A
Survey
of the Moon

A
SURVEY
OF THE MOON

Patrick Moore

*F.R.A.S., Director of the Mercury and Venus
Section of the British Astronomical Association
(Secretary of the Lunar Section, 1945-1955).*

83306

W · W · NORTON & COMPANY · INC ·
NEW YORK

TO PAUL JOHNSTONE
whose scientific interests lie
under his feet rather than above
his head, but who is nevertheless
a very wise man!

Acknowledgements

During the compilation of this book I have had immense help from Gilbert Fielder, I.C.I. Research Fellow at the University of London Observatory, who has not only read through the manuscript but has also made available to me certain unpublished researches of his own, notably in connection with the lunar grid system. I am more than grateful to him; but in expressing my thanks I must also make it clear that any errors and omissions are my responsibility alone, and that Dr. Fielder cannot be concerned in them. I should also point out that neither does he necessarily agree with all I have said, so that here too he must be exonerated in the event of my speculations proving to be wrong.

I am also very grateful to Leslie F. Ball, who is as noted as an astronomical artist as he is as a lunar observer. The drawings given here were prepared by him specially for this book.

Others who have helped include A. L. Helm, for translating some material from the·German for me, and the several observers who have allowed me to use their lunar sketches. Neither must I omit to thank the publishers, particularly Maurice Temple Smith of Messrs. Eyre & Spottiswoode and Eric P. Swenson of W. W. Norton & Co. Inc., who have made my task a very pleasant one.

I am also extremely grateful to W. H. Bromage, who has prepared the line drawings from my very unskilful originals. As his work includes the maps, it does indeed represent a major contribution to the book.

Last, but by no means least, I must thank Professor S. Miyamoto and M. Matsui, of the Kwasan Observatory in Japan. It will I think, be agreed that Mr Matsui's lunar photographs are quite exceptional in their quality, and it is a great privilege to be allowed to reproduce them here.

P.M.

Contents

CONTENTS

x

Plates

Foreword

When I was invited to write my book *Guide to the Moon*, in 1951, the Moon was very much a Cinderella in astronomical circles. It was energetically studied by amateurs such as myself, but professional workers were generally uninterested in it, and tended to regard it as a dull, dead world. The idea of sending a rocket to it, or of sending a vehicle on a 'round trip' to photograph the hidden side, was apt to be greeted with a sarcastic chuckle and a reference to boys' adventure stories.

Events have moved quickly since then – so quickly, in fact, that even the 'cranks' who predicted space-flight as long ago as the 1930's have been taken by surprise. I was one such 'crank', and I cannot resist telling a story against myself. In August 1958 I wrote an article for the periodical *New Scientist*, in which I discussed the prospects of photographing the far side of the Moon. I gave my own views as to what the reverse side might be like, and most of my guesses have proved to be accurate; but I ended: 'The practical difficulties are immense, and to hope for any early success is being highly over-optimistic.' Less than fourteen months later I was looking at pictures of the Moon's hidden face, taken by the Russian rocket Lunik III. . . .

Since 1957, when the first earth satellite soared into space, the whole situation has changed. The Moon is no longer neglected; it is still studied by amateurs, but professional astronomers have also begun to pay attention to it, and various ambitious projects are under way. By the time this book appears in print, a properly instrumented vehicle may well have been successfully brought down on to the Moon's bleak rocks.

Meanwhile, I have tried to give a picture of the Moon from the viewpoint of the observational astronomer, and I have made no attempt to deal with technicalities about rocket probes. Much of what I have written may prove to be wrong – but at least we now have every prospect of finding out, which did not seem very likely when I first began studying the Moon a quarter of a century ago.

PATRICK MOORE

East Grinstead,
1962

A
Survey
of the Moon

Chapter 1

The Lunar World

Thousands of years ago, at the dawn of human history, Stone Age men must have gazed at the Moon and wondered just what it was. It looked far larger and brighter than any of the stars, or even the five 'wandering stars' or planets; it moved quickly across the sky, changing shape regularly from a slender crescent to a full disk, and back again; it took second place only to the Sun. Surely it must be a god, or at least the home of a god?

Moreover, ancient peoples found the Moon very useful. In those far-off times, when lack of alertness meant certain death, dark nights were the most dangerous ones, and the Moon's radiance gave some defence against surprise attacks by human or animal enemies. Small wonder that the 'Queen of Night' was held to be divine, and that moon-worship held an important place in primitive religion.

The Moon was also helpful in the measurement of time. The interval between one full moon and the next was found to be more or less constant, and the first rough calendars were drawn up to conform with it. It was also noticed at a very early stage that the ocean tides were regulated by the Moon, although it was not known why.

Moon-myths probably go back as far as man himself. Some of the old stories are charming, and almost every country has its own legends. For instance, who has not heard of the Man in the Moon? It is true that by an effort of imagination, the dark patches on the lunar disk can be twisted into something like a human form, and the various myths are remarkably alike. According to a German tale, the Old Man was a villager caught in the act of stealing cabbages, and placed in the Moon as a warning to others. Another version, from the island of Sylt, makes him a sheep-stealer, and he is also a thief in a legend from Polynesia in the South Seas. Yet human beings did not monopolize the ancient Moon; hares, cats and frogs also found their way there at various times, each with their own particular legends.

1

To the people of Van, in Turkey, the Moon was a young bachelor, and was engaged to the Sun. Originally the Moon had shone in the daytime and the Sun at nights; but the Sun, being a girl, was afraid of the dark, and so she changed places with the Moon. According to another Turkish tale, the Moon was very fond of his mother, and used to follow her about everywhere, much to her annoyance. Once he followed her when she was washing dishes, and the mother was so angry that she threw the dishcloth in his face, which explains why the Moon's disk now appears stained.

One more story, this time from China, should certainly be told. It is said that there was once a great drought, and a herd of elephants came to drink at a sheet of water called the Moon Lake. They trampled down so many of the local hare population that when they next appeared, a far-sighted hare pointed out that they were annoying the Moon-Goddess by disturbing her reflection in the water. The elephants agreed that this was most unwise, and departed hastily.

True moon-worship still goes on in parts of Central Africa, and two thousand years ago the Moon was regarded as one of the most powerful of all the gods. Generally – though not always – it was male, and only the Sun was more important. The ruins of a large lunar temple have been uncovered at Ur, while the Egyptians had two moon-gods, Khonsu (also the God of Time) and Thoth. In Greece, Diana was the lunar deity, while the Japanese moon-goddess went by the name of Tsuki-yomi-no-kami. And from the Confessional of Ecgbert, Archbishop of York, we learn that the British Druids still paid homage to the Moon as late as the eighth century A.D.

However, the early peoples managed to find out at least something about the Moon itself. At first they believed that it actually changed shape from night to night – in Bushman mythology the Moon was believed to have offended the Sun, and was regularly pierced by the solar rays until he pleaded for mercy and was gradually restored! – but it was soon realized that this could not be so, because the 'dark' part of the disk could often be seen shining faintly alongside the brilliant crescent. We now know that this faint luminosity is due to the Earth shining upon the Moon. The correct explanation was not given until many years later, by the 'Forerunner', Leonardo da Vinci, but at least the earthlight showed our remote ancestors that

2

the Moon is always circular. It was also clear that the dark patches on the disk kept in the same positions, showing that the same face was always turned towards us. The nature of these dark patches was, of course, quite unknown; some races believed them to be reflections of earthly lands and seas, while others attributed them to dense lunar forests.

Then came the Greeks, who may be called the first 'scientists' in the proper sense of the word. Greek astronomy really begins with Thales of Miletus, who was born about 611 B.C. At first, naturally, the philosophers held very curious views about the Moon, and it is worth noting the words of Anaximander, a younger contemporary of Thales: 'The Moon is a circle nineteen times as large as the Earth; it is like a chariot-wheel, the rim of which is hollow and full of fire, as that of the Sun also is; it has one vent, like the nozzle of a pair of bellows; its eclipses depend upon the turnings of the wheel.' However, the later Greeks knew quite well that the Moon does not shine by its own light. They discovered that it merely reflects the rays of the Sun, so that moonlight is nothing more than what may be termed second-hand sunlight. They knew, too, why the Moon shows its monthly changes of shape. Democritus, who lived about 450 B.C., believed that there were lofty mountains and hollow valleys on the Moon's surface, and gradually the idea that the Moon is a rugged, rocky world began to gain popularity. Aristarchus of Samos, a philosopher of about three centuries before Christ, even had a very good idea of the Moon's distance from the Earth.

But the Greeks, enlightened though they were in many ways, could make no real progress in the physical study of the Moon – for the simple reason that they could not see it well enough. The Moon is almost a quarter of a million miles away, and no human eye can make out much detail at such a distance. Short of going there, which has become reasonably practicable only during the last few years, the only solution is to bring the Moon closer to us. It is the old problem of Mahomet and the mountain; and it was solved, in effect, by the invention of the telescope.

Toward the end of the thirteenth century, it was discovered that light is bent or 'refracted' when it passes through a glass lens. Spectacles came into use for correcting faults in the eye, and in or about 1608 Hans Lippersheim, a spectacle-maker of Middelburg

3

in Holland, found that by combining various lenses he could obtain a magnified picture of any distant object. Lippersheim's work came to the notice of the Italian scientist Galileo, who promptly copied it and improved it; and on a memorable evening late in 1609, the telescope was first turned toward the Moon.

Galileo saw at once that the lunar surface was not in the least like that of the Earth. There were no grassy plains, glittering oceans or spreading forests. Instead, he could make out rugged mountains, together with sunken amphitheatres bordered by circular ranges of hills, while the patches forming the legendary Old Man proved to be darker, more level plains. Truly, the Moon was a strange world.

Galileo and his successors spent a great deal of time in studying the Moon. Detailed maps were made, and a century ago it was popularly supposed that our knowledge of the lunar surface must be more or less complete. It was known that the Moon keeps the same face toward us because it turns on its axis in the same time that it takes to complete one journey round the Earth (27·3 days); that it is 2,160 miles in diameter, which is about the same as the distance across the Atlantic Ocean between England and America; that it lacks atmosphere and water, and that conditions are therefore quite unsuitable for life of the type we know. In fact, astronomers regarded the Moon as a dead, uninteresting globe, a burned-out planet of eternal silence where all change had ceased countlesss æons ago.

Things are very different today. The Moon has assumed a new importance in our eyes; we no longer worship it, and we no longer believe it to be the abode of either men or gods, but we do think that it is within our reach. Space exploration has begun, and in 1959 direct contact between the two worlds was made for the first time, when the Russian vehicle Lunik II landed upon the lunar rocks.

The idea of space-travel is far from new. It goes back to the ancient Greeks, and it has always fascinated both scientists and story-tellers. Yet until the present century it remained a vague dream, and only with the development of modern-type rockets has it become anything more. Nowadays we hear so much about space research in all its aspects that it is hard to remember that the pioneers of the 1930s were officially dismissed as cranks.

4

The Moon is the obvious first target, not because it is a friendly world – indeed, it is as hostile as could be imagined – but because it is so much closer than any other natural body in the sky. Lunik II hit the lunar surface only thirty-six hours after it had been launched, and a manned vehicle would not take much longer, whereas to reach the nearest of the planets (Venus) would take months. Also, the Moon is our companion in space, and is never far off, whereas Venus may sometimes be as much as 150 million miles away.

Many people still think that the only purpose of space research is to send a man to the Moon. This is quite wrong; indeed, nothing could be further from the truth. Manned flight is only one of the many branches of the new science of astronautics, and is not necessarily the most important one. Lunar flights by unpiloted vehicles are of tremendous value, and already they have given us information which we could never have obtained in any other way. The possibilities, too, are endless. For instance, medical research will benefit when it becomes practicable to set up a full-scale laboratory either in space or on the Moon, and this alone justifies the time and money which must be spent in the process.

And the Moon itself? Forbidding though it may be, it holds out a challenge for us – a challenge which must be taken up. Rocket experts have shown that the lunar trip can be accomplished, and meanwhile the astronomer must play his part by finding out all he can about the Moon as a world. Anyone who is going to visit a foreign land does not simply pack a suit-case and jump on board the first aeroplane; he buys a travellers' guide-book. The task at present is to draw up such a guide-book for the Moon. When the first explorers land there, which will not be so very far in the future, they will have many dangers to face, and they will need all the help which astronomical science can give them.

The new era has opened. Modern man sighs for 'new worlds to conquer', and the Solar System awaits his inspection. He has the ability, and he is gaining the knowledge. The main danger, at present, is his lack of adult self-control, but he will have only himself to blame if the rockets of the 1970s carry nuclear bombs instead of lunar probes.

Chapter 2

A Picture of the Universe

The Moon is a splendid object in our skies, and it is natural enough for us to think of it as a most important body. Actually, nothing could be further from the truth. Even the Earth is a very junior member of the Sun's family, and the Moon appears large and bright only because it is so close to us.

Before we can form a proper idea of the Moon's status, we must have at least some knowledge of the larger scheme of things starting near home, with the bodies in the Solar System.

The Solar System is made up of one star (the Sun), nine planets, thirty-one moons or 'satellites', thousands of small planets known as asteroids, and almost innumerable comets, together with small particles classed as meteors and meteorites. On the whole it is a compact family, and the Sun controls it firmly. Only some of the comets have any chance of escape.

The human brain is not capable of appreciating vast distances. We may talk about 'a million miles', but we cannot really understand what is meant. It is probably true to say that astronomers cannot understand great spans of time and space any better than ordinary people – the only difference is that, in general, the astronomers do not make the mistake of trying! Instead of using actual figures, then, let us image that the Sun has been reduced to a globe two feet in diameter. Using this as a basis, we can fill in the rest of the Solar System to scale.

The first of the nine planets, Mercury, will be represented by a grain of mustard seed, moving round the central globe at a mean distance of 83 feet. Venus will become a pea at a distance of 156 feet; the Earth, another pea at 215 feet; and Mars, outermost of the first group of planets, a small bead at 328 feet. Before going any further, let us put in the satellites. Mercury and Venus have none; the Moon will become another seed, moving round the Earth at a distance of $6\frac{1}{2}$ inches; and Phobos and Deimos, the two dwarf

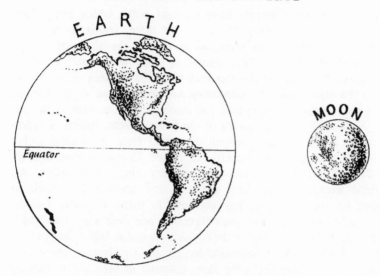

Comparative sizes of Earth and Moon

attendants of Mars, will be so tiny that we will have to use a microscope to see them at all.

All the four inner planets are solid and rocky, and have some points in common. Mercury, not much larger than the Moon, is an uncomfortable world with hardly a trace of atmosphere; Venus, the glorious 'evening star', has a considerable atmosphere – and unfortunately we cannot see through it, even with our most powerful telescopes, so that we have little idea what the actual surface is like, though conditions do not seem to be favourable for advanced life-forms. Mars, the red planet, has always been regarded as the one other world where intelligent life might exist, but modern research has shown that the chances are very slim. The atmosphere is of low density; there is little moisture, and most of the surface is a dusty desert.

Beyond Mars we come to the asteroids, about 1,000 feet from our two-foot Sun, and represented by grains of fine sand. Most of these Lilliputian worlds seem to be mere lumps of material, and it is possible that they are the shattered fragments of an old planet which somehow came to grief, though according to another theory they represent the débris left over when the main planets were

7

formed. A few asteroids have unusual paths which bring them nearer to the Sun than Mars; one of them, Icarus, even passes inside the orbit of Mercury, while one of the so-called 'Earthgrazers', Hermes, has been known to come within half a million miles of our own world – less than twice the distance of the Moon. On the other hand, the interesting asteroids known as the Trojans lie well outside the main belt, and move in the same path as Jupiter.

Next come the four giants of the Solar System. Jupiter is represented by an orange, one-fifth of a mile from the central globe; Saturn, a tangerine at two-fifths of a mile; Uranus, a plum at fourfifths of a mile; and Neptune, another plum at $1\frac{1}{4}$ miles. All these worlds have gaseous surfaces, and are intensely cold, so that we cannot expect any sort of life there. Of more interest to optimistic space-research enthusiasts are their satellites, which may possibly be reached in the centuries to come. Jupiter has twelve, four of which are of considerable size; the two largest, Ganymede and Callisto, have about the same diameter as Mercury, so that on our scale they will become mustard-seeds. Titan, the senior of Saturn's nine satellites, is rather larger than Mercury, and has even been found to possess an atmosphere – though since this atmosphere is made up mainly of methane (the gas known to miners as the dreaded 'fire-damp') it is certainly unbreathable. Uranus has five satellites, all rather small, while Neptune has two, one of which is the size of Mercury and the other very tiny.

Finally, far out at the boundary of the Solar System, we meet with barren, forbidding little Pluto, most recently discovered of the planets – another small bead on our scale, and with a curious orbit which sometimes carries it out more than two miles from the central globe in our model. There are some strange problems connected with Pluto, and some authorities consider that it is nothing more than a former satellite of Neptune which has broken away from the pull of its primary and moved off along an orbit of its own. It is quite possible that a tenth planet lies beyond Pluto, but if it exists it must be very faint, and its discovery will be largely a matter of luck.

Scale models are useful, but it may be as well to add a few precise figures. The Earth is 93 million miles from the Sun; our nearest planetary neighbours are Venus, at 67 million miles from the Sun, and Mars, at just over 141 million. At its closest to us, Venus may approach the Earth to within 25 million miles – roughly a hundred times as far as the Moon – but Mars never comes much within 35 million miles. Pluto, the outermost member of the solar family, moves at an average distance from the Sun of over 3,500 million miles, and no telescope yet built will show it as more than a dim point of light.

The junior members of the Solar System are the comets and meteors. A comet, unlike a planet, is not a solid body, but is made up of small particles enveloped in tenuous gas. Many faint comets have short periods, and Encke's Comet, for instance, completes one journey round the Sun in only 3·3 years, but the brighter comets have orbits which are so large and eccentric that they have periods of hundreds, thousands or even, perhaps, millions of years. The only conspicuous comet with a period of less than a century is Halley's, which was last near the Sun in 1910 and is due back again in 1986.

Meteors are small solid particles moving round the Sun in the manner of dwarf planets. Normally they are too faint to be seen. but if a meteor comes within the Earth's atmosphere it rubs against the air-particles and becomes heated by friction, destroying itself in the streak of luminosity which we call a shooting-star. Most meteors are smaller than grains of rice, and end their journey to the ground in the form of fine dust. They tend to travel round the Sun in shoals, and when the Earth passes through a shoal – as happens several times each year – the result is a shower of shooting-stars. The August shower, known as the Perseids, is the most spectacular. In addition there are non-shower or 'sporadic' meteors, which may appear from any direction at any moment.

Occasional larger bodies encountered by the Earth survive the drop without being destroyed, and are then termed meteorites. Most museums have meteorite collections, ranging from tiny specimens to large blocks. Major falls are very rare, and there have been only two during the present century, at least so far as we know. One took place in 1908, in the Tunguska region of Siberia, and the other in 1947, in the area of Vladivostok. However, there must have been many prehistoric falls, and giant meteorites are found here and there; the holder of the heavyweight record, the Hoba West Meteorite in Africa, has an estimated weight of over sixty tons. Oddly enough. there seems to be a fundamental difference between the meteorites and the ordinary shooting-stars, and it seems that there is a close association between meteorites and asteroids. Incidentally, it is worth noting that the Russian astronomer K. Florensky considers that the Siberian 'meteorite' of 1908 was in fact the head of a small comet, a view shared by other Soviet authorities.

Meteorites may sometimes produce craters, the most famous of which is the Coon Butte Crater in Arizona. Like other formations of the same sort, such as the Ungava Crater in North Quebec, Coon Butte is prehistoric. We will return to this subject later; it is relevant in any discussion of the Moon, since there are many authorities who believe that the lunar craters, too, were produced by falling meteorites.

Before leaving the Solar System, mention should be made of the interplanetary débris concentrated in the main plane, and which is responsible for the faint cone-shaped glow known as the Zodiacal Light. A still more elusive glow, the Gegenschein, is also due to particles of some sort, and it has been suggested that the Moon may have something to do with it, though the present evidence is very slender and uncertain.

So much for the Sun's family. It seems important to us, but we are too apt to deceive ourselves. All the bodies in the Solar System are relatively close to us, and beyond Pluto comes a vast stretch of 'empty' space; the absolute isolation of the Solar System is something which we find very hard to appreciate. For a moment, let us go back to our scale model. If we put our two-foot Sun inside the Tower of London, Pluto will be in the region of the Houses of Parliament; but what about the nearest star? We will not find it in England, or even in Europe. It will lie thousands of miles away, in the frozen wastes of Siberia, and all but the half-dozen closest stars will have to be placed clear of the Earth altogether.

We had better abandon our scale model, and look for a new unit of distance. Fortunately, there is a convenient one to hand. As long age as 1676 a Danish astronomer, Ole Rømer, discovered that light does not travel instantaneously, but moves at a velocity of 186,000 miles per second, so that it can leap from the Earth to the Moon in a second and a quarter. The 93-million-mile journey to the Sun would take just over eight minutes, but the nearest star could not be reached in less than $4\frac{1}{3}$ years! The distance covered by light in one year (the astronomical 'light-year') is somewhat under six million million miles, and this unit is often used in measuring the distances of bodies outside the Solar System.

A star is a sun – or, to put it more forcibly, our own blinding Sun turns out to be nothing more than a normal star, far less splendid than any of those which we can see on any clear night of the year. It would need at least 20,000 Suns to match the brilliance of Rigel, the white star in the foot of Orion; but Rigel is over 500 light-years away, so that the rays from it now entering our eyes started on their journey when Henry VI was King of England, and the Wars of the Roses had only just begun.* On the other hand, there are many stars much less luminous than our own. If we represent the Sun by an ordinary electric light bulb, the most powerful stars will be searchlights, while the feeblest will be tiny glow-worms.

All the stars are moving about at high speeds, but at their immense distances they appear to all intents and purposes fixed in the sky. Their individual or 'proper' motions can be measured, but only with delicate instruments and over relatively long periods, so that the constellations described by the Greek astronomers of over 2,000 years ago are almost the same as those which we see now. Only the Moon and the planets, together with the lesser members of the Solar System, are close enough to show obvious changes in position from night to night.

Our own system of stars, the Galaxy, is spiral in form, and has a diameter of about 100,000 light-years. It is not, of course, the only galaxy. Far away in space, so remote that their light takes millions of years to reach us, we can see many others; the most distant object known at present, the galaxy 3C-295 in the constellation of Boötes (the Herdsman), is thought to be about 5,000 million light-years away. Bearing in mind that we can only see a small part of the universe, we must realize that our Solar System is utterly insignificant, with the Moon one of the less important members of it. It is likely, too, that many of the stars are the centres of planetary systems of the same kind as our own.

One further point seems to be worth making here. The Russian rocket, Lunik II, reached the Moon in thirty-six hours; a journey to Mars or Venus would take less than a year; if we could build

* Some recent measures make the distance of Rigel as much as 900 light-years, which would take us back to the Battle of Hastings. If so, it must be more like 50,000 times as powerful as the Sun.

really powerful and efficient rockets, it would be possible to explore the more distant planets as well. Yet this may be the limit of our travelling. Interplanetary flight lies close ahead, but interstellar flight will probably remain nothing more than a dream.

The suns and galaxies have a fascination of their own, but we know that they are hopelessly beyond our reach; and in a way it is a relief to turn back from these remote regions to our nearby, familiar Moon.

Chapter 3

The Birth of the Moon

At the present time, we have to confess that the origin of the Earth itself remains something of a mystery. Many theories have been put forward, but each has its drawbacks, and the whole question remains very open. Therefore, we are bound to be even more uncertain about the birth of the Moon; but at least we have a few hard facts to guide us.

Our first piece of evidence relates to the age of the Earth, which is believed to be about 4,500 million years – or at any rate somewhere between 4,000 and 5,000 million years. There seems to be little doubt that this value is reasonably correct. We can make a good estimate of the age of the oldest rocks in the Earth's crust, because these rocks often contain radioactive materials (such as uranium) which decay steadily into lead; the extent to which the original uranium has decayed gives us a guide to the time which has elapsed since the rocks solidified. This is only one of several lines of investigation, but everything points to about the the same value for the age of the Earth as an independent body. It is probable that the Sun is older, and that all the planets, as well as the Moon, were formed at roughly the same epoch as the Earth.

In 1796 Laplace, a famous French mathematician, put forward a theory which was widely accepted for many years. According to him, the Solar System began as a vast cloud of tenuous gas, which slowly shrank and threw off rings, each ring condensing into a planet and leaving the Sun as the central remnant of the original cloud. The Earth, one of these newly formed bodies, contracted toward its own centre of gravity and threw off a ring of its own, which subsequently condensed into the Moon.

This sounds simple and straightforward, but Laplace's 'nebular hypothesis' has not stood the test of time. Mathematical arguments have shown that the matter left behind as the gas-cloud shrank would not form definite rings, and there are various other fatal

13

objections as well, so that the whole idea has been definitely abandoned.

Other theories have been put forward in plenty. Some of them involve the gravitational force of a wandering star, which is supposed to have passed close by the Sun and torn off a tongue of matter which broke up into 'drops' and produced planets, but here again the objections are so strong that all such passing-star ideas have joined Laplace's gas-cloud on the scientific scrap-heap. F. Hoyle once suggested that the Sun used to be associated with a companion-star which exploded violently and departed into space, leaving behind a certain amount of débris from which the planets were formed. Recently, however, most astronomers have declared in favour of a different sort of process, put forward by O. Schmidt in Russia and, in somewhat altered form, by C. von Weizsäcker in Germany.

According to von Weizsäcker, the Sun once passed through an interstellar cloud made up of dust and gas. When it emerged, it had collected a tremendous envelope of material, thinly spread and at a low temperature. During the millions of years which followed, the planets gradually built up by accretion until much of the cloud had been concentrated into a few large bodies. There is a vague resemblance to the old nebular hypothesis of Laplace. but the process suggested by von Weizsäcker is very different, and avoids the mathematical objections.

Of course we have no proof that von Weizsäcker is right, but to go into more detail here would be out of place,* and we have at least a reasonable starting-point. What, then, of the Moon?

It seems necessary to begin with a theory which has been completely discredited, but is still given in many books. This is the tidal hypothesis, first put forward in the latter part of the nineteenth century by G. H. Darwin, son of the great naturalist Charles Darwin.

Darwin started by assuming that the Earth and Moon originally formed one body, and that the Moon was thrown off as a fluid mass. According to a modified version of this idea, the Earth had cooled down sufficiently to possess a thin crust before the separation took place. The Earth, rotating rapidly on its axis, was in the state known as 'unstable equilibrium', so that it became elliptical in

---

* I have discussed the matter more fully in *The Planets* (London and New York, 1962).

form, rotating about its shorter axis. Two main forces were acting upon it – the tides raised upon it by the Sun, and its own natural period of vibration. When these two forces were 'in resonance', i.e. acting together, the tides increased to such an extent that the whole body became first pear-shaped and then dumbbell-shaped,

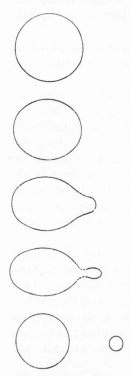

with one 'bell' (the Earth) much larger than the other (the future Moon). Eventually the neck of the dumbbell broke altogether, and a new world had been born.

W. H. Pickering, an American astronomer who paid a great deal of attention to lunar problems, went further, and pointed out that if this theory were correct, the thin crust of the otherwise fluid Earth must have been torn apart, leaving a huge hollow where the thrown-off mass had laid. Moreover, the shock caused by the final fracture would have been violent enough to crack the crust in other places.

A glance at a map or globe of the Earth shows that if the lands on the opposite sides of the Atlantic Ocean could be clapped together they would fit into each other. Allowing for the sea having washed away portions of the land here and there, and supposing Britain and France to be joined – as was the case, only ten thousand years ago – the relationship is striking. The 'bulge' of Africa fits into the hollow of

The Tidal Theory

South America, and the eastern coast of North America corresponds to the western coast of Europe. The Pacific Ocean, on the other hand, is roughly circular, and so vast that to an observer on Mars or Venus it would appear as a patch occupying much of the visible disk. According to Pickering, the great, rounded hollow which now forms the bed of the Pacific is nothing more nor less than the scar left in the Earth's crust by the breaking-off of the Moon, so that our satellite was born at the spot where our greatest ocean now rolls.

It is easy to continue the story. Pickering went on to explain

15

that the crust of the Earth cracked under the shock, and portions of it floated apart, to settle down eventually in the places where we now find Eurasia and the Americas. The crustal cracking exposed the intensely heated interior of the Earth, and the fragments of the crust floated as skin or scum on the hot, molten globe. The lava surface exposed beneath the broken pieces of crust cooled and solidified, and later, when water was able to settle on the surface, became the Atlantic Ocean.

The tidal theory sounds very plausible, and one can understand why it gained wide support. Unfortunately, later work has shown that almost everything about it is wrong.

To begin with, the Pacific Ocean is only a few miles deep, and can hardly represent the 'scar' left by the hurling-off of a body the size of the Moon. It used to be thought that the floor of the Pacific was different in nature from those of other oceans, indicating that the departing Moon had exposed deeper layers of the Earth, but we now know that there is no such difference; the floor of the Pacific is just the same as that of the Atlantic, the Arctic and all the rest. However, it is not worth following any of these points up, because it has become quite clear that the Earth and Moon could never have formed a single body at all.

There are two main reasons for this. First, mathematical arguments have shown that a large mass could not have been hurled off into space as Darwin and Pickering supposed; secondly, a body with the size and density of the Moon, moving round the Earth at a distance of less than 2·9 Earth radii (about 11,600 miles) could not survive as a single mass. In fact, the whole idea must be rejected, and it has been described here only because there are still some modern textbooks which repeat it.

The Moon is not the Earth's child. In fact, it is best to regard the Earth-Moon system as a double planet rather than as a planet and a satellite, since the Moon is much too large to be ranked as an inferior body. A few facts and figures will make the point clear.

Of the satellites in the Solar System, some are very small indeed – less than 100 miles in diameter; it has been suggested, though without definite evidence, that these dwarfs are really captured asteroids. Both the satellites of Mars come into this category; so do eight of Jupiter's attendants, at least one of Saturn's, and one of Neptune's. Of the rest, only a few are comparable in size with our Moon. Titan, in Saturn's family, has a diameter of about 3,500 miles,* which is appreciably greater than the 2,160 miles of the Moon. Then comes Triton, the senior attendant of Neptune (3,300 miles) and the four 'Galilean moons' of Jupiter – Callisto and Ganymede, about 3,200 miles; Io, 2,200 miles; and Europa, 1,900 miles.

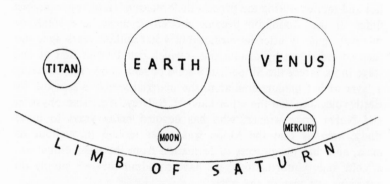

Diagram to show relative sizes of:

Saturn	=	*75,000 miles*
Venus	=	*7,700*
Earth	=	*7,900*
Moon	=	*2,160*
Mercury	=	*3,000*

indicating that the ratio Venus/Mercury is not unlike Earth/Moon but very different from Saturn/Titan

The interesting fact is that apart from the Moon, all the large satellites revolve round giant planets. Saturn, for instance, is over 70,000 miles in diameter, so that Titan is tiny in comparison. The Moon has one-quarter the diameter and 1/81 of the mass of the Earth, but Titan has a mere 1/20 the diameter and 1/4700 of the mass of Saturn. In the diagram, all four bodies are drawn to the same scale, together with the two innermost planets Venus and Mercury. It will be seen that the ratio Earth/Moon is not very different from the ratio Venus/Mercury, and there is every reason to rank the Moon as a small planet which happens to be associated with the Earth.

If so, the Moon was presumably born in the same way as our

* The exact figure is naturally uncertain; some authorities prefer 2,700 miles.

own world, and in the same region of space, so that the two have remained inseparable companions ever since. Yet even this is not certain; for instance, V. A. Firsoff believes that the Moon has been 'lost' and recaptured more than once.

It is a pity that we are so uncertain about the origin of the Moon, because it is important to find out whether the globe ever became hot and molten during the process of formation. Here, too, opinions differ. If the Moon did become molten, it must have solidified relatively quickly after its birth about 4,500 million years ago, and then cooled down by conduction – which could mean that at one stage in its career the Moon had a solid or semi-solid crust covering a layer of hot magma similar to the material which is sent out by Earth volcanoes. On the other hand H. S. Urey, American physicist and Nobel Prize winner, who has devoted many years to lunar study, believes that the Moon was never molten throughout its mass, and that the process of formation from the solar cloud was a 'cold' one. Unfortunately, we have to admit that we simply do not know one way or the other.

At any rate, it is very likely that at the beginning of its existence as an independent body, the Moon was much closer to the Earth than it is today. In those far-off times, the 'month', or period taken for the Moon to revolve once round the Earth, was of course much shorter than it is now. At a distance of about 12,000 miles, which is the minimum possible – if the separation had been less, the Moon would have been disrupted by the immense gravitational strain – the revolution time would have been a mere 6½ hours, and the length of the Earth's 'day' would also have been 6½ hours. In this case, the tides raised by the two bodies upon each other must have been extremely violent. Even at its present distance of almost a quarter of a million miles, the Moon still causes strong tides in our oceans; at 12,000 miles, the tides would have been truly Titanic. But the Earth is much more massive than the Moon, and has a greater pull, so that the Moon was the worse sufferer. These mutual tides had two important results. They slowed down the axial rotation periods of both Earth and Moon, and they pushed the Moon further away.

As the torn, tide-rent Moon receded – relatively quickly; by the start of the geological period known as the Cambrian, over 500 million years ago, it is thought that the distance had already grown to more than 200,000 miles – the persistent pull of the Earth raised a permanent 'bulge', or semi-solid tidal wave, in the lunar globe, and tended to keep this bulge turned toward the Earth, so slowing down the Moon's rotation. It may be helpful to draw a comparison with an engine wheel rotating between two brake shoes, as shown in the diagram. Similarly, the Earth's rotation period became longer as a result of tides raised by the Moon; and the process went on steadily. until the Moon's rate of spin had been so greatly reduced that relative to the Earth (though not, of course, relative to the Sun) it had ceased altogether. One face of the Moon was turned permanently earthward, the other permanently away, while the 'month' had become 27·3 of our modern days. Meanwhile. the Earth's rotation period had increased to almost twenty-four hours.

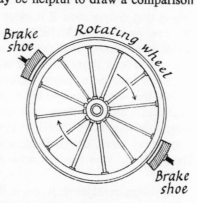

Engine-wheel between brake shoes

At present the Moon is still drawing slowly away from the Earth. and our 'day' is becoming longer, but both effects are very slight. The increase in the length of the Earth's day, for instance. amounts to something like one second in 120,000 years.*

The Moon will not go on receding indefinitely; it has been suggested that it will eventually start to approach again, finally entering the 'danger-zone' within 11,000 or 12,000 miles and being disrupted, ending its career as a ring of particles similar to the ring-system which we can see round the planet Saturn. But though it is true that all known satellites in the Solar System lie outside the danger-zone or Roche Limit (named in honour of the French mathematician Édouard Roche, who first drew attention to it) it is not likely that anything of the sort will happen. Neither must we be

* During the last decade it has been found that the Earth is not nearly so good a timekeeper as our best modern clocks. The rotation speeds up and slows down slightly for no apparent reason. Disturbances inside the Earth's globe are probably responsible, and in the long run these tiny irregularities tend to cancel out.

misled by drawing too close a comparison with Saturn's rings, even though this system may well have been produced by the breaking-up of an old satellite.

There are serious doubts as to whether the Moon would be turned into a ring-system even if it came within the Roche Limit, but in any case we have to take the time-scale of the universe into account. There is no chance that the Moon will come back to the danger-zone for at least thirty thousand million years, and long before then there will have been radical changes in the Sun. Many astronomers believe that within the next ten thousand million years, the relatively mild Sun which we know will have changed into a much larger, more luminous body than it is now – after which it may collapse into a very small, dense, feeble star of the sort known as a White Dwarf. If so, who can tell what will happen to the Earth-Moon system?

All things considered, it seems that the whole situation will alter drastically before the Moon is in peril of being disrupted, and when we have to deal with events so far in the future it is rather pointless to speculate. It would be strange to live on a ringed planet, and to be deprived of the Moon's friendly light; but we may be sure that nothing of the kind will happen in the foreseeable future, and probably it will never happen at all.

So far as we can tell, the Moon is unique in the Solar System, provided that we regard it as a junior planet associated with the Earth rather than as a mere satellite. What, then, are the chances that the Earth has a genuine satellite of much smaller size? This is an old problem, and is bound up with the whole question of the evolution of the Sun's family.

Theoretically, there are no obvious objections. Both the satellites of Mars, Phobos and Deimos, are less than a dozen miles across, and they are as unlike our Moon as it is possible to be, so that their origin must also have been different. As we have seen, they may be captured asteroids. Yet small though they are, they are visible with moderate telescopes when Mars is at its closest to us. I have seen Phobos unmistakably with the 12½-inch reflector in my own observatory.

This means that there can be no comparable body within close range of the Earth. It has been found that at a distance equal to that of the Moon, a 25-mile satellite would shine as a brilliant star, and a satellite one mile across would be visible in binoculars even if it were made up of darkish rock. At 2,000,000 miles, a 25-mile body would be seen with the naked eye, and even a one-mile satellite would be detectable with equipment used by the average amateur. Photographic maps of the sky are now so complete that we may be sure that an object of this kind would have been tracked down many years ago. If a minor satellite exists, it must be either much further away or else very small indeed.

In the nineteenth century, a French writer named Petit published a paper about a suggested second satellite moving at a distance of 4,650 miles from the Earth's surface, and with a period of 3 hours 20 minutes. It is not clear how Petit arrived at this conclusion, which is certainly wrong, but the idea was taken up by Jules Verne in his famous story *Round the Moon*, which appeared rather less than a hundred years ago. More will be said about Jules Verne later, but meanwhile it is worth repeating his description as seen through the eyes of one of his imaginary space-travellers, President Barbicane, observing through the porthole of the equally imaginary moon-projectile: *

As Barbicane was about to leave the window . . . his attention was attracted by the approach of a brilliant object. It was an enormous disk, whose dimensions could not be estimated. Its face, which was turned earthward, was brightly illuminated; it might have been taken for a small moon reflecting the light of the larger one. It advanced very rapidly, and seemed to be following an orbit round the Earth which would intersect the path of the projectile. It moved along in its orbit, and at the same time spun on its own axis. . . . The object grew enormously, and the projectile seemed to be rushing into its path. . . . The travellers instinctively recoiled. Their alarm was great, but it did not last long. The object passed within a few hundred yards and vanished, merging into the absolute blackness of space.

It is a graphic picture, and the second satellite was essential for the ingenious plot of Verne's story, but we need have no fear that

---

* My thanks are due to A. R. Michaelis for translating this passage from a first edition of Verne's book.

the true space-men of our own century will encounter anything of the sort. It is quite likely that minute bodies revolve round the Earth at a distance less than that of the Moon, but they will be so small that they will rank as meteoric débris and not as definite satellites.

Under the circumstances, the report of two satellite-like bodies, made in 1961 by the Polish astronomer K. Kordylewski, was most surprising. It remains quite unconfirmed, but it is of great interest.

Kordylewski began his search for minor satellites in 1951, using the equipment at Kasprowy Wierch and Lomnica in the mountains of Poland. On 6th March and 6th April 1961 he took photographs which, he claimed, showed two faint 'clouds' moving in the same path as the Moon, and presumably made up of meteoric material. The search had not been a random one; Kordylewski had been studying these special areas, because of the connection with the famous 'three-body problem'. To explain this, we must look at the remarkable asteroids known as the Trojans.

The Trojans lie far beyond the main asteroid belt, and move in the same orbit as Jupiter, at an average distance of about 483,000,000 miles from the Sun. There are two groups of Trojans, one of them sixty degrees ahead of Jupiter and the other sixty degrees behind. The asteroids do not, of course, keep together in a clump, and may be spread out by many millions of miles, but the sixty-degree points represent their mean positions, and there is no fear that any of them will go dangerously close to Jupiter.* In the diagram, A represents Jupiter, and B and C to two Trojan groups, with S marking the position of the Sun.

Kordylewski suggested that the same could be true of his 'clouds'. In the diagram, S now stands for the Earth and A for the Moon, while the 'clouds' are at B and C. The cloud at B would keep sixty degrees behind the Moon, and the cloud at C sixty degrees ahead. However, even if Kordylewski's report is confirmed – and this is very far from being certain, as there may be serious errors in interpretation – the objects cannot be proper satellites, and the idea of a loose collection of meteoric débris is much less improbable.

* For further details about this whole problem, see my book *The Planets* (London and New York, 1962). The description given here is very much over-simplified, and there are many complications to be taken into account, but I hope that the main principle is clear enough.

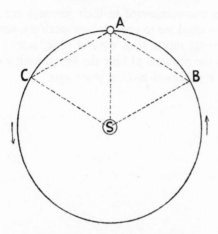

*Position of the Trojans relative to
Jupiter, and also Kordylewski's
reported objects relative to the Moon*

In passing, it may be worth referring to an old suggestion dating
back for centuries, according to which the Earth has a second
satellite lying behind the Moon and so permanently hidden from
us. This is ingenious, but completely unsound. For one thing, the
disturbances produced by other bodies in the Solar System, such
Mars and Venus, would soon destroy the lining-up of Earth, Moon
and second satellite. On the whole it seems likely that the Moon
is the Earth's only natural attendant; if there are other bodies moving round us they must be veritable dwarfs, pieces of débris a few
feet across.

It has also been suggested that the Moon itself may have a
satellite, and sixty years ago W. H. Pickering made a careful search
for it. He failed completely, and more recent photographic surveys
by Clyde Tombaugh and others have been no more fruitful. Tombaugh, the American astronomer who discovered the remote planet
Pluto in 1930 and who has also looked for minor earth satellites,
has used the powerful telescopes at the Lowell Observatory in
Arizona, and has stated that no lunar companion with a diameter
greater than fifteen feet is likely to exist.

There the matter rests at present, and it seems that the Earth and Moon are unaccompanied in their journeys round the Sun. It has been left to mankind to provide new satellites, and these bodies, made up of metal rather than natural rock, may eventually help us to clear up the problem of how the Moon itself came into being more than four thousand million years ago.

Chapter 4

The Movements of the Moon

Ancient peoples believed that the Sun, Moon and stars revolved round the Earth. This idea was natural enough, and nobody seriously questioned it until the third century B.C., when Aristarchus of Samos, one of the most far-sighted of the Greek philosophers, made the daring suggestion that the Sun and not the Earth might be the centre of the planetary system.

Unfortunately even the Greeks were not ready for so radical a change of view, and Aristarchus found few followers. Later philosophers went back to the old theory of a central Earth, and Ptolemy, the last great astronomer of Classical times, worked out a scheme of things which was universally accepted for many hundreds of years.* According to the Ptolemaic theory, The Earth lay at rest in the centre of the universe, with the Moon, Sun, planets and 'fixed stars' circling round it at various distances. Nowadays we know better. The Earth has been relegated to its true status of a very junior member of the Sun's family, and even the statement that 'the Moon revolves round the Earth' needs a certain amount of qualification, though it is good enough for most purposes.

In discussing the Moon's movements, we must obviously begin with the phases, which must have been as familiar to our cave-dwelling ancestors as they are to us. To make things as straightforward as possible, let us imagine that the Moon revolves round the Earth in a perfectly circular orbit. This is shown in the diagram, which, like those following, is wildly out of scale.

The Moon has no light of its own (a fact which the Greeks knew quite well). It shines only by reflected sunlight, and clearly the Sun can illuminate only half the Moon at any one time. In the diagram, the unlighted – and therefore non-luminous – 'night' hemi-

---

* To be strictly accurate, the scheme was not Ptolemy's own, but he certainly improved it and brought it to its highest degree of perfection. It was incredibly complex and clumsy, but at least it explained the apparent motions of the planets reasonably well.

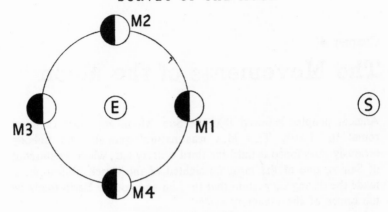

Phases of the Moon

sphere is blackened, while the shining or 'day' hemisphere is left white; E represents the Earth, S the Sun, and M1, M2, M3 and M4 the Moon in various positions in its orbit.

Look first at M1. At this moment the Earth, Moon and Sun are in more or less a straight line, with the Moon in the middle. The lighted half is turned toward the Sun, and the dark half toward the Earth; since the dark half does not shine, the Moon cannot be seen at all, and is 'new'. People often speak of the thin crescent moon as being 'new', but this is scientifically wrong; the true new moon is invisible.

From M1, the Moon moves along in the direction of M2. Gradually a little of the day-hemisphere begins to be turned toward the Earth, and the familiar crescent makes its appearance in the evening sky; very often the so-called dark side can be faintly seen as well, not because the Sun is shining on it, but because the Earth is doing so. Earthlight on the Moon is far more powerful than moonlight on the Earth – partly because the Earth is the larger, but also because it is a better reflector – and the intensity is great enough to make the Moon's night hemisphere dimly luminous. The effect is masked as more and more of the sunlit side appears. By the time M2 is reached, half of the day-hemisphere is visible, and the Moon is at First Quarter.

This term is liable to cause a certain amount of confusion, since at First Quarter the Moon appears as a half. Yet it is logical enough

26

really, since the Moon has then completed one-quarter of its journey reckoning from new moon to new moon.

From M2 the Moon moves steadily on toward M3, and more and more of the day-side comes into view. At this stage the Moon is said to be 'gibbous', i.e. between half and full. By the time M3 is reached, the night-hemisphere is turned wholly away from the Earth; the lighted half faces us, and the Moon is full. Once again the Earth, Moon and Sun are more or less lined up, but this time the Earth is in the mid-position.

As the Moon moves on toward M4, the day-side begins to be turned away again. Passing through the gibbous stage, the Moon has become a half-disk by the time it arrives at M4 – the phase known as Last Quarter – and again approaches the Sun's line of sight, becoming a narrowing crescent and finally disappearing into the morning twilight. After 29½ days it has come back to M1, and is again 'new'.

A discrepancy may be noticed here. The Moon takes only 27⅓ days to go once round the Earth; why, then, is the interval between successive new moons over two days longer?

The answer is that the Earth itself is moving round the Sun. The next diagram will make the situation clear. Once again S stands for the Sun, with E1 and E2 the Earth in different positions, and the

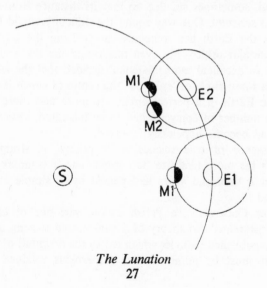

The Lunation
27

Moon at M. When the Earth is at E1 and the Moon at M1, the Moon is of course new. $27\frac{1}{3}$ days later the Moon has completed one full circuit, and has arrived back at M1; but meanwhile the Earth has moved on to E2, and the Moon must travel further along its orbit, to M2, before the three bodies are properly lined up again. The extra time taken to cover the distance between M1 and M2 takes just over two days, which accounts for the difference.

There are technical terms for these two periods. The $27\frac{1}{3}$ day revolution-time is known as the Moon's 'sidereal period', while the interval between one new moon and the next is the 'lunation' or 'synodic month'.

Our next correction has to do with the shape of the Moon's path, which is definitely not circular. Ptolemy was basically right when he said that the Moon goes round the Earth, but in almost every other respect he was hopelessly wrong. It was not really his fault; great man though he undoubtedly was, he could not bring himself to break away from tradition.

Ancient astronomers held that the circle was the 'perfect' form, and this meant that all the bodies in the sky must have circular orbits, since nothing short of perfection could be allowed in the heavens. Unfortunately for this idea, it was obvious that the Moon does not always look the same size; sometimes its disk is larger than usual, sometimes smaller, so that its distance from the Earth cannot be constant. One way round the difficulty would be to suppose that the Earth lies some way away from the centre of the Moon's circular orbit – but even this would not do, and Ptolemy, who was an excellent mathematician, decided that the Moon must move in a small circle or 'epicycle', the centre of which itself moved round the Earth in a perfect circle. As more and more problems arose the number of epicycles had to be increased, until the whole system had become hopelessly involved.

The essence of true science is simplicity. A straightforward scheme is far more likely to be correct than a complex one; and after over a thousand years had passed by, a simple explanation was found.

Nicolaus Copernicus, a Polish canon, was one of the first to revive Aristarchus' old theory of a sun-centred system, and it was his book, published in 1546, which led to the downfall of Ptolemy's theory. It must be admitted that Copernicus retained many of

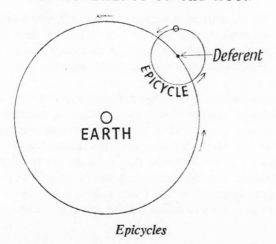

Epicycles

Ptolemy's mistakes – he still believed that all orbits must be circular, and he was even reduced to bringing back epicycles – but he paved the way for Johannes Kepler, who developed the theory and worked out the three Laws of Planetary Motion which still bear his name. The first of these Laws was announced in 1609, at about the time when Galileo first turned a telescope toward the Moon. It stated that the planets move round the Sun in paths which are not circular, but elliptical, with the Sun lying in one of the foci of the ellipse. The same held good for the Moon; it moved in an elliptical orbit, with the Earth in one of the foci.*

The fact that the Moon's orbit is not circular explains the changes in apparent size. At its closest, or 'perigee', the distance is 221,000 miles reckoned from the Earth's centre; at its furthest, or 'apogee', the Moon recedes to 253,000 miles, giving an average of 238,900 – just under a quarter of a million miles. The changes in distance are quite considerable, and the Moon's apparent diameter at apogee is only nine-tenths of the value at perigee. On the other hand, it would be most misleading to think of the orbit as being highly

---

* The accepted way of drawing an ellipse is to fix two pins in a board, an inch or two apart, and fasten them to the ends of a length of cotton, leaving a certain amount of slack. Then draw the cotton tight with a pencil, and trace a curve, keeping the cotton tight all the time. The result will be an ellipse, with the pins marking the foci. In practice, of course, what usually happens is that the thread breaks and the pins fall out.

elliptical. The eccentricity amounts to only 0·05, which is not very much. If the orbit were drawn to a scale of, say three inches in diameter, so that it could be fitted on to a page of this book, it would be indistinguishable from a circle unless it were carefully measured.

The next correction is of rather different type. We have seen that the Earth-Moon system should be regarded as a double planet rather than as a planet and a satellite. Therefore, we cannot say simply that the Moon moves round the Earth; more properly, both bodies are travelling round their common centre of gravity.

To understand this more clearly, it will be of help to picture an ordinary gymnasium dumbbell. Balance it on a post by the joining arm, and twist it; both bells will revolve round the centre of gravity

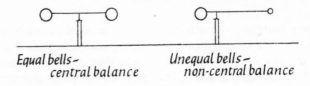

Equal bells–
central balance

Unequal bells–
non-central balance

Centre of gravity demonstration

of the system, i.e. the point where the arm is supported. Ordinarily this point will be in the middle of the arm, since the bells are of equal weight. If one bell is heavier than the other, the balancing point will be closer to the heavier bell; and the greater the difference in weight between the two bells, the greater will be the distance of the supporting point from the middle of the arm.

The same holds good for the Earth and Moon, which may be compared with the two bells. There is no joining arm, but the force of gravity may be said to act in much the same way. The Earth has 81 times the mass of the Moon, and so the centre of gravity is shifted well toward the Earth – so far, in fact, that it actually lies inside the terrestrial globe, though some way from the middle of the Earth. It is around this balancing-point, or 'barycentre', that the two bodies are revolving.

Even now there is yet another correction to be made to our original diagram, which showed the Moon going round the Earth in a conveniently circular orbit. This new complication arises because, strange as it may seem, the Sun's pull upon the Moon is more than twice as powerful as the Earth's.

The Earth is moving round the Sun at a mean velocity of 18½ miles per second, or roughly 66,000 m.p.h. Relative to the Earth, the Moon's orbital speed is only about one-third of a mile per second, so that it too is moving at about 66,000 m.p.h. relative to the Sun; and to an observer in space the Moon would appear to be a perfectly normal planet, travelling in an elliptical orbit with the Sun in one of the foci. The path of the Moon is always concave to the Sun, as is shown in the diagram.

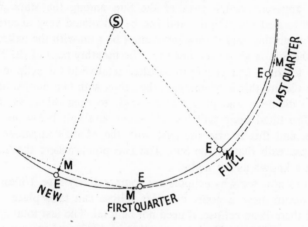

The Moon's orbit always concave to the Sun

Although the Sun's pull is so strong, there is no danger that the Moon will part company with the Earth and move away on its own. This is because the Sun attracts the Earth and Moon almost equally. The Moon is more strongly pulled when it lies between the Sun and the Earth, around the time of new moon, and less strongly when it is on the far side; but the force on the two bodies is always much the same, and all that the Earth has to do is to overcome the slight difference. This it can easily manage, and so Earth and Moon keep together in their never-ending journey.

Next let us turn to eclipses, which have been carefully studied from the very early days of science, and which caused a great deal of alarm and despondency before astronomers found out why they occur.

Although the Sun is so much larger than the Moon, it is also so much further away that it appears as almost exactly the same size in the sky; in each case the mean angular diameter is just over half a degree. Consequently, when the Earth, Moon and Sun move into a straight line, with the Moon in the middle, the lunar disk blots out the Sun, and we see a solar eclipse. If the Moon's orbit were really as simple as shown in the first diagram, we would have a solar eclipse at each new moon. This does not happen because the Moon's path is inclined at an angle of about five degrees relative to the orbit of the Earth.

The apparent yearly path of the Sun among the stars marks what is termed the ecliptic, and can be calculated very accurately, even though the stars themselves cannot be seen with the naked eye when the Sun is above the horizon. The monthly path of the Moon is easy to chart, and proves to be tilted relative to the ecliptic. One way to picture this is to compare the orbits with two hoops, hinged along a diameter and placed at an angle to each other, as shown here. The tilted hoop will lie half above and half below its companion, and this is also the case with the Moon's apparent path compared with that of the Sun. The two points where the 'hoops' cross are known as the nodes.

We can now see why eclipses are comparatively rare. Unless new moon occurs near a node, no solar eclipse can take place – and even if there is an eclipse, it need not be total. The last total eclipse of the Sun visible in England was that of 1927, and we must wait until 1999 for the next.

An eclipse of the Moon is quite different in nature, since it is due to the Moon passing into the shadow cast by the Earth. Lunar eclipses will be described in Chapter 13; meanwhile it is obvious that they, too, depend on the lining-up of the Moon, Earth and Sun, and can take place only when the Moon is full. More than

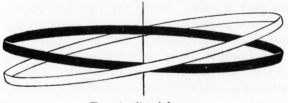

Two inclined hoops

a dozen lunar eclipses will be visible from Britain before the end of the present century.

The Moon's orbit is not absolutely unchanging for revolution after revolution. The effects due to the gravitational pulls of the Sun and Earth change, owing to the changing distances, and measurable effects are also produced by the planets, particularly Venus. The result of all this is that the nodes shift slowly round the sky, completing a full circuit in just over eighteen years.

We will return to eclipses later; meanwhile, let us turn to another famous phenomenon – Harvest Moon.

Everyone knows that the Moon rises in an easterly direction and sets toward the west. This apparent motion is due to the real rotation of the Earth from west to east. The Moon is also moving in its orbit from west to east, and so it appears to travel eastward among the stars, covering about thirteen degrees per day. Anyone who takes the trouble to check the position of the Moon on two successive nights, using near-by stars as reference-points, will soon see just what is happening.

The apparent path of the Moon in the sky is not very different from that of the Sun; the angle between the two is only five degrees, which is not very much even though it is sufficient to prevent eclipses from happening every month. At full phase, the Moon is opposite to the Sun in the sky, and to observers in the northern hemisphere of the Earth it is visible due south at midnight.

In the diagram, the angle of the ecliptic compared with the horizon is shown for spring and for autumn. In spring, around March, the angle is at its greatest. In twenty-four hours the Moon moves from position 1 to position 2, and it is clear that the 'retardation' – that is to say, the difference in rising-time from one night to the

Harvest Moon

33

rest – will be considerable. The situation in autumn is different. The angle is not nearly so sharp, and although the Moon moves across the starry background by the same amount – in other words, the distance between 1 and 2 is the same in each diagram – the retardation will be much less. In September, the retardation may be reduced to about a quarter of an hour.

In September, then, the full moon seems to rise at much the same time for several nights running. This is termed Harvest Moon, since in olden times the farmers found it very useful. The following full moon (Hunter's Moon) behaves in a similar fashion, though the retardation is greater. It is often said that Harvest Moon and Hunter's Moon look unusually big, but this is not so, as even rough measures will prove.

The Earth has a rotation period of 23 hours 56 minutes, but that of the Moon is $27\frac{1}{3}$ days. This means that the Moon keeps the same face towards us all the time. A surface feature, such as a crater, will not seem to shift about; if it lies near the centre of the disk it will always remain there, and will never be seen near the edge or 'limb'.

There is no mystery about this curious state of affairs. The Moon has a captured rotation, to use the scientific term, because of the tidal friction in past ages. Such behaviour is not unique. Mercury always keeps the same hemisphere turned toward the Sun, and all the large satellites of the giant planets do so with respect to their primaries.

It has sometimes been argued that the Moon cannot rotate at all, but this is clearly wrong. A simple experiment will show that we would see all parts of a non-rotating Moon. Put a chair in the garden to represent the Earth, and imagine that your head represents the Moon. Stand behind the chair, a foot or two away from

Chair demonstration

it, and fix your eyes upon some object beyond, such as a tree. Now walk in a circle round the chair, keeping your eyes fixed on the tree. When you have reached the far side of the chair, so that the tree is in front of you and the chair behind, you will find that your back, not your face, will be pointing to the chair. To keep your face turned chairward all the time, you must turn as you walk – in other words you must rotate upon your axis, completing one rotation for each journey round the chair.

From this it will be seen that the Moon keeps the same side toward the Earth, but not toward the Sun. From Earth we can never see the reverse hemisphere of the Moon, but daylight and night conditions there are just the same as on the familiar side.

It might therefore be thought that we would be able to study exactly 50 per cent of the total surface of the Moon, while the remaining 50 per cent would be permanently averted. Actually, conditions are not so straightforward as this, and altogether we can study 59 per cent of the surface area (though, of course, no more than 50 per cent is visible at any one moment). The remaining 41 per cent remained completely unknown until the Russian rocket, Lunik III, sent back photographs of it in October 1959.

The most important factor in this connection is termed libration in longitude. It is due to the fact that the Moon's path round the Earth* is not circular, but elliptical. Kepler's Second Law, announced 350 years ago, states that the velocity of a planet round the Sun, or of a satellite round a planet, depends upon its distance, and the rule may be summed up quite neatly by the phrase 'the nearer, the faster'. Thus Mercury, at 36,000,000 miles from the Sun, moves much more rapidly in its orbit than the Earth, at 93,000,000 miles.

This law may be applied to the Moon. As we have seen, its distance from us varies between about 221,000 miles at perigee to about 253,000 at apogee. When near perigee, it is moving at its fastest, while by the time it reaches apogee it has slowed down. In fact, the Moon's velocity in orbit is not constant, whereas the speed of axial rotation does not change at all – a situation which has far-reaching results.

The diagram should make the position clear. We begin with the

* Or, more accurately, around the barycentre.

35

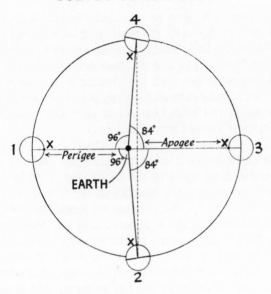

Libration in longitude

Moon at perigee, in position 1, and take X as marking the centre of the disk as seen from Earth. After a quarter of its journey, the Moon has reached position 2; but since it has travelled from perigee, it has moved slightly quicker than its mean rate and has covered 96 degrees instead of only 90. As seen from Earth point X lies slightly east of the apparent centre of the disk, and a small portion of the 'far side' has come into view in the west, so that in fact we are seeing a short distance round the mean western limb.

After a further quarter-month the Moon has reached 3. It is now at apogee, and the point X is again central. A further 84 degrees is covered between positions 3 and 4, and point X is displaced toward the west, so that an area beyond the mean eastern limb is uncovered. At the end of one revolution the Moon has arrived back in position 1, and X is once more centrally placed on the disk as seen from Earth.

Libration in longitude means, then, that the Moon sways slightly to and fro, allowing us to peer alternately beyond the mean east and west limbs of the earth-turned hemisphere. In addition, there is a libration in latitude; because the Moon's orbit is perceptibly inclined, we can sometimes see for some way beyond the mean northern or southern limb. Finally there is a diurnal or daily libration, due to the axial rotation of the Earth; at moonrise an observer at A can see slightly beyond the mean western edge, and at moonset slightly beyond the eastern edge, as shown in the next diagram.

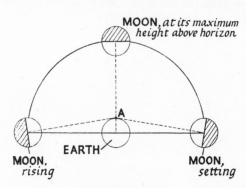

Diurnal libration

The sum total of all these librations is that at one time or another we can study 59 per cent of the Moon's surface. Of course, the so-called libration zones – those which are periodically brought into and out of view – are difficult to map, since all the features there are seen at an inconvenient angle and are badly foreshortened.

One further peculiarity of the lunar motion is certainly worth mentioning. This is the secular acceleration, or apparent speeding-up of the Moon in its orbit. If we take the position of the Moon as measured centuries ago, and predict the present position by adding on the correct number of revolutions, the results will not agree; the Moon will have moved too far, i.e. too quickly.

Fortunately the ancient astronomers have left us reliable records, as they observed eclipses. A total eclipse of the Sun can happen only at new moon, and therefore the moment of totality is also the exact moment of new moon. Eclipse records go back for thousands of years, and it was by comparing these records with modern measures of the Moon's position in the sky that the apparent speeding-up was discovered. It is due partly to Venus and Mars, which pull on the Earth and make our orbit round the Sun less elliptical.

and partly by the tidal effects described in Chapter 3. The effect is very slight, but over hundreds of years it mounts up enough to be measured with some accuracy.

We must agree, then, that the Moon's movements are by no means so simple as they look at first sight. The account given here is very brief, and perhaps over-simplified; much remains to be said, and to explain the lunar motions completely taxes the ability of the world's greatest mathematicians.

Chapter 5

The Moon and the Earth

Whether we regard the Moon as a sister planet or as a mere satellite, we must at least agree that it is our companion in space. Astronomically speaking it is never far away from us, and it may well be expected to produce significant effects upon the Earth. This is indeed the case. In particular, the Moon is the main cause of the tides.

In the far-off ages when the Moon and Earth were closer together than they are now, the tides raised by the two worlds upon each other must have been tremendous. As the Moon drew away, the tides lessened; but even today, when the separating distance has grown to almost a quarter of a million miles, they are still very marked.

It is probably true to say that so far as mankind is concerned, the tides are much more important than moonlight. We could easily do without the friendly light which the Moon sends us – as in fact we have to do for at least one week out of every four – but without the tides, our shipping problems would be increased. Moreover, the tides offer us a source of almost unlimited power, and the only trouble about this is that at present we do not know how to harness it.

The diagram on page 40 shows how the tides are caused. For the sake of simplicity, let us imagine that the whole Earth is covered with a shallow, uniform ocean. Immediately under the Moon, where the lunar gravitational pull is strongest, the waters will tend to heap up in a bulge, and there will be another bulge on the far side of the Earth. Here, M represents the Moon, and AX the Earth's axis; the water-shell is shown by dashed lines, and is, of course, drawn as much larger and more elliptical than it could ever be in fact.

As the Earth spins on its axis, the water-heap does not spin with it, but keeps underneath the Moon. The result is that as the Earth rotates, the water-heaps remain more or less stationary. They pass right round the Earth's surface at every revolution, and each point on the globe will have two high tides per twenty-four hours.

The Moon is moving in its orbit, so that the water-heaps shift slowly as they follow the Moon around; on an average, the high tide at any particular place will be fifty minutes later each day. Neither will the two daily high tides be equal. Consider a point C, which, in the diagram, has a high tide. Twelve hours later C will have moved round to C^1, and will experience another high tide – but this high tide will not be so great as the first, because the Earth's axis, AX, is tilted with respect to the path of the Moon. If the original tide is represented by CD, the second will be given by C^1D^1, which is decidedly less (though the drawing is, needless to say, hopelessly out of scale). This difference is known as the 'diurnal inequality' in the tides.

There are other complications to be taken into account, too. When the Moon is near perigee, and is at its closest to the Earth, its pull is stronger than at the time of apogee, and the tides are correspondingly higher; in fact, the difference amounts to over twenty per cent. Neither can we disregard the Sun. Solar tides are much weaker than those caused by the Moon, but they are evident, none the less. At new or full moon – the positions when the Moon is said to be at 'syzygy'* – the Sun and Moon are pulling in the same direction, and produce the strong tides known, rather misleadingly, as spring tides. The much lower neap tides occur when the Moon is at quadrature, i.e. First or Last Quarter, so that its gravitational pull works against that of the Sun. There will be neap tides when the Moon has moved to the position shown in the neap-tide diagram.

The actual tides are not so simple and orderly as they would be if the Earth were genuinely surrounded by a shallow, uniform water-shell. The seas are of various shapes and depths, and local effects are very important. At Southampton, for instance, two high

* This hideous word is in common use, and is so tongue-twisting that it is easy to remember!

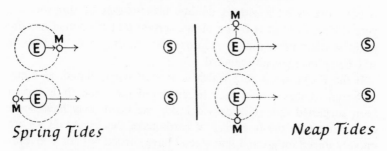

Spring Tides   Neap Tides

tides take place in succession as the rising water comes up the
two narrow straits separating the mainland from the Isle of Wight
– the first up the Solent, then up Spithead. In the Bay of Fundy in
Nova Scotia, and also along some coastal areas in South America,
the tidal range is fifty feet or so, while in other places it amounts to
less than one foot. Moreover, the waters take some time to heap
up, and maximum tide does not occur directly under the Moon.
There is an appreciable lag, and the highest tide follows the
Moon after an interval which varies according to local conditions. Naturally, the lag is usually greatest for shallow coastal
areas.

The Moon pulls upon the solid body of the Earth as well as
upon the oceans, and land tides are easy to measure with suitable
instruments. A rather curious fact has emerged from studies of
them. Although the body of the Earth behaves as though it were
more rigid than steel, it also proves to be perfectly 'elastic'; after
being distorted by the tidal pull, it returns to its original shape
without the slightest delay, rather in the manner of an elastic band
which is first stretched and then let go. However, land tides amount
to only about 4½ inches instead of many feet, and in everyday life
they are too minor to be noticed at all.

Tidal effects are also traceable in the atmosphere. Although they
are unimportant in the normal way, it is conceivable that they may
have some influence upon radio reception. Long-distance wireless
communication is made possible by the presence of reflecting layers
in the upper part of the atmospheric mantle, known as the ionosphere. In 1939 Appleton and Weekes showed that the Moon causes
tides in the ionosphere, and more recently P. A. Howell has maintained that radio reception is easiest at about the time of full moon.

Other workers have serious doubts; observations of this sort are very difficult, and it is by no means certain that the Moon has the slightest effect upon radio conditions, though the whole question is still being energetically studied.

If the Earth has a core which is at least partly liquid, as many authorities believe, tides may be produced there too. It has even been suggested that tides caused inside the Earth may have some connection with the frequency of earthquake shocks. Again we are on very uncertain ground, but since I have carried out some investigations on my own account I feel justified in discussing the possibility in slightly more detail.

In 1938 C. Davison, the British authority upon earthquakes, had come to the conclusion that there was a definite connection between earthquake frequency and the phases of the Moon. During the 1950's the Bulgarian astronomer N. Boneff announced that in his view the shocks were most common at around new and full moon, when the Moon and Sun were pulling along the same line; and this was supported independently by G. P. Tamrazyan, in Russia. From an analysis of earthquakes in California up to the end of 1935, Maxwell Allen had suggested that there was definite evidence of some sort of lunar control. Yet apparently there had been no real attempt to carry the survey over the whole world, and so a great deal of doubt remained.

Earthquake records are collected and analyzed at Kew Observatory, in London. Unfortunately there are no published lists showing the violence of individual earthquake shocks, but some sort of guide is given by noting the number of recording stations reporting each tremor; an earthquake recorded by, say, one hundred stations is likely to be much stronger than one reported by only half a dozen. On this basis, I took the Kew records for the period 1931-1953 and worked out an 'earthquake activity number' for each day, after which I tried to correlate these numbers with the phases of the Moon. No positive results emerged. The investigation was comparatively rough, since my daily numbers were very arbitrary; but so far as they go, they certainly do not support the theory that the Moon has any effect upon the frequency of the shocks. Once again, it is best to say that the whole question remains open. Of course it is true that many earthquakes have occurred near full moon – but the Moon is full once a month, and a search for coincidences will nearly always reveal them.*

The Moon and the weather are often said to be linked, but actually there is no connection between them, and no faith can be placed in the various attempts to associate the phases with rainfall, cyclones or changes of temperature. Admittedly the weather often does change at full moon, but we must bear in mind that the weather usually changes every two or three days in any case – in England, at least – so that once again the 'relationship' is due to nothing more than the law of averages. Between 1956 and 1960 I kept records of the weather-changes at my home, East Grinstead in Sussex, and found no trace whatsoever of any connection with the phases of the Moon. I have no doubt that the same would be true of any particular place in the world.

An old country saying tells us that 'the full moon eats up the clouds', and the sky often does clear as the full moon rises; but at the same time, the Sun must be setting – and nobody can deny that the weather and cloud conditions are very strongly dependent upon the Sun! Thunderstorms and meteors have also been linked with the Moon's phases, but again without the slightest justification.

All the same, one or two atmospheric effects are worth mention-

---

* It is easy to show this, and I have selected only one out of the many dozens of examples which could be given. In 1952 an American radio engineer produced a paper in which he claimed that certain 'planetary configurations' had a marked effect upon wireless transmission. The frequency-curves in his paper looked most impressive at first sight, but he had been forced to bring in so many 'configurations' that it became clear that he was, no doubt unintentionally, coincidence-hunting. When the paper was described to the British Astronomical Assoiation in 1952, it was shown that the 'configurations' were even more closely related to (1) the light-fluctuations of the variable star Delta Cephei, and (2) the frequency of matinée performances at the Folies Bergère in Paris. With regard to (1), Delta Cephei is 600 light-years from the Earth, so that its rays now entering our eyes started on their journey about the time of King Edward III, and it does not seem very likely that they have much to do with the present positions of the planets in their orbits – yet the frequency curves fitted in very well. I am hardly qualified to comment on case (2), particularly since I have not been to the Folies Bergère since I last attended a scientific conference in Paris some years ago.

Coincidence-hunting can be quite amusing, though completely useless. I have no doubt that by selecting suitable qualifications it would be possible to draw graphs showing a link between – say – the periods of the minor planets, the price of bananas, and the number of goals scored by the Aston Villa football club. Astrologers are particularly good at this sort of thing.

ing, even though they belong strictly to the science of meteorology and have no actual connection with the Moon itself.

Everyone knows the expression 'once in a blue moon'. Blue moons are certainly very rare, but they are seen occasionally. The most striking example of recent years was that of 26th September 1950. I saw it from East Grinstead, and noted that 'the Moon shone down from a slightly misty sky with a lovely shimmering blueness – like an electric glimmer, utterly different from anything I have seen before'. Many people saw it from various parts of the world, and blue suns were also recorded. As is always the case, dust particles in the upper air were responsible, due in this instance to giant forest fires raging in Canada. The dust-pall in the New World was much more striking. At Ottawa, car headlights had to be switched on at midday, and in New York a game of baseball was played under arc-lights.

Haloes, or luminous rings round the Moon's disk, are comparatively common, and can be beautiful. They are due not to dust, but to moonlight catching a layer of ice-crystals in the atmosphere about 20,000 feet above the ground. These crystals make up the type of cloud known as 'cirrostratus'. If the cloud is lower and denser, the Moon merely looks watery. Both watery moons and haloes are said to be the forerunners of rain, and this is often true, as cirrostratus cloud itself is often a sign of approaching bad weather. Paraselenæ, or 'mock moons' – brilliant images of the Moon some way from the actual disk – are also due to ice crystals, but are very rare.

When the Moon shines upon water droplets in the atmosphere it may produce a rainbow in the same way as the Sun, although since moonlight is feebler than sunlight* the lunar rainbows are rarer, fainter and less brightly coloured. Yet occasionally a striking one is seen. Flying some 2,000 feet above North Scotland on 28th March 1945, I was particularly fortunate; most of the rainbow circle could be seen, and even some delicate, fugitive hues, giving a lovely effect. As I was the navigator of the aircraft, I could spend little time in looking at the rainbow, but I am glad to have seen it.

The celebrated 'moon illusion', which has been the subject of a

---

* About half a million full moons would be needed to equal the light of the Sun.

good deal of research, is not an atmospheric phenomenon at all, and in fact it remains something of a puzzle. For some reason, the full moon seems to appear larger when close to the horizon than when high in the sky. Indeed, the casual observer is apt to say that it looks twice the size, whatever the state of the sky – particularly at the time of Harvest Moon. Actually, the low-down moon is slightly more distant than the high-up one; the observer is brought toward the Moon as the Earth turns, and so the high moon is a little the larger – though the difference amounts to less than two per cent, and is therefore negligible. Why, then, should the low moon look the bigger? It is not really so, as measures prove; some trick of the eye is responsible.

The illusion has been known for many centuries, and was often explained by saying that we automatically compare the horizon moon with near-by objects such as trees and houses, so that it looks large by comparison. This theory is still given in some textbooks, but it is not correct, as the illusion is still well-marked even when the Moon rises above a perfectly featureless sea horizon.

Some years ago E. G. Boring, at Harvard, carried out experiments which indicated that the illusion was due to the behaviour of the eye itself, because the unconscious effort of raising the eye to look at a high-up object causes the Moon to give the impression of being slightly smaller than it really is. Boring's work was followed up in 1959 by H. Leibowitz and T. Hartman, at Wisconsin, who experimented with disks seen at eye-level and overhead. They concluded that the illusion is due to the fact that human beings have more visual experience with objects in the horizontal plane than in the vertical, and that children were more affected than adults.

In 1962 L. Kaufman and I. Rock published some results which confirm the theory put forward by Ptolemy 2,000 years ago, according to which any object seen across filled space, such as the Moon seen across terrain at the horizon, is perceived as being more distant than an object just as far away but seen through empty space, such as the Moon at the zenith. If the images of these objects in the eye are in fact of equal size, the one that appears farther away will seem larger.

It is generally said that the illusion is not noticed by people who have lost the sight of one eye, or who deliberately cover up one eye for the entire evening. I was therefore surprised when, in 1961, I met a one-eyed observer (trained in science) who told me that he was always conscious of the effect. Yet interesting though the illusion may be, it is due to the human observer and not to the Moon, so that further discussion of it here would be out of place.

One elusive phenomenon, so far not properly explained, is the Counterglow or Gegenschein – a very faint luminous patch in the sky, seen exactly opposite to the Sun. It is visible only when the sky is exceptionally dark and clear; the slightest glow from artificial lights is enough to hide it. From England I have seen it only once – in 1942, from Devon, when the whole country was blacked-out as a wartime measure against German air-raids.

It is thought that the Gegenschein is due to sunlight being scattered by interplanetary dust, though other theories have been put forward. F. L. Whipple has suggested that the dust producing the glow must lie fairly near the Earth, and that it comes from the Moon. If the lunar surface is thickly coated, it is not impossible that meteors hitting the Moon may have hurled up dust-particles so violently that the material has left the moon altogether and escaped into space; but the idea does not seem very likely, and in any case it is very doubtful whether the lunar dust can be as deep as would be required.

Let us now consider the possible influence of the Moon upon living things.

Everyone has heard of the so-called connection between mental illness and the full moon, but few doctors have any faith in it, and stories about 'moon-madness' seem to lack foundation. Arguments about the whole matter have gone on for a long time, but there is no positive evidence that the Moon's phases affect human minds, and neither is there any obvious reason why they should do so.

Of course, certain small creatures regulate their habits according to the Moon; but as all these creatures are aquatic, it seems reasonable to suppose that the tides are responsible, and not the Moon directly. Land animals are in a different class. Fifty years ago, many farmers still believed that it was unwise to sow crops at new moon, and L. Kolisko of Stuttgart, who carried out long-term experiments between 1926 and 1935, reported a marked connection

Chapter 6

Observers of the Moon

Even a small telescope will show that the Moon is very different from the Earth. In place of our own prairies, forests and ice-fields, we find a rugged, rocky surface – barren, waterless and unprotected by atmosphere. On the Moon, perhaps more than anywhere else in the Solar System, we see Nature's work unaltered by the passing of time.

Lofty mountains rise from the plains, mingling with ridges, hillocks and valleys; here and there a brilliant peak glitters against the grey background, and the curious whitish streaks or rays run for immense distances across the surface. But the most striking features of all are the craters. There are hundreds upon hundreds of them, ranging from tremendous walled enclosures large enough to contain a dozen English counties down to tiny pits so small that they are at the extreme limit of visibility. Some have smooth interiors; some contain high central mountains; some have been

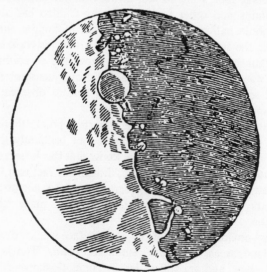

Galileo's drawing of the Moon

between plant growth and lunar phases – for instance she said that tomatoes sown two days before full moon were stronger, juicier and more tasty than those sown two days before new moon. Kolisko's results looked quite impressive, but she went on to draw some wild conclusions which tended to discredit the whole series of experiments (for instance, she believed that the Easter full moon was particularly powerful, and had a special significance for the whole of the following year). Later work by Rohmeder, Becker and others has given negative results, and on the whole it is safe to say that even if a relationship does exist, which is most unlikely, it is of no practical importance.

It would be pointless to discuss all the various superstitions which have grown up around the Moon, such as the old tale that it is unlucky to see the new moon through glass; neither need we waste any time on astrology, the so-called science which hindered the progress of true astronomy for so many centuries. According to astrologers, the positions of the Sun, Moon and planets in the sky affect human destinies. The belief still lingers on in some countries, particularly in India, where there was widespread alarm when, in 1962, the five brightest planets all happened to be in the same region of the sky, and some of the astrologers forecast the end of the world. Yet it has long since become clear that an astrologer with genuine mystical powers is about as common as a great auk.

It seems, then, that the Moon's main effects upon us concern the movement of the Earth and the regulation of the tides. Once we try to take matters any further, we are treading upon very uncertain ground.

Meanwhile, there has been a new and interesting suggestion which, if confirmed, would show a real link between the two worlds. It has been said that the mysterious objects known as tektites once formed part of the Moon, and have been hurled across space to the Earth.

Tektites are small, dark, glassy-looking objects which are found only in certain areas of the Earth. Most of them are less than an inch long, and even the largest known example is smaller than a hen's egg. They contain about eighty per cent silica, and are not difficult to identify, because they are unlike any other natural objects so far discovered.

Their distribution is remarkable. The widest 'tektite field' is in Australia, covering much of the southern part of the continent; at least two more fields occur in the region of the East Indies, and there are a few others in Asia and the American continent. The main European field lies in Moravia. No tektite has ever been found in Britain.

Originally, it was – naturally – thought that tektites must be of terrestrial origin. Even a casual glance showed that at one stage they had been very strongly heated, and the obvious answer was

Tektites

that they had been hurled out of active volcanoes. The main trouble about this idea is that the tektites are found in areas well away from volcanoes of any sort, active or extinct. Also, some tektites at least seem to have been heated not once, but twice. The first heating must have been very thorough, but the second was less violent, and affected only the layers near the surface.

This might be explained on the volcano theory – or so it was thought. Suppose that a tektite were heated inside a volcano, and then hurled out at a speed great enough to carry it beyond the densest part of the Earth's atmosphere? As it fell back toward the ground, it would encounter friction against the particles of atmosphere, just as a meteor does, which would explain the second (surface) heating.

However, D. Chapman has shown that this explanation, simple

though it may sound, does not fit the facts. It seems that the second heating of tektites was too strong to be accounted for in any such way. When a body is hurled upward, either by a volcano, a rocket vehicle or in any other manner, it can behave in one of three ways. Depending upon the speed which it is given, it can either escape into space, enter a path round the Earth, or come to a stop and then fall back to the ground. Therefore, a tektite which began its career inside an Earth volcano would have to follow the third course, as otherwise it would never return. This means that it must have started its drop, from a point beyond the top of the dense layers of atmosphere, with zero velocity. Yet a tektite has been so violently heated that a simple drop through the air, starting from rest, will not do. All the signs show that the tektite must have rushed into the air from outer space when it was already moving very quickly indeed. Of course, the greater the velocity, the greater the heating-up by friction against the air.

All this is very remarkable. Tektites are not in the least like ordinary meteors or meteorites; they have had their two heatings, and the first one has been so intense that it may well have taken place inside a volcano. And if Earth volcanoes cannot have been responsible – well, there must once have been plenty of active volcanoes on the Moon.

We can work out a possible sequence of events. Tektites were born inside lunar volcanoes; they were hurled out so violently that they escaped from the Moon altogether, and cooled down when they had reached what is often, though rather vaguely, called 'outer space'. Then they came into the Earth's atmosphere, and were heated again as they fell to the ground. Each tektite-field would be related to some specific lunar eruption, but few eruptions would produce material moving in a suitable manner to hit the Earth, which explains why tektite-fields are so rare.

This is speculation, and other suggestions have been made; for instance H. H. Nininger believes that the tektites were expelled from the Moon as a result of large meteors striking the lunar surface. Yet it looks as though the total mass of known tektites is too great for this to be the correct answer, and if tektites really come from the Moon it is more likely that they began their careers inside volcanoes there.

By no means all scientists agree that tektites are lunar,* and it would be much too sweeping to say definitely that when we handle tektites we are handling pieces of material which once formed part of the Moon; but it is an intriguing possibility, and we must admit that the tektites, small and unspectacular though they may look, are among the most baffling objects ever found.

This is one of the problems which will probably be cleared up soon after the first expeditions have landed on the Moon. Meanwhile, it is time for us to turn our attention to the lunar world itself.

---

* Various less rational ideas have been put forward from time to time. It has been maintained that tektites are artificial, and that our remote ancestors were remarkably good at glass-making; that they are pieces of special material produced by the people of Ancient Atlantis or some equally mythical country, and so on. The latest of these weird theories has come from a Russian, A. Agrest, who has claimed that tektites mark the traces left by nuclear-powered space-ships which once visited Earth from another planet. Agrest's views were summed up rather neatly by two more Russians, V. Gubarev and M. Rostarchuk, who said that 'the traces point not to outer space, but to ignorance'. Every science attracts eccentrics, but astronomy has surely had more than its fair share!

broken and ruined by other craters, so that only disjoined parts of their original walls still remain.

Modern astronomy really began in the winter of 1609-1610, when Galileo turned his newly made 'optick tube' toward the Moon. The little telescope was feeble by our own standards, but it was quite good enough to give Galileo a spectacular view of the lunar surface. During the next few years he even constructed a map – rough and inaccurate, of course, but marking the start of true lunar study or 'selenography'.*

Galileo also tried to measure the heights of some of the mountains on the Moon. His method was not capable of any real accuracy, and his results were somewhat wide of the mark; but he concluded that some of the peaks reached altitudes of about $5\frac{1}{4}$ miles, which is at least not so very far from the truth.

While Galileo was observing the Moon from Italy, news of the invention spread. During 1610 telescopes, or 'perspective cylinders' as they were then called, were brought to Britain. Strangely enough, the first lunar observations made in our islands came not from London, Bath or York, but from the isolated country village of Traventy, in Pembrokeshire, where Sir William Lower used one of the cylinders to look at the Moon. Lower described the broad plains, ring-mountains and other features just as Galileo had done, and said that about half-moon he could see 'the mountains shining like stars', while the full moon resembled a tart that his cook had made – 'there some bright stuff, there some dark, and so confusedly all over'. He was not an astronomer in the proper sense of the word, and never seems to have attempted any serious observations, but his comments are of historical interest.

Lower and Galileo agreed on one important point: there were no half-tones on the Moon. Objects were either brilliantly lit, or else immersed in black shadow. We now know that this is because of the almost complete lack of atmosphere, though the fact that the Moon is an 'airless world', to use the general term, was not proved until many years after Lower and Galileo had made their first observations.

The most obvious feature of the Moon's face was its division into bright upland areas, and dark, smoother plains. The latter were christened 'seas', and are still called by romantic names such as the

* A word derived from the Greek: Selene, the moon-goddess.

Sea of Serenity (Mare Serenitatis) and the Sea of Nectar (Mare Nectaris). Galileo himself seems to have known that there is no water in them, but most astronomers of the time thought differently; it was believed that the Moon might well be a smaller edition of the Earth, with lakes, oceans, and – presumably – inhabitants. Of course, it was impossible to find out much with the early telescopes. The Moon is almost a quarter of a million miles away, and Galileo,

Hevelius' Lunar Map

53

using a maximum magnifying-power of 30, could see it only about as well as he could have done with the naked eye from a distance of 8,000 miles. No wonder that small details escaped him, and that his map of the surface was very crude.

During the next thirty years, several charts were made by various observers, but it was not until 1647 that the first reasonably good map was produced by Hevelius, a city councillor of Danzig. Hevelius built an observatory on the roof of his house, and equipped it with the best instruments available at the time; he was a patient and skilful observer, and his map, just under a foot in diameter, remained the best for over a century. He also made height-measures of some of the lunar peaks, and although his results were naturally rough by modern standards they were much more accurate than Galileo's.

Hevelius gave some thought to the best method of naming lunar features. He finally decided to give them terrestrial names, and this was the system followed in his map. For instance, the crater now known as Copernicus was called 'Etna'; another large crater, the modern Plato, was 'the Greater Black Lake'. The whole system was clumsy and feeble, and only four of Hevelius' names are still in use.

Copies of the map exist, but the original copper-plate of it is no longer to be found. Apparently it was melted down and made into a teapot after Hevelius' death!

Riccioli, an Italian priest, worked out a much better scheme of nomenclature. In 1651 he published a map in which each large crater was named after a famous scientist or philosopher. Riccioli's motives have often been questioned, and it has been suggested that he put forward this system out of sheer vanity. Certainly he allotted large and important craters to himself and his pupil, Grimaldi, upon whose observations the map was based; but at any rate his system soon replaced that of Hevelius, and nearly all the names he gave (more than 200 altogether) are still used. Later astronomers have added to the list, and at the present time over 700 names are recognized, some of them those of living astronomers.*

* Descartes, a seventeenth-century French philosopher, once made the cheerful suggestion that the spirits of those people honoured at being placed on the Moon went to reside in their own particular craters after death. As some lunar maps attach my own name to a small and entirely unimportant crater near the Mare Humorum (Sea of Humours), I rather hope that Descartes was wrong.

No system can be completely satisfactory, and Riccioli's has its weaknesses. Some strange people seem to have found their way on to the Moon. Julius Cæsar is there, presumably because of his association with calendar reform, and Alexander the Great and his friend Nearch also appear; there are even a couple of Olympians, Atlas and Hercules. (One crater has been given the rather startling name of Hell. This does not, however, indicate any remarkable depth; it was named in honour of Maximilian Hell, a Hungarian astronomer of the eighteenth century.) On the other hand Riccioli 'gave away' all the largest and most important formations, so that later astronomers had to be content with second-best. Thus we find Newton tucked away near the Moon's South Pole, while Mädler, greatest of all lunar observers, is represented by a very insignificant crater on the Sea of Nectar. Moreover, Riccioli did not believe in the Copernican System, according to which the Earth moves round the Sun; he firmly believed the Earth to be the centre of the universe. Thus, to use his own words, he 'flung Copernicus into the Ocean of Storms' – the great plain of the Oceanus Procellarum – and Galileo joined him there in the guise of a very obscure crater which is none too easy to identify at first sight.

Yet despite the criticisms made then and later, Riccioli's system was obviously a good one, and it has stood the test of time. His map, however, was little or no better than that of Hevelius.

For the next hundred years, little progress was made in charting the lunar surface. At last, in 1775, a German astronomer named Tobias Mayer produced a comparatively accurate map almost eight inches across, and this remained the best for a long time; but true 'selenography' really began four years later, when Johann Hieronymus Schröter founded a small private observatory at Lilienthal, near Bremen, and began to study the Moon.

Schröter was not a professional astronomer. For much of his career he was chief magistrate of Lilienthal, with ample means and leisure to carry on his hobby, and he collected several large telescopes – two made by William Herschel, the most skilful instrument-maker of the age, and two even larger constructed by Schräder of Kiel, one of which had a 19-inch mirror. For thirty years he worked away, drawing, measuring and charting. To a great extent he was breaking new ground, and it was he who first studied the interesting features which we now call the clefts. He did not actually

55

discover them, and this honour must go to Christiaan Huygens, a Dutch astronomer of a century earlier, but Schröter was the first to pay any serious attention to them.

Schröter, like Riccioli, has been much maligned, and with even less reason. It is perfectly true that he was not a good draughtsman. His drawings are crude and schematic, and the detail is put in very clumsily. Some of his ideas, too, were strange; he believed that he had found important changes on the lunar surface, and he was prepared to admit that the Moon was a world peopled by intelligent beings. On the other hand he was a completely honest observer, and never drew anything unless he could be quite certain that he had seen it, while his measures of mountain-heights were far better

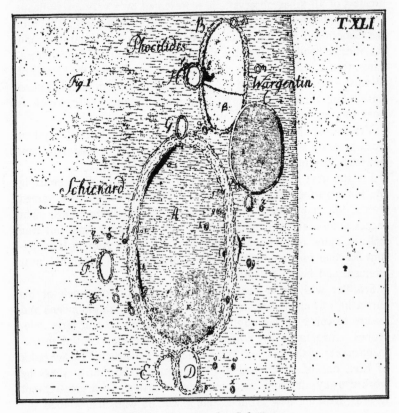

Lunar drawing by Schröter

than those of his predecessors. He did not produce a complete map, but he did make hundreds of drawings of different parts of the Moon; and his work has never received sufficient credit except, perhaps, in Germany.*

It is sad to relate that Schröter, most peaceful of men, became a victim of the Napoleonic Wars. In 1813, when he was sixty-eight years old, the French, under Vandamme, occupied Bremen: Lilienthal fell into their hands, and Schröter's observatory was burned to the ground, along with almost all his notes, manuscripts and unpublished observations. The loss could never be made good, and the old astronomer, his life's work more or less wrecked, lived for only three years longer.

The mantle of Schröter fell upon three of his countrymen, Lohrmann, Beer and Mädler. All were clever draughtsmen as well as being good observers, and between them they explored every square mile of the Moon's visible surface – but it must be remembered that they had Schröter's work to use as a basis. The credit for founding the science of precise lunar observation must go to the Lilienthal amateur, and to him alone.

Wilhelm Lohrmann, a land surveyor of Dresden, published an excellent map on a larger scale than Mayer's, and started out to construct a chart showing even more detail. Unfortunately he had completed only four sections when his eyesight failed him, and he had to give up. He died in 1840.

However, a tremendous advance was made by a Berlin banker, Wilhelm Beer, and his friend Johann Mädler. These two used the 3¾ inch refracting telescope at Beer's home, and studied the Moon patiently for over ten years, finally producing a map which has been the basis for all later studies. They followed it up with a book, *Der Mond*, which is a masterpiece of careful, accurate work. *Der Mond* appeared in 1838, and it is surprising to find that it has never been fully translated into English.

Oddly enough Mädler, who did most of the mapping, never used any but the 3¾-inch refractor for his lunar work. A refractor is more effective, inch for inch, than a reflector; but even so, the difference

* For instance, it has been said that Schröter's telescopes were of poor quality, so making his work unreliable. This may possibly be true of the 19-inch Schräder reflector, but it was certainly not true of the smaller Herschel instruments which Schröter used almost all the time.

between Mädler's telescope and Schröter's 19-inch is remarkable. It is true that Mädler's probably gave a sharper image, but Schröter's extra aperture must have given him a distinct advantage when studying very delicate detail.

Beer and Mädler's book had a tremendous effect upon lunar studies, and, strange to say, actually held them back to some extent. Schröter had believed the Moon to be a living, changing world, but Beer and Mädler went to the other extreme, and considered that it must be completely dead. Their opinions naturally carried a great deal of weight. Neither of them did much more lunar work after 1840, when Mädler left Berlin to become director of the Dorpat Observatory in Estonia (then, as now, part of Russia), and nobody else seemed inclined to follow in their footsteps. The general opinion was that *Der Mond* must be the 'last word' on the subject, and that as the Moon was a changeless world there was no point in observing it any further.

Whatever the cause, the quarter-century following the publication of *Der Mond* was extremely unproductive. Observers turned their attention elsewhere, and the Moon, relegated to the status of a lifeless and uninteresting globe, was shamefully neglected.

Luckily there was one astronomer, Julius Schmidt, who did not agree. He began to observe the Moon when he was only a boy, and he continued to do so until his death in 1884. After acting as assistant at various German observatories he was appointed to the directorship of the Athens Observatory, in 1858, and it was in Greece that much of his work was done.

Schmidt not only revised and completed the map begun by Lohrmann, but also issued one of his own which will stand up to comparison with the best modern charts. Before this map appeared, however, a great deal had happened, and Schmidt was primarily responsible. It was the 'Linné affair' which reawakened popular interest in the Moon.

At various times Lohrmann, Beer and Mädler, and Schmidt himself had recorded a deep crater in the Mare Serenitatis (Sea of Serenity); Mädler had named it Linné in honour of Carl von Linné, the Swedish botanist. Then, in 1866, Schmidt announced that the crater was no longer there. It had vanished from the Moon, or at least altered in appearance beyond all recognition.

This was startling, to put it mildly. Could the Moon be less dead than Mädler had thought? It was a revolutionary idea, and yet, coming from an observer with Schmidt's experience, it could not be disregarded. Amateurs and professionals alike were interested, and once more telescopes were pointed at the lunar surface. Even now the Linné mystery has not been cleared up, and we will return to it later.

Up to less than a century ago most of our knowledge of the Moon's surface had been gained by the work of German observers. Britons and Americans had done relatively little, but this was altered during the years following the Linné announcement.

The first of the important British lunar works, written by Edmund Neison, appeared in 1876. Neison's map was not much more than a revision of Mädler's, but the book itself, containing a description of every named formation, was of tremendous value – in fact it still is, and even now copies of it may be picked up occasionally. Just how much actual observation Neison himself did is not clear, though it must have been considerable. He provides a link between the past and the near-present; he was only twenty-five when he wrote his book, and died as recently as 1938, though, amazingly, he seems to have taken no practical interest in the Moon for the last sixty years of his life.

At about the time that Neison's book was published, a new society devoted entirely to studies of the Moon was formed in England. This was the Selenographical Society, and for ten years or so it was very active. In 1883, following the death of its president (W. R. Birt) and the resignation of its secretary (Neison) it was disbanded, but seven years later the newly founded British Astronomical Association set up a Lunar Section and carried on the work.

From the start, the B.A.A. has been made up chiefly of amateurs; and since the Moon is a body upon which valuable work may be done with modest telescopes, there has been no shortage of observers. Ever since 1890 the Lunar Section has kept up its activity, and eleven full-length *Memoirs* have been published, as well as dozens of papers and reports scattered through the monthly *Journal* of the Association. Thomas Gwyn Elger, first Director of the Lunar Section, published a book on his own account in 1895, illustrated by an outline map which is still extremely useful.

Meanwhile, the camera had started to make its presence felt. The very name 'photography' was first coined by an astronomer –

J. F. W. Herschel, son of the even more famous William Herschel – and its application to the Moon was seen as early as 1839, when François Arago described the invention in his speech to the Chamber of Deputies in Paris. Arago's words are worth remembering. He said: 'We may hope to make photographic maps of our satellite, which means that we will carry out one of the most lengthy, most exacting, most delicate tasks of astronomy in a few minutes.' This hope has not been realized, and even today we still lack a really first-class photographic lunar map, but at least a start has been made, and all modern charts are based upon photographic measures.

In March 1840 J. W. Draper, of New York, made a Daguerreotype of the Moon, using his long-focus 5-inch reflector. The image was one inch in diameter, and light and dark areas were shown, but the exposure-time needed was a full twenty minutes. Ten years later J. A. Whipple, at Harvard, obtained a good series of Daguerreotypes showing the Moon at different phases, and some of these pictures, enlarged to a scale of five inches to the Moon's diameter, were shown at the Great Exhibition held in London in 1851. They caused a great deal of interest.

The development of the wet collodion process helped matters considerably, and in 1852 some good results were obtained by a British amateur, Warren de la Rue. Later, using dry plates, de la Rue in Britain and Rutherfurd in the U.S.A. were able to take photographs which were of definite astronomical value. Others, too, began to join in the work, and after 1890 lunar photography became a recognized branch of research. The plates taken at Paris by Loewy and Puiseux were used to draw up the first real photographic atlas, and were of good quality; the atlas appeared in 1897, and was followed in 1904 by another due to W. H. Pickering, using equipment at the Jamaica station of the Harvard College Observatory. Pickering's programme was an ambitious one, as he covered the surface of the Moon five times, showing each area under five different states of illumination. It cannot be said that his photographs are anything like as sharp as those of the Paris observers, but they have been proved to be very useful.

Yet once again there came a period of relative neglect. Professional astronomers in general had no time to spare for selenography, and tended to regard the Moon as rather dull and parochial. Even photography of lunar features lapsed; some trial exposures were made around 1919 with the new 100-inch reflector at Mount Wilson, in California, but on the whole the Moon was regarded as the province of amateurs.

Nobody can deny that the amateurs rose to the occasion. In Britain, for instance, Walter Goodacre, who succeeded Elger as director of the B.A.A. Lunar Section, published a book in 1930 containing a detailed map as well as a full account of each named formation. Even larger was the map compiled by H. P. Wilkins, director of the Lunar Section between 1946 and 1956. Wilkins began lunar work in 1909. His first map, dating from 1924, had a diameter of 60 inches, and this was followed by a gigantic chart 300 inches across. The final edition, reduced to a scale of 100 inches, appeared in 1959, and Wilkins was at work on a further revision at the time of his sudden and deeply regretted death on 23rd January 1960.

Lunar charting was by no means confined to Britain. In America the amateurs of the Association of Lunar and Planetary Observers, founded by W. H. Haas in 1947, were equally active, and work was also carried out in many other countries of the world, particularly Japan. This, then, was the state of affairs when the spectacular advances in space research changed the whole situation.

As we have seen, professional interest in the Moon had largely lapsed. It is true that the International Astronomical Union published a map in 1935, drawn by W. H. Wesley and M. A. Blagg and based on the positions of lunar features measured earlier by S. A. Saunder and J. Franz, but it was hardly a success; it was not clear enough to be really useful, and was defective near the Moon's limb. But when the rockets began to fly, and it became clear that the Moon would be reached much earlier than most people had thought possible, selenography once more became 'respectable'. A really detailed, accurate map was needed.

The obvious solution was a complete photographic chart, similar to Pickering's series or the Paris Atlas, but much larger and sharper. This was attempted by G. P. Kuiper and his colleagues at the Yerkes Observatory in America, and appeared in 1959. It was based on the best photographs available – including those taken at the high-altitude Pic du Midi Observatory in the French Pyrénées, which are superb – and it represents a major contribution. Yet even so, it does not meet the requirements. Over-enlargement has led to blurring of the fine detail, except in areas near the centre of the

Moon's disk, and many of the limb areas are poorly represented.

This is not the fault of the observers, or of their equipment. The trouble lies with the Earth's inconvenient, unsteady atmosphere. When a time-exposure is made, there is bound to be slight disturbance in the air, and the most delicate detail is lost. We have to admit that in recording fine features on the surfaces of the Moon and planets, the camera is still less effective than the eye. The photographic plates are most useful for accurate measures of the positions of recorded objects – for which they are, needless to say, invaluable.

Further programmes are planned. A mapping project organized in Europe, from Manchester University, seems to have made little progress, but a small and very clear atlas has been produced by the Japanese observers S. Miyamoto and M. Matsui. As the Moon becomes more and more accessible, the work will go on; we may not yet have achieved all that Arago had hoped to do 'in a few minutes', but we are well on the way.

This review of the history of selenography is very sketchy and incomplete, but if we are to form a complete picture of lunar science we must know at least a little about what has gone before. Mayer, Schröter, Mädler and the rest are not mere voices from the past; their work lives on.

Chapter 7

Features of the Moon

When we first look at the Moon through a telescope, the whole surface seems a tangled confusion, so crowded with detail that any attempt to map it all would be doomed to failure. Before long, however, the impression wears off, and a good deal of order begins to emerge from the outward chaos. In particular, the various features sort themselves out into well-defined types, and a few evenings at the telescope – or, for that matter, studying photographs – will lead to quick recognition of the chief features.

There are over 700 objects considered worthy of separate names,* and the total number of recorded features amounts to several tens of thousands, so that to describe them all would require a book the size of an encyclopædia. However, the charts given here will, I hope, serve to indicate at least some of the more interesting and important formations.

One thing is clear at once: all the charts and photographs are shown with south at the top and north at the bottom. This may seem curious, but astronomical pictures are always turned round in this way. A telescope gives an inverted image, and to correct this for normal use on Earth an extra lens-system is introduced. Every time a light-ray passes through a lens it becomes slightly weakened. This does not matter in the least when we are looking at a ship or an aircraft, but in astronomy it is vital to collect all the light we can without losing any of it. Therefore, the correcting lenses are left out, and all views are upside-down. There is no other fundamental

* Unfortunately, the names are not the same in all the maps. The official nomenclature used in the International Astronomical Union map of 1935 is inadequate; new names were added by various selenographers such as Wilkins; and recently, in the Yerkes photographic atlas, Kuiper has made things even worse by dropping some of the old-established names and altering others. Some years ago I was drawing up a paper dealing with the area of the crater Hausen, near the south-east limb of the Moon, and found that six different maps gave six different Hausens! In this book I have, in general, followed the names given in Wilkins' map.

difference between an astronomical refractor and an ordinary hand-telescope.

Most maps are drawn to mean libration (though on a small scale the differences for any particular limb are not noticeable), and for convenience are divided into four quadrants, the first being north-west, the second north-east, the third south-east and the fourth south-west. Wilkins' large map includes special limb-charts drawn to maximum libration. Remember that objects close to the Moon's edge are very foreshortened, and a large crater is very easily confused with a mountain ridge.

Newcomers to lunar study are often confused by the rapid changes in appearance caused by the changing lighting. A peak or crater can alter beyond all recognition in only a few hours, simply because we depend so much on shadows. When the Sun is rising or setting over an elevation, the shadow cast is long and prominent; when the Sun is high above the object the shadow becomes very short, perhaps vanishing completely – just as we can see the shadow of a tree or post shortening as the Sun rises over it – and as there is no local colour on the Moon, the feature will not be visible at all unless it is definitely brighter or darker than the surrounding country. The effect is even more noticeable with the craters. A walled formation is at its most striking when it is on or near the 'terminator', an expression which needs some description.

The terminator is the boundary between the day and night sides of the Moon. It must not be confused with the limb, which is the Moon's apparent edge as seen from the Earth. The limb remains in almost the same position, and though it does shift slightly, owing to the various librations, the effect is hardly perceptible except in areas well away from the centre of the disk. On the other hand the terminator sweeps right across the disk twice each lunation, first when the Moon is waxing ('morning terminator') and then when it is waning ('evening terminator'), so that even an hour's watch will

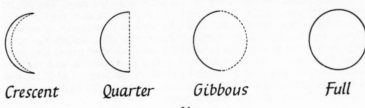

Crescent   Quarter   Gibbous   Full

reveal definite movement. In the diagram, the full, gibbous, half and crescent phases of the Moon are shown, with the limb drawn as a continuous line and the terminator dotted.

Owing to the roughness of the Moon's surface, the terminator does not appear as a smooth line. As the Sun rises, the first rays naturally catch the mountain-tops and higher areas before the valleys and crater-floors, so that the terminator presents a very jagged and uneven appearance. Peaks glitter like stars out of the blackness, while their bases are still shrouded in night, so that the summits appear completely detached from the main body of the Moon; ridges make their first appearance in the guise of luminous threads, while a crater will show its rampart-crests and the top of its central mountain while its floor is still perfectly black. On the other hand, a low-lying area will appear as a great dent in the terminator and take on a false importance for a few hours. Even with a small telescope, it is fascinating to watch the slow, steady progress of sunrise upon the bleak lunar landscape.

The result of all this is that the features shown on lunar maps cannot be seen properly all at the same time. In fact, it is more or less true to say that full moon is the worst possible time to start observing, as the limb appears complete all round the disk and the shadows are at their minimum. Moreover the mysterious bright rays, described below, drown most of the other details, causing the Moon to take on the look of a blurred, speckled circle of light.

Of course, the vast dark plains known as seas catch the eye at once. They take up much of the visible disk, and cover a large part of the eastern hemisphere – which explains why the last quarter moon, when the eastern side is shining on its own, is much less brilliant than the first quarter moon, when the western half is visible.

There are nine important seas and a number of lesser ones, though nearly all of these are combined into one great connected system in the same way as our own water-oceans, and usually there are no hard and fast boundaries. On first acquaintance, the names are perhaps rather confusing. Latin is still the universal language, and therefore astronomers use Latin rather than English names; the Sea of Showers becomes 'Mare Imbrium', the Sea of Vapours 'Mare Vaporum', and so on.* Other names are even more romantic

* 'Mare' (plural, maria) is Latin for 'sea'. Ocean is 'oceanus', bay 'sinus', marsh 'palus' and lake 'lacus'.

- for instance we have a Sea of Nectar, a Bay of Rainbows and an Ocean of Storms – but we have to admit that they are rather inappropriate. Showers, rainbows, nectar and storms are very much out of place on the glaring, tangled rocks of the lunar world.

The seas, with their Latin names and English equivalents, are listed in the Appendix. The Latin versions are used on all serious lunar charts, and it will be best for us to keep to them here. It is not as though they were in any way difficult; one soon becomes used to them.

We know, of course, that there is no water on the Moon now, and that the so-called seas are dry plains without a trace of moisture in them. Once, earlier in lunar history, they may well have been seas of lava, though it does not seem likely that they were ever filled with water. At any rate, it is certain that they were still unsolidified long after the adjacent regions had become permanently rigid. This is shown by their treatment of the features bordering them. We can see traces of the old wall between the Mare Humorum and the Mare Nubium (third quadrant); the mountainous border between the Mare Imbrium and the Mare Serenitatis has been widely breached, while various 'coastal' craters such as Lemonnier have had their seaward walls ruined and levelled. It is true that water could act in this way – most people must have seen the gradual wearing-away of a boy's sandcastle as the incoming tide laps over it – but almost all astronomers agree that water is not the answer.

Many of the major seas are more or less circular, with lofty, mountainous ramparts. Look, for instance, at the most impressive of all – the Mare Imbrium or Sea of Showers, in the second quadrant. It seems oval in shape, but this is because it is foreshortened; really it is almost circular, hemmed in by four mountain arcs, and large enough to hold Britain and France put together.

The foreshortening effect is even more striking with the Mare Crisium, not far from the western limb. This is a conspicuous sea, separate from the main system. It measures 260 miles in one direction and 335 in the other – but the longer diameter is along the east-west axis, which comes as a great surprise to the unwary observer. The third of the almost circular, well-bordered seas is the Mare Serenitatis, almost exactly equal in area to Great Britain, and lying in the first quadrant, west of the Mare Imbrium. Less perfect, but still basically circular, are the Mare Nectaris and the Mare

Humorum, which take the form of lesser features on the borders of major seas.

The obvious conclusion is that there is no essential difference between a large lunar crater and a small sea. Mare Crisium, as we have noted, has a mean diameter of about 300 miles, and is not the smallest of the maria. The dark-floored crater Grimaldi measures over 120 miles across, and if it had happened to lie near the middle of the disk instead of near the limb it would probably have been ranked as a minor sea. Even more of a borderline case is one of the features on the reverse side of the Moon, described in Chapter 15. This is the Mare Moscoviæ (Moscow Sea), which is a dark patch about 185 miles in diameter. Its details are not yet known, of course, but already there is a definite doubt about whether it should be termed a crater or not.

In fact, the division of the largest walled formation into 'maria' and 'craters' is quite arbitrary, a point which many people do not appreciate. On the other hand the less well-defined dark areas, such as the Oceanus Procellarum – covering two million square miles, much more than our own Mediterranean – are less regular, and are of different type. My own theory is that they are overflows from the crater-like seas, but this will be discussed more fully in Chapter 9.

J. E. Spurr, an American geologist who paid a great deal of attention to the Moon, christened the bright upland material 'lunarite' and the dark mare-material 'lunabase', two terms which seem eminently suitable. Lunabase is not, however, confined entirely to the seas. Some craters have their floors covered with it, and there are also small splashes of it here and there in the uplands.

Any casual glance shows that the Moon is a mountainous world. The bright regions, found chiefly in the southern hemisphere, are packed with detail; peaks, craters, valleys and ridges jostle against each other in a wild tangle, and it looks almost as though there is scarcely a square mile of level ground anywhere.

Some of the peaks are of great height. Recent measures show that the Leibnitz Mountains, on the south-west limb, may reach 30,000 feet, in which case they are higher than Everest. But there are quite a number of things to be borne in mind before we say simply that the Moon's mountains are higher than those of our own world, so let us examine the position rather more closely.

It is wise to begin with the region of the vast Mare Imbrium, the largest of the circular-type seas. Here there are various mountain borders. The Apennines separate the Mare Imbrium from the smaller, darker-hued Mare Vaporum, and they make a magnificent spectacle when seen at their best; their peaks cast long, sharp shadows across the plain, and give the impression of a true range, more rugged and bleak than anything on the Earth. The highest peak, Mount Huygens, rises to almost 20,000 feet, and there are other crests of at least 15,000 feet; the whole chain is over 600 miles long, stretching from the lofty Mount Hadley in the north to the grand crater-ring of Eratosthenes in the south.

The Apennines break off near Eratosthenes, and there is a wide gap, so that the Mare Imbrium links up with the even vaster though less perfect Oceanus Procellarum. Then comes another range, the Carpathians – much lower than the Apennines, and rising to no more than 7,000 feet anywhere, but over 100 miles long. When the Carpathians too come to an end, there is another broad gap in the Mare border.

In the north, the Mare Imbrium is bounded by the Alps, which do not, however, join up with the Apennines; there is a gap between

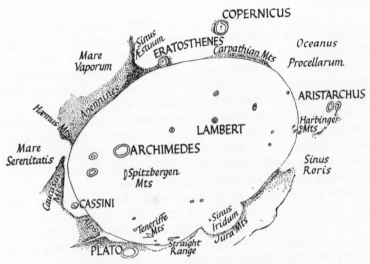

The mountain walls of the Mare Imbrium

68

the two ranges, so that the sea-floor is connected with that of the neighbouring Mare Serenitatis. The Alps are by no means the equal of the Apennines, but they have an interest all their own, largely because of the presence of the remarkable Alpine Valley. Near here, too, is the crater of Plato, one of the most famous formations on the Moon. Further east lies the Sinus Iridum, or Bay of Rainbows, bordered by the Jura Mountains; when on the terminator, so that the Juras catch the sunlight while the Bay is in darkness, the 'jewelled handle' effect defies description. And beyond the Bay, the mountain border is resumed up to the abrupt ending near the Sinus Roris, or Bay of Dew.

The other surviving part of the Mare border is represented by the relatively modest Harbinger Mountains, which do not take the form of a definite range, but are better described as clumps of hills.

The general picture is shown in the drawing – and one fact stands out at once. The Apennines, the Alps, the Carpathians, the Juras and probably the Harbingers all form part of the circular wall of the Mare Imbrium. The Mare itself is depressed below the outer country, and it seems that we are dealing with a 'crater' on a tremendous scale. In other words, the mountain ranges are 'crater walls', and not normal mountains of Earth type.

The same is true of the borders of the Mare Serenitatis, where we have the Caucasus and Hæmus ranges; of the Mare Humorum, where we find the Percy Mountains, and so on. Mountain chains on the bright areas do not exist. Even the Altai range, which runs south-eastward from the crater Piccolomini, is not properly a chain of mountains, and Spurr's revised name of the 'Altai Scarp' is more suitable.

If this interpretation is correct (and it must be added that by no means all astronomers agree with me!) then the chief ranges on the Moon are not strictly comparable with Earth ranges such as the Himalayas or the Rockies. It is unfortunate, too, that the mountains which seem to be the very loftiest on the lunar scene, the Leibnitz and the Dörfels, lie so close to the limb that they are very difficult to study. About 1951 D. W. G. Arthur suggested that they too might be the walls of large seas which lay on the hidden side of the Moon. The photographs sent back from Russia's Lunik III seem to show that Arthur was wrong, since there are few major seas on the reverse hemisphere, but the question is still open.

There are, of course, smaller ranges which do not make up the boundaries of seas. Particularly notable is the Straight Range, near Plato, a little chain forty miles long and rising to less than 6,000 feet, but curiously regular, with an abrupt beginning and an equally abrupt ending. Close to the small, bright crater Euclides we find the Riphæan Mountains, which rise to no more than 4,000 feet. V. A. Firsoff considers that the Riphæans represent the last traces of the wall of a destroyed crater, or even a minor Mare, and he is probably right.

Whatever view we take, the Moon's ranges are of the greatest significance to the 'selenologist', the lunar equivalent of a geologist, but we must beware of drawing too close a comparison with the mountain chains with which we are familiar on Earth.

There are many separate mountain-peaks on the Moon. In the uplands they are to be found in their hundreds, but those on the seas are more impressive. They are not so lofty as the summits of the chain-mountains; but all the same, some of them would rank with the famous peaks of our own world.

Look, for instance, at Pico on the Mare Imbrium, 100 miles south of Plato – a mountain mass with broad slopes, and foothills studded with pits and craterlets. It may not look impressive on the map, but the highest of its crests rises to a good 8,000 feet above the plain, so that it is twice the altitude of Scotland's much-vaunted Ben Nevis. Not very far off is another superb mountain, Piton; and there are many other examples.

Less important peaks are very common indeed, and the Moon is dotted with hills, some of them no more than mere mounds. Even the crater-floors are not free from them, and the smoothest parts of the maria are very far from flat, although it is naturally difficult to recognize slight differences in level unless we catch them under a very low sun.

There is another point to be borne in mind. On Earth, the forces of erosion, such as the wearing-away of heights by wind, water, and weathering in general, are constantly at work; they never cease for a moment. But the Moon is to all intents and purposes without atmosphere, and no wind or water can exist there now, so that we would expect the Moon's peaks to be sharper and more jagged than our own. This is possibly true, but it is not likely that the peaks are of the immensely delicate, steep-rising form shown in most science-fiction books. The slopes may be quite steep, but are not so sharp as is often thought.

Galileo was the first to make a serious effort to measure lunar mountain-heights. As the Sun rises, a peak will – as we have seen – catch the first rays before the lower-lying country around, and so will appear as a bright point detached from the main body of the Moon. All that Galileo did was to time how long the mountain remained illuminated on the night-side of the terminator, after which its real distance from the terminator, and therefore its height, could be worked out.

This is all very well – in theory. Unfortunately the terminator is so irregular, owing to the Moon's uneven surface, that its position cannot be properly measured, and in consequence Galileo's results were very inaccurate. It is true that he did give altitudes of about 30,000 feet for some of the peaks, and this would have been correct for (say) the Leibnitz or the Dörfels, but these were not the ranges which Galileo measured. He seems to have concentrated on the Apennines and the Caucasus, which are much lower, and so his calculated heights were nearly double the true values.

The modern method is to measure the shadow cast by the peak itself. The position of the peak is known, and so is the angle at which the Sun's rays strike it at any particular moment, so that the height relative to the neighbouring surface can be calculated. The general principle is shown in the diagram. Of course, there are many complications to be taken into account, but the method itself has a perfectly straightforward basis.

An extra annoyance is that we cannot measure lunar mountain heights from 'sea level', as we do on Earth. There is no water on the Moon, and so we have no exact standard of reference. We can measure the heights relative to the surrounding country, or we can measure them relative to the mean surface-level, but neither course is really satisfactory. All we can really do is to give a result which is at least of the right order of magnitude. The one inescapable fact

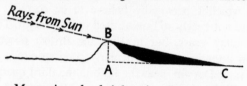

Measuring the height of a Lunar Peak

71

is that the Moon's mountains are much higher relatively than those of the Earth, whether we regard them as true mountain ranges or as the walls of vast crater-like formations.

Wherever there are mountains, there will be valleys, and this is so on the Moon. Some of them are mere passes, while others are highly spectacular. Yet here again we must be wary of jumping to conclusions. The Rheita Valley, in the fourth quadrant, is long enough to stretch from London to Birmingham, and at first sight looks almost as though it had been scooped out by a gigantic chisel, but a closer look shows that it is not a valley at all. It is a crater-chain from beginning to end, and there is nothing genuinely valley-like about it.

Quite different is the Alpine Valley, near Plato. Over 80 miles long, it is definitely not a crater-chain, and there have been suggestions that it was carved out by a great meteor crashing through the mountains. The death-blow to this attractive idea is given by the fact that there are much smaller parallel and transverse valleys near by. I first noticed them in 1949, and they have since been fully confirmed by G. Fielder at the University of London Observatory. They are not conspicuous, and are seen only under suitable lighting conditions, so that they are not easy to photograph.

The Alpine Valley itself is a superb sight in even a small telescope. It has no equal on the Moon, and not even the hardiest and most experienced of lunar observers is likely to tire of looking at it.

It is not easy to decide just what is a genuine valley and what is a mere gap between two roughly parallel ridges; the term is a very broad one. Many of the valleys, too, resemble that of Rheita in that they are really crater-chains.

Next let us turn to those extraordinary features known as domes. As their name suggests, they are surface swellings, and give the impression that they were produced by some internal force which pushed up the Moon's crust without being able to break it – an impression which I personally believe to be correct.

Domes are not nearly so rare as used to be thought. They escaped notice for many years, but in 1932 the British observer Robert Barker drew attention to a particularly good specimen – the dome inside the crater Darwin, near the limb in the third quadrant, which Barker described as 'a huge cinder-heap, a lunarian dust-heap which bristles with roughness'. A few more came to light, mainly because of the work by S. R. B. Cooke in America, but still they were regarded as lunar oddities.

In 1957 I began a systematic search for domes, working together with P. J. Cattermole. Much of the observational work was done with my 12½-inch reflector, which is a modest instrument indeed, but which proved quite powerful enough to show that domes existed not in ones or twos, but in dozens. By 1961 we had catalogued over seventy, but this naturally represents only a tiny fraction of the total.

Several interesting facts emerged. First, the domes are not spread about at random, but occur in clusters. For instance, there are eight inside the crater Capuanus, not far from the border of the Mare Humorum in the third quadrant, while other rich areas lie near Arago on the Mare Tranquillitatis, near Prinz in the Harbinger Mountains, and on various parts of the Oceanus Procellarum. There is, for instance, a superb example of a dome near the little crater Milichius.

Secondly, many of the domes proved to have summit pits, giving them a striking resemblance to true volcanoes. Some of the pits were clear enough to be seen even in a 6-inch telescope, and can be photographed, though most of them were much more delicate. It seems, indeed, that summit pits are the rule and not the exception. It may even be that every genuine dome will turn out to have a summit pit, though close studies with very large telescopes will be needed to clear the matter up.

Quite independently, in 1959, G. P. Kuiper announced the discovery of a dozen such objects, and termed them 'extinct volcanoes'. His work was carried out with the 82-inch telescope at the McDonald Observatory in Texas, and was in close agreement with ours, since all his 'volcanoes' were included in our earlier published lists.

The trouble is that one cannot always tell what is a true dome and what is not. In fact, is there a basic difference between a dome and a rounded hill? I suspect that there is; but the dome-slopes are gentle, and not easy to measure with any accuracy at all, so that we cannot tell for certain whether or not there is a complete gradation from relatively steep-sided elevations down to the much less abrupt surface swellings.

It is often said that domes appear dark when the Sun is low over them. Cooke's explanation was that the objects are seamed with minute fissures which are shadow-filled under oblique lighting, causing the whole dome to look dark. This fits in very well with Barker's description of the Darwin dome (which may not, however, be typical of the class). On the other hand, recent studies have not convinced me that all domes do indeed take on a dark appearance under low illumination, and here too more work remains to be done.

Domes in rough areas are unpleasantly hard to detect, and no doubt many of them have escaped notice; but there is one good example in the Altai area, near Piccolomini in the fourth quadrant, so that we cannot assume that domes are confined to the maria and the floors of craters.

Every Earth geologist is interested in 'faults', and so is every selenologist, since faults on the Moon are very common indeed. Look, for example, at the Mare Humorum; to quote V. A. Firsoff, it is 'fairly ringed by faults and fractures on all sides'. This is only one of the many heavily faulted areas.

There are a few particularly outstanding faults; one near Bürg, for example, in the first quadrant. But the most striking of all is the remarkable feature known as the Straight Wall, near the edge of the Mare Nubium in the third quadrant – not so very far from the crater Thebit, which will be described later. The name is not appropriate. The Straight Wall is not straight, and it is most certainly not a wall. The surface of the plain to the east is about a thousand feet lower than on the west, so that the feature is of the nature of a fault. It begins at a clump of hills known as the Stag's-Horn Mountains, and ends at a small craterlet sixty miles to the south. Well before full moon it shows up as a dark line, since it is casting shadow to the east; then it vanishes, and for some days it cannot be identified at all, though the Stag's-Horn peaks can usually be traced. Then the Wall reappears as a bright line, since the slanting rays of the Sun are shining upon its inclined face.

It used to be thought that the Straight Wall must be almost sheer, and that an observer on the Moon standing east of it would be confronted with a near-vertical cliff between 800 and 1,000 feet in height. Recent work has not borne out this idea. In America, J. Ashbrook has analyzed shadow measurements of it, and has come to the conclusion that the angle of slope is about 45 degrees. I suspect that it may be less sharp even than this. At any rate, it is the most perfect formation of its kind, and is one of the show-places of the Moon.

Ridges, too, abound on the Moon, and are of various types. There are the so-called wrinkle-ridges (a name due originally, I believe, to Spurr) which are low, snaking elevations of considerable length, seen excellently near the Mare borders; and there are ridges further on the seas, which, as I pointed out in 1952, are usually the walls of old 'ghost craters' which have been so completely destroyed that only fragments of their borders remain. Yet in general the Moon is criss-crossed with ridges and faults, and this leads us on to a feature of vital importance – the lunar grid system.

The term 'grid system' is also due to J. E. Spurr. Strictly speaking, Spurr was not an astronomer; he was a geologist, and he did little or no actual work at the telescope, preferring to base his studies upon photographs. This was no disadvantage at all, since he was able to bring all his geological experience to bear upon lunar research. His various books are devoted mainly to his own theories of the origin of the surface features, but even those who disagree with his conclusions must admit that many of his comments are extremely apt. Since then the grid system has been investigated by various authorities, notably by Fielder and Firsoff in England.

As we have seen, the Moon is criss-crossed with faults and ridges. Sometimes the faults are due to almost vertical slippages, while in other cases the movements are more nearly horizontal; generally speaking the ridges form parts of the walls of craters, though often enough the craters themselves are too broken to be properly recognizable. Following a very detailed and lengthy study, Fielder has found that there are two principal families of ridges and faults, running in specific directions and nearly at right angles to each other. This makes up the grid system, though it is complicated by the presence of other, less obvious families such as those of the Alps and Caucasus region.

The very existence of such a system points to the lunar crust having been subjected to strain of some kind over very long periods, and there is no need to stress its significance when we come to consider how the various features (including the craters) were produced.

Meanwhile, let us note that, as Fielder has pointed out, small craters in some regions are non-circular, and have their longest axes in the direction of either one or other of the families of the main grid system.

The general pattern is clear enough – when one knows that it is there. The remarkable thing is that it escaped notice for so long, which may be an instance of the old cliché that it is only too easy to overlook the obvious.

Finally, before we turn to the craters themselves, something must be said about the lunar clefts (also termed rills or rilles). One of the most famous lies near the centre of the disk, near the small but quite prominent crater Ariadæus. It can be seen with any small telescope when the lighting is suitable, and it looks remarkably like a crack in the Moon's surface, running for well over 100 miles. Close to it is a curved cleft associated with the 4-mile crater Hyginus. Most spectacular of all is the lovely winding valley-cleft running out of Herodotus, the companion-crater of the glittering Aristarchus near the junction of the Mare Imbrium and the Oceanus Procellarum. It starts inside Herodotus, broadens out into a formation which has been nicknamed the Cobra-Head, and winds its way across the plain, ending at a small craterlet. Then, too, there are whole systems of clefts, such as that in the region of Triesnecker – again in the region of Ariadæus and Hyginus.

R. B. Baldwin, who wrote an important book about the Moon in 1949, described the Triesnecker clefts as 'irregular cracks, very jagged in appearance, which seem to be bottomless'. Yet this is completely wrong. The clefts are not bottomless, and seem indeed to be relatively shallow – not more than a mile or so in depth, whereas they are up to three miles wide. They are not jagged, since the slopes are not particularly steep. And they are not cracks; as Fielder and Kuiper have independently shown, they are collapse features, and there is no analogy at all with Earth-type river-beds or ravines, as has often been suggested in the past.

Here, too, the distribution is not random. Some parts of the Moon are riddled with clefts, while other areas lack them completely. Their origin is intimately bound up with that of the formation of the craters – and, of course, with that of the grid system.

On the other hand we have already noted that there are some so-called clefts which prove to be not clefts at all, but crater-chains.

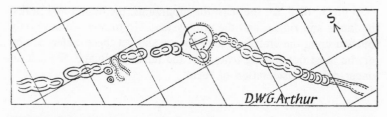

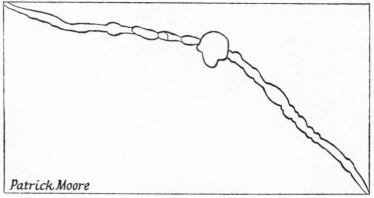

The Hyginus 'Cleft'

This is largely true of the Hyginus Cleft. According to D. W. G. Arthur, this feature is a crater-chain throughout its length. My own observations show that this is not quite accurate, since there are parts which show no crater-like enlargements, but there can be no doubt that craters lie along most of its length – the most conspicuous of them being, of course, Hyginus itself. Like the Ariadæus Cleft and the Herodotus Valley, it is visible with any small telescope, and is extremely easy to identify.

Note, too, the more delicate cleft associated with the crater Birt, near the Straight Wall. Here we have a genuine cleft which nevertheless begins with a chain of small craters, and ends with another chain. Again we find that there is the closest of relationships between the various features of the Moon's surface.*

* Many of the comments in this chapter are based upon the work of G. Fielder, who has studied the whole problem very carefully. I am also most grateful to Dr. Fielder for providing me with information which is so far unpublished – particularly with reference to the grid system.

So much, then, for the seas, the mountains, the domes and peaks, the faults and ridges, and the grid system. Up to now we have only touched upon the craters of the Moon – and yet these craters are by far the most dominating feature of the lunar landscape. We can no longer defer consideration of them.

Chapter 8

The Craters of the Moon

Who has not heard of the craters of the Moon? They dominate the whole lunar scene; no area is free from them, and they seem to be everywhere. They are found on the smoothest parts of the plains, the wildest regions of the uplands, and even on the summits of mountains.

Strictly speaking, the name 'crater' is rather a misleading one, since it conjures up the impression of a very deep, steep-sided hole. Moreover, the features are on a vast scale, and far larger than anything of the sort found on Earth. The famous craters of Hawaii would cut a very poor figure if transferred to the Moon, and would certainly not be honoured with separate names. Quite apart from this, a lunar crater is so different in form from a terrestrial volcano that it must be regarded only as a 'distant relation'.

When a crater is seen on the terminator, so that its floor is filled with shadow, it looks immensely deep. This is true enough, since some of them have walls rising to more than 15,000 feet above their floors; the deepest of all, Newton, has a depth of about 30,000 feet. Yet it is important to remember that all craters are relatively shallow in relation to their diameters, so that they are more like saucers than pits.

As a typical example, let us take Theætetus, on the Mare Imbrium (second quadrant). It is 32 miles across, so that its area is greater than that of the Isle of Wight, and the walls rise to 7,000 feet above the interior. This sounds a considerable height, and indeed it is; but the crater-floor itself is depressed 5,000 feet below the plain, so that an observer standing on the Mare Imbrium looking at Theætetus' outer rim would be confronted only with modest-looking elevations much lower than Scafell. Neither are the slopes steep. Even with a small crater, it is rare for the angle of slope to reach 40 degrees, and for the really large formations it is much gentler than this.

With a large crater, such as Ptolemæus, a grand formation almost

79

at the centre of the Moon's Earth-turned hemisphere, the saucer-like form is very evident. Ptolemæus has a diameter of over 90 miles, but its walls rise to less than a mile above the bottom of the floor, and less above the outside plain. This leads to a result which may seem surprising at first sight. Anyone standing inside Ptolemæus or a similar crater would have no impression of being inside a walled formation – because he would be unable to see the ramparts at all. The Moon's horizon curves more sharply than that of the Earth, because the Moon is a smaller globe, and the crater-walls would be below our observer's horizon, so that he would seem to be standing on a flattish plain.

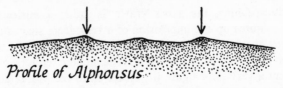

Profile of Alphonsus

The same is true of Clavius, which, with its diameter of 146 miles, has an area greater than that of Switzerland. The walls are three miles above the deepest part of the interior, but still they would be invisible to anyone standing in the middle of the vast amphitheatre. With smaller craters the relative depth is greater, but the idea of a sharp-sided well is very wide of the mark. Our first impressions of lunar craters as gaping holes in the surface, banked with mountains rising almost sheer from the shadowed depths, will have to be drastically revised.

There is one factor common to all craters, large and small. All are basically circular, even though they may have been battered or distorted by later outbreaks. Remember that the best-defined of the seas, such as the Mare Crisium and the Mare Imbrium, are also more or less circular, so that there is evidently no fundamental difference between a mare and a crater.

The craters away from the centre of the disk appear as ovals, but this is merely an optical effect due to foreshortening. For instance Gauss, in the first quadrant, is almost perfectly circular, but it lies so near the limb that it appears as a long ellipse. In the libration areas, at the limit of our view, it becomes very difficult to map the features at all accurately, and it is often almost impossible to tell whether an object is a foreshortened crater or merely a ridge. The

Theophilus   Plato   Pythagoras

Crater foreshortening. In reality, all these three craters are
practically circular.

only way to find out is to study it under all possible angles of
illumination. The largest craters, more suitably termed walled
plains, must also be the oldest, and were presumably born in the
early days when the Moon was at its most violent. Many of them
are now so broken and ruined that they are scarcely recognizable.
For instance Janssen, in the fourth quadrant not far from the Mare
Australe, must once have been a noble object, with high continuous
walls rising to thousands of feet above its sunken floor; but it has
been so roughly treated by later outbreaks and crustal disturbances
that it is now no more than an enormous field of ruins, broken by
craters, ridges, pits and clefts, with its walls breached in dozens of
places and completely levelled in some. Only when it is right on
the terminator, and filled with shadow, does it give a faint impression of its former self.

The term 'field of ruins' has also been applied to Bailly, on the
south-east limb of the Moon. Here we have a vast enclosure over
180 miles from side to side – unfortunately so badly placed that it
is very much foreshortened – and as the diagram shows, it covers
an area over half that of England. Were it darker-floored and more
centrally placed on the disk, it
would probably have been
ranked as a minor sea instead
of an outsize crater.

However, quite a number of
the walled plains have managed
to escape relatively unharmed.
Clavius is a case in point. Admittedly it contains several
craters which are large in their
own right, and form a chain
across the floor; yet the walls
are fairly continuous, and when

81

the Sun is rising or setting over it it causes an apparent dent in the terminator which may be seen without any optical aid at all.

Newton, near the Moon's South Pole, has the distinction of being the deepest of all the craters, but it is a compound formation, and is never well seen, partly because of its closeness to the limb and partly because it lies in a particularly rough area. Because of its depth and its position, neither Sun nor Earth can ever be seen from parts of its interior; the rocks have lain there undisturbed for millions of years, and eternal blackness and silence reigns, since no friendly gleam of sunlight can penetrate there. The bottom of Newton Crater must be one of the most desolate spots in the whole Solar System. We cannot form any real picture of what it must be like.

One or two of the walled plains are notable for the darkness of their floors. For instance Plato, on the southern border of the Mare Imbrium – large enough to hold Devonshire comfortably – has a steel-grey amphitheatre, one of the levellest places on the whole Moon even though it contains a fair number of craterlets and pits. An even darked walled plain is Grimaldi, near the east limb, whose floor makes it recognizable under any conditions of lighting.

Before leaving the walled plains, let us note their tendency to arrange themselves in lines. A chain of tremendous formations runs down the western limb, from Furnerius near the Mare Australe as far as the dark-floored Endymion in the north, and even more striking lines of plains may be seen near the centre of the disk. When well placed, the three great formations Ptolemæus, Alphonsus and Arzachel are particularly imposing.

Coming now to the generally smaller formations, we find that they may be divided broadly into two classes: formations with central peaks, and those without. Some craters have floor-mountains which rise to thousands of feet, though they never attain the height of the surrounding rampart; others have lower, many-peaked central elevations, and sometimes the so-called central mountain is nothing more than a low mound. There are even formations which have central craterlets instead of peaks, while sometimes the entire floor is featureless except for low hummocks and pits.

There are craters of all sorts. Look, for instance, at the superb Theophilus, in the fourth quadrant near the edge of the Mare Nectaris; it is 64 miles across and over 14,000 feet deep, with a magnificent central elevation and massive walls. It has broken into a second formation of similar size, Cyrillus, where the central peak is relatively minor; south lies the third member of the trio, Catharina, which has no central peak at all, and whose floor is extremely rough. Equally notable are Archimedes, Aristillus and Autolycus, on the Mare Imbrium. But rather than describe several craters it will be better to select one, Copernicus on the Oceanus Procellarum, which shows many of the features seen in its lesser companions. It has been nicknamed 'the Monarch of the Moon', and only Theophilus is worthy to be ranked as its equal.

Copernicus has massive walls rising in places to 17,000 feet above the inner amphitheatre. The distance right across the crater, from crest to crest, is 56 miles, but the true 'floor' is only forty miles across, since the rest is blocked with rubble and débris resulting from huge landslides from the ramparts. Copernicus seems calm enough now, after its hundreds of millions of years of silence; but we can picture the scene during its formation, when vast rocks were being hurled about as though they were feathers in a gale. Truly the Moon has had a troubled history.

The central heights are made up of three distinct, multi-peaked masses, while lower hills and mounds litter the whole area of the floor. The outer slopes of the walls are comparatively gentle, and are lined with ridges and valleys which radiate outward. Spurr has suggested that they were formed by water pouring down the outer slopes from the crater orifice, much in the way that narrow channels are formed in a sandbank when water is running down it, but on the whole it seems that there is never likely to have been much liquid water on the Moon. It it worth noting that other craters, such as Aristillus, show similar gullies.

Another feature of Copernicus is the terracing of the inner walls. Terracing is common in lunar craters, but is particularly well-developed in 'the Monarch of the Moon', as any telescope will show. In some formations there are three or four terraces, and just occasionally a complete concentric inner ring – a crater within a crater, so to speak.

It is impossible to do justice to Copernicus by written description. Its nickname is well-earned, and the more it is studied the more imposing it seems to become.

Copernicus must have been formed fairly late in the Moon's

history, so that it has escaped damage, but other craters have not been so lucky. Those on the sea-coasts have had their seaward walls battered down and levelled, so that they have been turned into huge bays; Fracastorius on the border of the Mare Nectaris is a good example, and so, probably, is the famous Sinus Iridum or Bay of Rainbows. In some cases the ruins of a seaward wall can still be seen, and even, as with Hippalus on the Mare Humorum, the wreck of a central mountain.

The Sinus Iridum is the most splendid of the bays. It leads off the Mare Imbrium; the ground-level drops gradually to the east, and low, discontinuous remnants of the old west wall can still be traced between the two jutting capes which bound the strait separating the Bay from the main Mare. When the terminator passes close by, the mountain peaks of the eastern border (the Juras) catch the light, producing the 'jewelled handle' effect described earlier.

Old craters right on the seas have been even more damaged, and have been drowned by the Mare-material, so that they now show up as ghosts – marked sometimes by low, discontinuous walls, sometimes by ridges, sometimes by nothing more than a slight change in the colour of the plain.

Look, for instance, at Stadius on the Mare Nubium. It is large enough to hold the whole county of Sussex, and must once have been a noble formation, but nowadays it is in a sad state. The Mare material has flowed across it, breaching the ramparts and leaving them shattered and ruined. The loftiest summits cannot now be more than a couple of hundred feet above the plain, and for long stretches the wall cannot be traced at all, while the amphitheatre has been filled up and speckled with dozens upon dozens of tiny pits. Unless it is caught under very oblique lighting, it is difficult to find. Its neighbour Eratosthenes, only about 100 miles off, has escaped completely, and must have been born far later than the crater whose pathetic remnants we now call Stadius.

It is tempting to go back to our comparison with a boy's sand-castles. Suppose that he digs two holes, each time piling the sand in a ring – one at a point reached by the highest tide, the other lower down the beach? The first formation will have its seaward wall broken and its floor flooded, as Fracastorius and Sinus Iridum have been; the second will be overwhelmed by the rising water, and may be compared with old Stadius. The analogy is reasonable enough, though it should not be taken too far.

The arrangement of the various craters is most significant. Like the great plains, they tend to line up, and also frequently occur in pairs or groups. There are 'twins' in which the two craters are quite separate, as with Aliacensis and Werner, which lie in the fourth quadrant close to the great chain of which Walter is the senior member; in other cases the second formation has broken into the first, as with Steinheil-Watt in the fourth quadrant and Sirsalis-Bertaud in the third. When this happens, the intruding formation is always slightly but perceptibly the smaller of the two. If the craters are of volcanic origin, this is only to be expected; the major outbreaks came at an early stage, when the Moon was at its most violent, and the smaller craters which followed later were able to disturb formations which already existed. The rule holds good in over 99·9 per cent of cases – the only important exception being the Sinus Iridum, which may be in a class of its own.

Craterlets, with diameters ranging from more than a dozen miles down to only a few yards, pepper the whole Moon. Some are complete miniatures of the larger craters, even to the central hills; others are mere pits, with depressed floors but virtually no true walls rising above the outer level. Spurr has called these pits 'blow-hole-craters', and the name seems very appropriate.

The more powerful the telescope used, the more craterlets will the observer see. I remember making a close study of one of the flattest parts of the Moon, using the 33-inch refractor at the Meudon station of Paris Observatory. The best photographs at my disposal showed nothing at all, but the refractor enabled me to map more than twenty minute pits, to say nothing of mounds and hummocks.

The lining-up of craters is as marked with the small formations as it is with the large ones – perhaps even more so. As we have seen, some of the so-called clefts, such as that of Hyginus, are basically composed of small craters which have run together, often with the loss of their dividing walls. This makes us rather suspicious; can all the clefts have tell-tale bulges along their lengths?

The answer seems to be a definite 'no', and most of the finer clefts are not made up of craterlets. On the other hand, there are plenty of crater-chains which cannot possibly be mistaken for clefts. Some years ago I was mapping a small area not far from Wargentin, the famous lunar plateau, and found four distinct crater-chains within a hundred square miles. After all, there is nothing surprising in this. The great plains arrange themselves in such a way; why should not the smaller ones do likewise? We have a complete series from the 'giants' down to the 'strings of beads'.

Here and there we come across real lunar freaks, and perhaps the most remarkable of all is Wargentin, close to the large walled plain Schickard in the third quadrant. Here the floor is not sunken, but is raised above the outer surface by about a thousand feet. What may have happened is that some blockage caused the molten magma to be trapped inside the amphitheatre when the crater had only just been formed, so that instead of subsiding and flowing away, as usually happened, the magma solidified where it was. The true floor of Wargentin is therefore hidden, and all we can see is the top of the lava-lake. In places the floor is level with the top of the old rampart, but in others there are still traces of a wall – one segment rises to as much as 500 feet. Still, the general impression is that of a flat plateau, not a crater at all. Wargentin is large enough to hold the whole of Lancashire, and it is a great pity that it is not nearer the centre of the disk, as there are no other plateaux anything like so large. A few smaller ones exist, but are neither so perfect nor so prominent.

The Moon is full of puzzles, but it is probably true to say that the most baffling problems of all are set by the bright rays. Not even the most casual observer can overlook them when the Moon is near full, but so far nobody has been able to find out precisely what they are.

Unlike most other details, the rays are best seen under a high light. In fact they are very obscure when close to the terminator, and become conspicuous only when the Sun has risen to some height over them. Of the dozens of ray-systems on the surface, two stand out as being incomparably more splendid than the rest – those associated with the craters Tycho and Copernicus.

Tycho is a well-formed crater in the southern uplands, 54 miles across, and with high terraced walls including peaks which rise to more than 12,000 feet above the amphitheatre. There is also a central peak. Magnificent though it is, Tycho lies in a crowded area, and would not be particularly remarkable if it were not for the rays. When it first emerges from the lunar night, it appears to be a perfectly normal crater, even though somewhat brighter than average. Gradually the rays increase, and by full moon they dominate not only the surrounding area but also the whole of that part of the disk. There are dozens of them, streaking out in all directions from Tycho as a focal point; they cross craters, peaks and valleys, uplands and maria, clefts and pits without deviating appreciably from their courses.

Non-astronomers often think that Tycho marks the pole of the Moon. This is a natural mistake, but in fact Tycho lies some way from the polar point.

Strange to say, the rays cannot be followed right into Tycho. There is a ray-free area round the rampart, showing darkish under a high light, where they stop short. However, there can be little doubt that whatever may be the exact nature of the rays, Tycho is responsible for them.

One famous ray is said to stretch from Tycho right across the Mare Serenitatis and across the northern limb. Actually, the situation is not so clear-cut as this, and it seems that the ray is 'renewed' along its course, so that it is something more than an extra-long member of the Tycho system.

The rays associated with Copernicus are different from those of Tycho. They are not so brilliant, and at full moon, when they are best seen, they appear less bright than the gleaming crater-ring of Copernicus itself. Neither are they so long as Tycho's, though they spread widely over the surrounding plain.

Here and there over the disk other ray-centres can be made out; Kepler on the Oceanus Procellarum, Olbers close to Grimaldi in the east, Anaxagoras in the north, and so on. We also find very small craters surrounded by bright patches, and sometimes with short ray-systems. At full, the rays confuse the whole lunar scene so thoroughly that even the experienced observer may have trouble in finding his way about.

It is easy to see that the rays are not continuous white streaks. When closely examined they are found to have definite structure, and so they cannot be surface cracks or anything of the kind – though this is obvious in any case, from the way in which they cross all other types of formations and drown them in light.

Reports of shadows cast by rays have been made from time to

time, but none seem to be reliable, and it is more than likely that the rays are due to surface deposits of some sort. Salts have been suggested, but on the whole ash seems to be the best answer. This idea is supported by the fact that some of the lesser systems are grey, not brilliant white, so that they are not unlike the background hue of the surface, and are difficult to make out at all.

This, then, is the lunar picture – a scene of apparent chaos which, upon examination, turns out to be not quite so chaotic after all; where craters and peaks mingle with grey plains, valleys and faults, and mountainous chains. In so brief a description much must remain unsaid, but here, as in other things, an ounce of practice is worth a ton of theory. The amateur who takes a small telescope and turns it toward the Moon will find so many wonders awaiting his inspection that he will be quite unable to appreciate them all at once. Remember, too, that it may not be long now before men from Earth will have the chance to tread the bleak lunar rocks and explore for themselves.

Chapter 9

The Moulding of the Surface

In some ways the Moon is a convenient world. Not only is it exceptionally close to us on the astronomical scale, but it is virtually without atmosphere, so that there are no clouds or mists to hide its surface, and everything is sharp and clear-cut. Powerful telescopes can show an immense amount of detail, and tiny pits only a few hundreds of yards across may be recorded with absolute certainty.

This being so, we might reasonably expect to know a great deal about the way in which the Moon's surface was moulded. After all, we speculate about Venus, which is always a hundred times more remote and whose surface is permanently hidden by a dense atmosphere; we discuss the dark areas on Mars even though we can never, even with our best telescopes, see Mars as clearly as we can see the Moon with the help of ordinary field-glasses; we can analyze the light from the stars and tell, with great confidence, what elements exist there. Yet the Moon, as always, guards its secrets jealously, and will probably not yield them up until the first lunar voyage has taken place. The plain, unwelcome truth is that we are still very much in the dark as to how the Moon's craters were formed.

One thing may be said: the craters in general are very old indeed, and this is also true of most of the other features of the Moon's disk. Let us try to correlate lunar history with the story of our own world. Geologists can carry their studies of the Earth back far into the past, and usually begin at the so-called Cambrian Period, around 500 million years ago; events before that are classed as Pre-Cambrian, and are not so well known, since we have very few Pre-Cambrian fossils to guide us. It seems that all the large craters of the Moon are Pre-Cambrian, in which they are at least as ancient as the oldest terrestrial fossils.

This is not proved, and it may be that the Moon's period of great activity did not end quite so early; but it is a reasonable theory, and is probably not very wide of the mark. The basic fact should never be forgotten. Tycho, for instance, is often called a 'young' crater. It may well be 'young' according to lunar standards; but even so, it is probably at least 500 million years old. Ever since animal life first appeared on Earth, the Moon has been calm, silent and almost changeless.

Some time ago I had a party of boys at my observatory, and showed them the half-moon through my telescope. Their reactions were rather interesting. One or two said that the surface looked like grey sand into which stones had been dropped; others compared it with porridge, but most said that the general view reminded them of dead volcanoes.

It is undeniable that the lunar scene is essentially volcanic in appearance. A century ago it was regarded as certain that the craters were due to surface disturbances on the Moon itself, so that they were genuinely 'volcanic', using the term in a broad sense. It is only recently, during the last sixty or seventy years, that serious doubts have begun to creep in.

Nowadays the whole question is highly controversial, and fierce arguments have been raging. Some authorities, notably R. B. Baldwin, H. C. Urey and G. P. Kuiper, believe the craters to be meteoric, so that they were formed by bodies hitting the Moon's surface. On the other hand a second school, including V. A. Firsoff and J. Green, holds the view that the meteor theory is untenable, and that volcanic activity of some sort is the correct answer. Z. Kopal, of the University of Manchester, attributes some of the craters to impact and others to vulcanism. Indeed, every student of the Moon has his own ideas. A. Paluzíe-Borrell, of Spain, has referred to the meteors v. volcanoes controversy as the 'Hundred Years' War', and it is quite true that new battles are being fought every month.

I do not pretend to be unprejudiced. Meteor craters must exist on the Moon, just as they do on the Earth; but I believe that so far as the major craters are concerned, the impact theory has so many weak links that it will have to be abandoned. The main trouble is to find something better. My own ideas, outlined later in this chapter, may turn out to be completely wrong, but at least we now have a real hope of finding out; as soon as we can obtain specimens of the lunar crust, and subject them to analysis in our laboratories, we ought to know the truth.

90

But before turning to meteors and volcanoes, it will be as well to pause and consider some of the less widely supported theories which have been put forward from time to time.

Of the frankly eccentric ideas, the best-known is undoubtedly the Ice Theory, which was originally put forward by Ericson, of Norway, in 1885. It was supported by S. E. Peal, a tea-planter of Ceylon, who wrote a book about it four years later, and more recently by two Germans – H. Hörbiger,* whose remarkable views about ice extended far beyond the Moon, and by a perfectly serious seleno-grapher, P. Fauth, who died only in 1943. It supposes the craters to be nothing more than lakes of frozen water, and, to quote Peal : 'As the lakes slowly solidified in the cooling crust, the water vapour rising from them formed a local, dome-shaped atmosphere, which became a vast condensed snowy margin and piled as a vast ring.' This would make the Maria actual sea-surfaces, solidified, while the entire Moon would be coated with a thick layer of ice.

Fauth, the only modern supporter of this strange idea who may be termed an astronomer in the proper sense of the word, considered that the ice came from space in a sort of cosmic rain, forming a layer round the Moon's rocky core over 100 miles thick. However, the noon temperature at the lunar equator exceeds 200 degrees F., which does not seem very suitable for the permanent existence of either ice or snow; and in any case, an icy crater-rampart would not keep its shape for long. A wall of ice would soon flatten out under its own weight. Effects of this sort can be seen after any heavy winter snowfall in England.

It may not be impossible that isolated patches of ice persist in shaded areas, as has been argued recently by Z. Kopal; but this is very different from a general 'cold shell', and Fauth's theory is worth mentioning only as a curiosity. Fauth himself carried out a great deal of good work in other branches of lunar study, and it is a pity that his unswerving devotion to ice made him distort plain facts, so reducing the value of his labours.

The ice theory may seem strange, but an even more peculiar idea was put forward in the 1940s by a certain Herr Weisberger, of

---

* Hörbiger's name seems to have been attached to a very large walled plain associated with the crater Hell, and extending to the east of the Walter chain. I am not sure who put it there, but I imagine it must have been Fauth. On some maps the enclosure is named Hellplain.

Vienna, who solved the whole problem very easily simply by deny-
ing that there were any lunar mountains or craters at all. He
attributed the surface markings to storms and cyclones in a dense
lunar atmosphere, and seemed most surprised when the astronomical
world failed to treat him with due respect.

It was of course difficult to surpass Herr Weisberger, but a
Spanish engineer, Sixto Ocampo, did so in 1949, when he announced
his Atomic Bomb theory. After explaining that the Moon does not
rotate upon its axis (!), Señor Ocampo went on to prove that the
Moon used to be inhabited by advanced beings who indulged in an
atomic war, and destroyed their civilization, producing vast craters
in the process. He added that the craters are of different types
because the opposing armies used different sorts of weapons, one
kind of bomb producing a crater with a central peak and the other
kind a crater with a flat floor. The Alpine Valley and the Straight
Wall were engineering works. After the fall of the bomb which
produced the ray-crater Tycho, the lunar seas were 'fired' and were
expelled at great speed, falling back on to the Earth and causing
the Biblical flood.

Señor Ocampo presented his paper to the Academy of Arts and
Sciences at Barcelona, and was most annoyed when they declined
to publish it. It was eventually printed in a small South American
periodical, together with a letter in which the author complained
that an unscrupulous British writer had stolen his theory and was
planning to publish it as original work, thereby depriving Spain
of the glory of the discovery.

It should not be supposed that Herr Weisberger and Señor
Ocampo have the monopoly of weird ideas. Remember, there is
still an International Flat Earth Society which holds meetings in
London, while the members of the German Society for Geophysical
Research maintain that the Earth is in fact the interior of a hollow
sphere, so that the Sun is inside it.* Space forbids any discussion of
the theories of D. P. Beard, who, in 1917, put forward the idea that
the Moon had once been ocean-covered and that the present craters
are limestone formations similar to our coral atolls, or M. W.
Ovenden, one of the present Secretaries of the Royal Astronomical
Society, who has stated that no large lunar-type volcanic craters

* I once put these two societies in touch with each other. The ensuing
correspondence was most enlightening, but hardly relevant here.

can exist on Earth, since they would soon be rubbed away by friction as the Earth rotates beneath its atmosphere. Instead, let us turn to theories which have rather more of a scientific basis.

Some years ago the Bulgarian astronomer N. Boneff put forward a detailed account of a process involving tidal action. According to Boneff, the craters were formed when the Moon's crust had just solidified, and the Moon, much closer to the Earth than it is now, was rotating on its axis comparatively quickly. The hot, viscid interior was much more affected by the tidal pull than was the thin crust, and so at each rotation of the Moon on its axis the molten lava surged upwards, breaking through the weak points of the crust. The action was rather like that of a pump. Gradually the large craters were built up; as the Moon receded and the axial spin slowed down, so the tidal effects lessened, and the formations produced were smaller. At last the crust became too solid to be broken by the surging magma inside, so that crater-building ceased altogether.

Boneff explained that the Earth's crust was not then solid enough to register any similar craters, though, as we have seen, he did not rule out the possibility that the Moon still influences the frequency of earthquake shocks. Moreover, if it is agreed that the Moon will one day approach the Earth once more, Boneff maintains that it may yet be capable of covering our lands and drying seas with lunar-type craters before it is itself torn apart by the Earth's pull. The last paragraph of his paper is worth quoting: 'An Earth without a Moon, surrounded by a ring of minute bodies and entirely covered with formations of the lunar type, except perhaps at the poles – that is the probable state of the Earth-Moon system, if it still exists, after many thousands of millions of years.'

It is a sombre picture, but not one which we need take very seriously. Apart altogether from the fact that the time-scale is wrong, the whole theory is unsound. The central mountains in lunar craters, for instance, present hopeless difficulties, and there are other objections which are equally fatal. It is an ingenious idea, but evidently it is nothing more.

Ingolf Ruud, of Norway, has put forward a 'direct contraction' theory, according to which the crust of the Moon shrank round a less-yielding interior and thinned and stretched at its weakest points, with the formation of circular craters. On Ruud's theory the smallest formations are the oldest, and the greatest of all the circular plains, the Mare Imbrium, the youngest. This flies in the face of observation; and as neither the central peaks nor many of the other features of the craters can be satisfactorily explained, it seems that the theory must be rejected. The same holds good for the mechanism proposed by A. Fillias, of France, which involved expansion of the Moon's interior against a rigid crust.

There is, however, one idea which avoids both the Scylla of meteors and the Charybdis of vulcanism, and is worthy of serious consideration. This is due to K. H. Engel, a Czech astronomer who has for many years lived and worked in the United States.

Engel believes that the craters and other features were formed by the spontaneous solidification and crystallization of a fairly shallow lava-layer. He has carried out practical experiments on a large scale, and the results are most interesting. There are obvious difficulties, of which Engel himself is well aware, but it is at least a worthwhile line of research, and deserves to be followed up even if it proves to be completely wrong in the end.

Having 'cleared the air', so to speak, it is time for us to turn to the two main theories of today. Since I do not pretend to be impartial, it is only fair to give first innings to the meteoric impact hypothesis, according to which the craters (and, for that matter, the main seas) were produced by a sort of cosmical bombardment of the Moon in past ages.

The idea was originally put forward in 1824 by a German astronomer, Franz von Paula Gruithuisen. Gruithuisen was an enthusiastic observer, though admittedly he was inclined to let his imagination run away with him; and his theory received a certain amount of attention, but later in the century it was more or less forgotten. Then it was revived, first by R. A. Proctor in England (who, however, abandoned it eventually) and G. K. Gilbert in the United States. Again it fell into disfavour, but the situation altered abruptly with the publication, in 1949, of a book called *The Face of the Moon*, by R. B. Baldwin of Chicago. Baldwin dealt with the whole matter in great detail, and presented a case which appeared to be highly convincing.

From what follows, it will be clear that I disagree with much of what Baldwin has said. My views are entirely different from his, and I simply do not believe that the major craters of the Moon are meteoric at all. This is not to suggest that I have anything but the greatest admiration for his book, to say nothing of his numerous other contributions to lunar study. I am quite ready to believe that when the matter is finally cleared up, as it will be when the first expeditions land on the Moon, Baldwin will be proved right and I will be proved wrong. Meanwhile, we agree to differ – and there is no harm in this, as is, I feel, shown by the cordial correspondence which has passed between us.

Following the publication of Baldwin's work, the meteor theory achieved popularity. Others who came out strongly in favour of it were H. C. Urey, G. P. Kuiper, E. Öpik and T. Gold, though all these authorities disagreed over matters of detail. Urey, in 1956, wrote that it was no longer necessary to go on discussing the merits of impact *v.* vulcanism, since the whole question had been settled. Yet with the greatest respect to a Nobel Prize winner and one of the world's great scientists, I suggest that matters are not quite so clear-cut as this. Even the most ardent supporter of the impact hypothesis must admit that there are horribly weak links in the chain of argument.

One 'objection', however, proves to be no objection at all. It has been maintained that a falling meteor would cause a circular crater only if it fell straight down, and that a meteor landing at an angle would result in an elliptical formation. Yet this is not so, as practical experiments prove. On arrival, the meteor would penetrate for a definite distance into the Moon's crust, and would act in the manner of a tremendously powerful explosive, so that a circular crater would result.

Also, it cannot be too strongly stressed that meteor craters must exist on the Moon. Meteorites land on the Earth from time to time, some of them producing craters; the Moon must have had its fair share, and some of the impact scars may be of quite considerable size. It is, therefore, worth saying something about some of the famous meteor craters found on Earth.

As was pointed out in Chapter 2, most shooting-stars are very tiny objects. Meteorites, which are probably related to the minor planets or asteroids, are much larger, but also much less common. Crater-producing meteorites are rarer still. Of the two major falls of the present century, one – the Siberian object of 1908 – fell in marshy ground, and by the time that a scientific expedition reached the site, years later, no craters remained. The other, in the Vladivostok region of Siberia in 1947, was equally unproductive, since the meteorite apparently broke up before landing, and came down in fragments scattered over a rather wide area. In fact, all known meteorite craters are prehistoric.

The most celebrated of them is the Barringer Crater in Arizona. It is visible from Highway 66, which runs between Flagstaff and Winslow. The crater has a diameter of 4,150 feet, with a maximum depth of about 700 feet; the wall rises to 150 feet above the surrounding plain. There can be no doubt that it was caused by a meteorite, and it is certainly very old, though the date of its formation is not known even approximately. One estimate of its age is 50,000 years. According to estimates by L. LaPaz, of the University of New Mexico, the meteorite which caused the crater had a mass of over a million tons, and a probable diameter of around 200 feet.

Other meteorite craters are found in the United States, Arabia, Australia and the Baltic island of Oesel. Less than twenty were known when Baldwin wrote his book; other, less well-preserved specimens have been added to the list since then, but the craters are by no means common.

One interesting formation has come to light in Northern Quebec, near Lake Ungava. It was found in 1950 by a Canadian prospector named Chubb, and described by him as being 'an immense hole looking like a great teacup tilted at an angle'. As soon as the discovery became known, a Toronto research team headed by V. Meen went to investigate. It was established that the crater is two miles across and 1,500 feet deep, part of the floor being occupied by a lake. Once again the age is most uncertain, but the impact must have taken place many thousands of years ago.

The largest Earth crater which seems probably (though not certainly) to be of meteoric origin is that at Deep Bay, Saskatchewan. Here the diameter is eight miles, which is large by terrestrial standards, though very small on the lunar scale. If the Barringer Crater were transferred to the Moon it would hardly be visible, and would appear only as a tiny speck even when seen through a powerful telescope; even the Deep Bay Crater would be a very minor feature, and would certainly not be honoured by being given a separate name.

Baldwin made a close study of the forms of lunar craters, Earth meteor craters and bomb pits, and suggested that they were basic-ally of the same type. He produced graphs showing that the depth-diameter ratios were similar, the general rule being that a smaller crater was deeper in proportion to its size, and from this he con-cluded that all the lunar craters were due to impact.

The question of the depth-diameter values is most interesting. Take, for instance, a well-preserved Moon crater such as Theophilus. The diameter (D) is 64 miles, and the average height of the wall above the deepest part of the floor (h) is around 2·7 miles. 64 divided by 2·7 is about 24; this, then, is the D/h or depth-diameter value for Theophilus. For Ptolemæus, diameter 90 miles, the D/h value is as much as 112; for the 12-mile crater Bessel, on the Mare Sereni-tatis, D/h is 15. The figure for the Barringer Meteor Crater works out at rather less than 6.

We will return to this later. Meanwhile, it is clear that even allowing for the effects of erosion, meteor craters on Earth are rather surprisingly small and rare.

Another point stressed by Baldwin is that it is quite easy to produce artificial impact craters which look very much like lunar ones. There is an immense difference in scale, but a photograph of tiny artificial craters, suitably enlarged, can look quite like a scene on the Moon; even central peaks and short rays can be produced.

We have seen that some of the domes, as well as rounded hills, are crowned by small, symmetrical pits. Baldwin attributed these features to sheer chance hits. When his book appeared, in 1949, a dozen such objects were known, and random bombardment indicated that there should be just about this number, so that Baldwin wrote: 'The agreement is excellent. The case for the meteoritic nature of the lunar craters is even more solidly founded, and the volcanic hypothesis is correspondingly weakened.'

The long chains of great craters, such at the Ptolemæus and Walter groups, were explained quite simply as being due to tricks of the eye. When the Sun rises over a formation, the interior of the crater is thrown into shadow, and the crater itself is at its most conspicuous; the Ptolemæus chain, for instance, is striking at about half-moon. This, according to Baldwin, leads to a false impression, since chains aligned in – say – an east-west direction would not catch the eye nearly so much.

According to the modern version of the impact theory, the

circular maria too are of meteoric origin. The most important of all is the Mare Imbrium, produced by the fall of a body which might be ranked as an asteroid or even the nucleus of a comet.* An impact capable of producing a Mare 700 miles across would indeed be on a vast scale, and Baldwin has stressed that the effects reached far across the Moon; there are what he describes as radial valleys scooped out of ancient rock formations, attributed to débris sent out immediately after the collision, and representing an exaggerated version of the gullies down the slopes of craters such as Aristillus. Fielder has pointed out a clearly-marked 'wheeling movement' of the grid markings around a centre located in the Mare Imbrium.

On the impact theory, the Mare Imbrium meteorite was the greatest of all the collisions which the Moon suffered during its bombardment. Smaller circular maria, such as the Mare Crisium and the Mare Nectaris, were regarded as lesser-scale copies of it.

Then there are the mysterious rays. Various mechanisms have been suggested, but in any case it is clear that if the ray-centres such as Tycho are meteoric, then the rays must have been formed at the same time, so that they represent material sent out across the Moon in long lines. It follows that the ray-craters are among the youngest formations on the whole lunar surface, as otherwise the streamers would have been more broken and distorted than they actually are. Urey has drawn attention to the exceptionally prominent ray coming from Tycho and stretching across the Mare Serenitatis, passing close to Bessel; he suggests that in fact the ray extends right round the Moon, and that we can observe what seems to be the 'other end' of it coming over the south limb.

Finally, valleys such as the Rheita formation and the Alpine Valley are said to be due to collisions with high-velocity meteorites made of nickel-iron. According to G. P. Kuiper, the Rheita Valley is a crack due to a meteoric impact.

So much for the points in favour of the meteor theory. Now let us examine the arguments which can be mustered against it.

As we have seen, there can be no doubt that impact craters exist on the Moon. The point at issue is, quite simply, whether the major formations are due to bombardment, or whether they were produced by forces in (and on) the Moon itself. For the moment it will

* As was noted in Chapter 2, most Russian authorities now believe that the Siberian object of 1908 was the nucleus of a small comet.

be best to retain the term 'volcanic' for the second of these alternatives, even though it is by no means ideal.

Of course, there is a slight chance that with the large craters, too, the origins are different. It is not likely that the central peaks are volcanic and the crater-walls meteoric, but Kopal has suggested that craters such as Tycho are due to impact while others, such as Alphonsus, are not. This seems an unnecessary complication, and one would expect a noticeable difference in form between the meteor and the non-meteor formations, whereas no such indications can be found. Consider, for instance, Tycho and Theophilus. For reasons which are given below, Theophilus is not likely to be an impact crater; if it were, it would have destroyed much of the older crater Cyrillus, which adjoins it. The D/h ratio for Theophilus is 24. With Tycho, it is also 24. The agreement is almost perfect; does it therefore seem probable that the two craters are completely different in character?

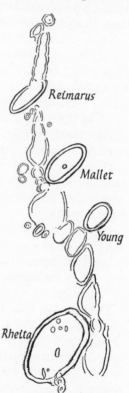

First, then, let us consider the chain-craters of modest size. There can be little doubt that these are volcanic (using the term in its broadest sense). The chains are widespread over the Moon; there are features such as the Hyginus Cleft, which is a crater-chain at least in part, and there are numerous others, not all of which are associated with clefts. Moreover, there is a steady gradation from the 'string of beads' up to formations such as Vogel, in the Hipparchus area, which consists of several craters which have run together.

If we draw upon our imagination and suppose that we have to deal with a string of meteors falling obligingly in a line, the results would still be wrong. There would be a generally disturbed area, certainly not a chain of craters some of which retain their separate walls. But it is pointless to go into further detail, since even the most convinced supporters of the impact

The Rheita Valley

theory agree that the chain-craters are not due to meteoric falls.

There is, however, a further point in this connection. This concerns Kuiper's statement that the Rheita Valley is due to impact. If so, the formation would be genuinely valley-like, but nothing is further from the truth, as is clear when the area is studied visually with a large telescope. The Rheita Valley is made up entirely of craters throughout its length, and could not possibly have been formed in the way suggested by Kuiper.

The Alpine Valley is in a different class, but here we have to reckon also with the parallel and transverse valleys, difficult to record photographically and to be seen visually only under ideal conditions of lighting. I first noted them in 1949, and they have since been fully confirmed by Fielder. This argues against the main Valley having been formed by a missile slicing through the mountains, though it gives no positive proof.

Nobody denies that it is possible to make artificial 'lunar-type' impact craters. What is often forgotten is that such craters may also be produced in other ways. F. Benario, in America, has done it very simply by using plaster of paris, hydrogen peroxide and Alka-Seltzer tablets. Another method, used in 1959 by A. G. Gaydon and R. C. M. Learner, is equally instructive. Gaydon and Learner put powder (sand, together with salt, magnesium oxide and magnesium chloride) in a flask, pumped the flask free of air, and then let in a mild air-flow through a hole in the bottom. Various forms of blow-holes were observed, leading to the suggestion that the Moon's craters may have been caused by fountains of dust blown out by trapped gases.

Experiments of this sort are useful, but we must always bear in mind the tremendous difference in scale. Moreover, the production of artificial craters cannot be said to provide much evidence either way, since the results can be interpreted to support either impact or vulcanism.

This is also true of the argument that Earth meteor craters resemble those of the Moon. I remain to be convinced of the truth of this; unfortunately I have never seen the Barringer Crater, which is by far the most perfect example, but judging from its photographs it does not look particularly lunar. With terrestrial vulcanoids, however, things are rather different. Particularly interesting are the craters in the Richat area of French West Africa, where there are formations of two sorts; single-walled crater-like depressions with diameters ranging from 550 to 1,650 yards, and large circular areas with diameters up to 30 miles. Geologists state that the main features were produced by the rise and subsequent fall of molten volcanic material below the Earth's crust. Moreover, three of them (Temimichat-Ghallaman, Ténoumer and Richat itself) lie in more or less of a straight line.

Here again I must depend on the accounts of other observers; but I have made a first-hand study of some of the volcanic formations in Iceland, notably the spectacular Hverfjall and Lúdent, which lie near the village of Reykjahlið in the Lake Myvátn

Hverfjall   *Lúdent*

Icelandic vulcanoids near
Reykjahlið

area. Hverfjall, visible from the main road, is quite a landmark. It is circular, with walls which rise to between 200 and 300 feet above the floor; it is three-quarters of a mile across, and has a central peak 80 feet high. Evidently it was formed by a single outbreak, when a huge gas 'bubble' rose to the top of the magma reservoir and burst, puncturing the surface and leaving Hverfjall behind in testimony of the event. The inner and outer slopes of the wall are quite gentle, and I found that I could more or less walk up them; no true climbing was needed. Close by are Lúdent, which has an intruding crater, and the smaller Hraunbunga.

There is an obvious similarity with the craters of the Moon. It may of course be a superficial one, but certainly the whole scene is as 'lunar' as can be imagined. The analogy is by no means perfect, and, in particular, the floor of Hverfjall is not appreciably depressed below the outer country. All the same, it looks as though lunar craters are more closely related to these Icelandic volcanoes than to the Barringer Meteor Crater. Photographs taken from the air speak for themselves.

In any case, there are features on the Moon which do look remarkably like conventional Earth volcanoes. These are the lunar domes, which were described earlier, and with which we may, for the moment, include the rounded hills with summit pits. Baldwin, as we have seen, knew of a dozen or so, and explained them as chance hits. I was by no means satisfied, and during 1952 and 1956

101

I spent some time at the Observatory of Meudon, near Paris, using the great 33-inch refractor to search for more. I found over fifty. The list has been added to since, and there seems to be no longer any doubt that the 'hit or miss' idea simply will not do.

Yet the crucial point of the whole controversy concerns the way in which the craters are spread over the surface of the Moon. If they were produced by bombardment, the distribution would be essentially random. On a volcanic theory, we would expect a certain orderliness – just as is the case on Earth.

Even a casual glance at a map of the Moon shows that the crater

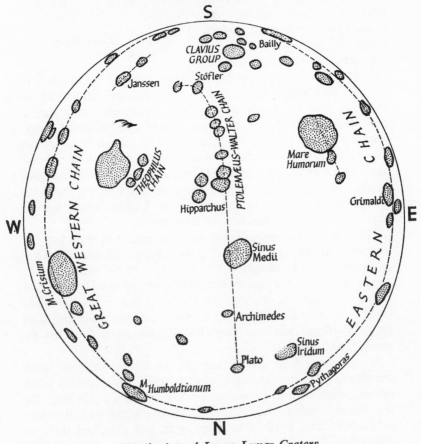

Distribution of Large Lunar Craters

distribution is not random, or anything like it. Baldwin's dismissal of the long chains of walled plains as being due to lighting effects fails to stand up to analysis. There is a chain down the central meridian of the Earth-turned hemisphere, made up of the Walter group, the Ptolemæus group, and perhaps Clavius in the south and Archimedes and Plato in the north; a chain down the west limb, extending from Vlacq down to Endymion, and including the Mare Crisium; another down the east limb, reaching from Bailly to Schickard, Grimaldi and Pythagoras. These are shown on the chart, which is a perfectly fair one, since the craters shown have been selected only by size. (A Mercator chart is even more informative, but the inevitable distortions make it an inconvenient projection for this sort of work.) No such chains extend from east to west, and it seems, then, that we are dealing with formations which were born along lines of weakness in the Moon's crust – connected no doubt with the influence of the Earth, since the lining-up of the chains with the central meridian can hardly be due to chance.

The only loophole for an impact theory might be to suppose that the craters really were produced by chains of meteors which fell at about the same time. Baldwin himself has, however, pointed out that the craters in any particular chain are of widely differing age – for instance, Vendelinus in the western chain is obviously much more ancient than its neighbour Langrenus – and so this argument is equally untenáble.

Groups and pairs are also extremely common, as we have seen; there are the separate 'twins' such as Aliacensis and Werner, and the joined ones of the Sirsalis and Steinheil type. The same sort of arrangement extends down to much smaller craters, such as Messier-Pickering in the Mare Fœcunditatis and Beer-Feuillé in the Mare Imbrium.

Note, too, that with 'twins', either joined or separate, the two craters are always of the same sort. I do not know of one case in which one 'twin' has a central peak and the other has not. The two are always basically alike.

Next let us turn to the almost innumerable cases in which one crater breaks into another. The rule here is, as we have seen, that the smaller crater is the intruder, and the larger one the sufferer. Of course there are great formations which have much smaller craters inside, or on their walls; Clavius is the classic example, and con-

103

centric craters such as Vitello are also notable. But the general principle is best shown by the two drawings given here. One is of Thebit, near the Straight Wall; the main crater is broken by a second (Thebit A) which is in turn disturbed by a third (Thebit D). The second is a freehand sketch, since it could not be drawn from actual observation; nothing like it exists on the Moon.

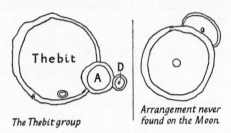

The Thebit group   Arrangement never
                                     found on the Moon

It has been said that there are a few exceptions to the rule. The Sinus Iridum may be one; if we regard it as a crater, it has had its seaward wall broken by the Mare Imbrium. Other possibilities are Burckhardt, near the Mare Crisium, and Maurolycus in the uplands of the fourth quadrant. However, I am not convinced about either of these, since the broken craters have been so distorted that it is difficult to tell whether or not they really break the general law. In any event, the exceptions amount to far less than 0·1 per cent of the total.

On the impact theory we would expect a good many departures from the rule; it is impossible to believe that all the large meteors fell first! If we adopt the volcanic principle, there is no objection at all; the earliest outbreaks would be the most violent, and smaller craters would be produced later as the Moon calmed down.

There is, however, another most important point. I first discussed it some ten years ago, but at the time it seemed so obvious that I did not realize it had not been appreciated. Since then, Kopal has mentioned it independently. To explain it, let us look again at the drawing of Thebit.

Suppose that Thebit itself were formed by a meteoric impact. Later, a second meteorite fell on or very near the wall, and produced the crater A. In such a case, there would have been a major 'moonquake' in the lunar crust — and the wall of Thebit itself would have been ruined for miles around the point of the new

104

impact. This is not what is seen. Thebit's wall remains perfect and undamaged right up to the point of the junction. Always it is the same; never is there any sign of ruin or débris. Could an impact-produced Theophilus have failed to level long stretches of the wall of the older Cyrillus, and could Tralles have been similarly merciful with regard to Cleomedes?

The answer must surely be 'No' – and this indicates that the craters were not produced either by impact or by explosive vulcanism. The process must have been much gentler, which was why I originally put forward the idea of uplift and subsidence.

As a last objection, let us look at the rays which come from Tycho and other craters. By impact, the rays must have been formed at

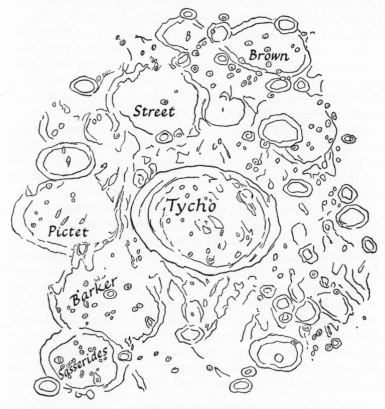

Region of Tycho
105

the same time as the crater lying at the focal point of the system, since the streamers pass over all other formations with nothing more than mild distortion. This would make Tycho one of the youngest craters in its area, if not the youngest of all. It is 54 miles across; if it had been produced by a falling meteorite, the resultant ground-tremors would have been disastrous to its neighbours such as Pictet, Street and Brown. The same argument holds good for other ray-craters lying in crowded areas.

It is, moreover, very difficult to see how the material could have been spread out in such long, straight lines. Urey's suggestion of a ray coming from Tycho and stretching right round the Moon is untenable; it would mean that the particles would have been sent into circular paths, whereas in fact the paths would have been elliptical. Moreover, the ray which finally passes over the northern limb is not a mere continuation of the original ray from Tycho, and generally speaking the rays are not simple streaks. They have definite structure, and are associated with small, bright craterlets. My own ideas about them are given below; but in any case it is hardly likely that they were produced in one cataclysmic outburst at the same time as the formation of their parent craters.

All these considerations seem, to me at least, to show that the impact hypothesis will have to be abandoned so far as the large craters are concerned. It needs too many special assumptions, and it has too many fatally weak links. The next step is to find something better, and this brings us on to the various volcanic theories.

Actually, the term 'volcanic' can be misinterpreted, since a lunar crater is so unlike a volcano of the Vesuvius type. Moreover, many people still connect it with the delightful fiery fountain idea proposed by two English amateurs, J. Nasmyth* and J. Carpenter, in 1874. Nasmyth and Carpenter pictured a central volcano erupting violently and showering débris around it on all sides, so that the matter ejected from the central orifice built up the crater wall. As the eruptions became less violent, inner terraces were formed, and in the dying stages of activity, when the explosions were only just powerful enough to lift the material out of its vent, the central peak was built up. Craters without central peaks were explained by supposing that the explosions ceased rather suddenly, so that the

* The inventor of the steam-hammer. His telescope is now on exhibition at the Science Museum in South Kensington.

Nasmyth & Carpenter's Volcanic Fountain

floor was covered by lava which welled up from inside the Moon.

The idea sounds very plausible at first sight. The terraces, the hill-top craters, the flooded craters and even the famous plateau Wargentin are accounted for, and the ringed formations do give the superficial impression of having been built up in this way. Unfortunately, there are various fatal objections. It is beyond all belief that a circular wall over 100 miles in diameter, and sharply defined (as is the case with Clavius, for instance) could have been formed in such a fashion; the slope-angles are wrong, and the walls are far too massive. Moreover, the central peak of a lunar crater is always considerably lower than the rampart, which would not be expected on the volcanic fountain theory. It is also true that many craters which lack central peaks show no sign of interior flooding.

The explanation given for the bright rays is equally untenable. Nasmyth and Carpenter thought that the crust of the Moon had cracked in places, much as a glass globe does when it is struck, and that lava had oozed out of the cracks, forming the rays; but we may now be sure that the rays are mere surface deposits, not connected with fissures of any kind.

As long ago as 1665 an entirely different process was suggested by Robert Hooke. Hooke was a genius in many fields; he has never been given as much credit as is his due, partly no doubt because he left a reputation for peevishness and ill-humour, but mainly because he lived at the same time as a still greater genius, Isaac Newton. Yet Hooke's interests were just as wide as Newton's, and his contributions to science were tremendous.

He made some drawings of lunar craters which were remarkably good considering the low-powered telescopes which he had to use, and he put forward the idea that the craters might be the remains of great bubbles which rose during the period when the lunar

107

surface was molten; when they burst, they left a solidified rim behind. This again sounds plausible, and one cannot refrain from drawing a comparison with the bubbles seen in boiling porridge or boiling mud. Yet here too we come up against hopeless difficulties, because a bubble of the size needed to form a crater as large as (say) Clavius can be discounted on dynamical grounds.

There are many modern variations on the volcanic theme, and to list them all would take many pages. Rather than do so, I propose to put forward my own theory. I do so with diffidence, and with the full knowledge that there is probably not much original work in it; it is merely an attempt to build up a general picture. Whether there is any truth in it remains to be seen.

On this form of the volcanic theory, we begin with a Moon which had a solidifying crust lying over a layer of hot, viscous magma. This is an idea supported by some authorities, but not all. If it proves to be incorrect, the sequence of events suggested here will have to be drastically modified, or else abandoned altogether; but one has to start somewhere, and we cannot claim to have anything like an adequate knowledge of the Moon's past history.

In those far-off times, the distance between the Earth and the Moon was less than it is now, and the tidal effects on the Moon were greater. The axial rotation was rapidly slowed down, and when the main crater-building period began the rotation was already 'captured' – that is to say, the same hemisphere of the Moon faced the Earth all the time. Lines of weakness were produced in the lunar crust, and at any particularly weak point the hot magma would tend to force its way to the surface, forming a 'feed-pipe', so that the whole of the surrounding area would be lifted up in a dome. If the pressure were not strong enough for any further development, the activity would cease, and the dome would remain – as many domes actually do; but generally, so much gas and material would be forced out through the feed-pipe that the pressure below would relax abruptly, so that the dome would subside with comparative suddenness. This would lower it into the hot magma, and the skin of the old dome would melt.

This process might be repeated several times, with the eventual production of walls low above the outside surface, but much higher above the continually remelted interior. Terraces would be produced; and as the floor gradually congealed, hills and minor craters

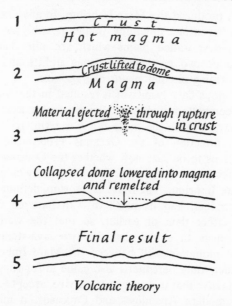

1
 Crust
 Hot magma

2
 Crust lifted to dome
 Magma

3
 Material ejected through rupture in crust

4
 Collapsed dome lowered into magma and remelted

5
 Final result

Volcanic theory

would arise in it. Often the dying stages of ejection from the feed-pipe would result in the building-up of a massive central elevation, naturally lower than the outer surface-level, while in other cases a final phase of remelting inside the now-deepening hollow would destroy all detail, even to the central peak (if one had ever been formed). In a few cases, such as Wargentin, the rising rush of magma was trapped when its lower escape-vent became blocked, so that it solidified where it was.

The early surface activity was naturally the most violent, because the Moon was then at its hottest and tidal strains were at their maximum – so that the oldest craters were the largest, and were broken into by the smaller ones which arose later. Craters tended to appear along the lines of crustal weakness, so that they formed strings and chains, while very often two similar weak points in the crust resulted in twin craters.

Probably the very first crater-like formations were obliterated, partly by later outbreaks and partly because the crust may not have been sufficiently solid to preserve them. Yet they may have left their mark, and resulted in low-lying areas which were later covered with Mare-material (Spurr's lunabase) from violent outbreaks such

109

as that which produced the Mare Imbrium. In any case, at a fairly early stage in the surface moulding, though possibly after the formation of the oldest walled plains which are still visible (such as Janssen), one or two particularly strong uplifts and subsidences took place, forming circular plains of huge size.

The tremendous cataclysm which resulted in the Mare Imbrium gave rise to complete remelting of the crust over a wide area, and magma (or lava, to use the more familiar term) rolled across the plain in the direction of the Oceanus Procellarum, making it impossible for us to be sure now whether the Oceanus were due to an earlier subsidence or whether it were merely a lava overflow from the Mare Imbrium. The Mare Humorum, definitely a separate subsidence product, had its northern wall battered down by the rolling lava either then or earlier, so that the wall was finally breached to such an extent that the two lava-streams met and mingled. The mountain wall between the Mare Imbrium and the somewhat older Mare Serenitatis also came in for rough treatment, but was so massive that it managed to survive, except for one stretch between the modern Apennines and Caucasus; it may well have acted as a vast groyne, protecting the western area from more extensive remelting.

Other dome-collapses gave rise to the Mare Nectaris, the Mare Crisium and the Mare Humboldtianum, though the lighter and patchier lunabase areas such as the Lacus Somniorum and the Mare Frigoris were no more than lava overflows. Craters such as Letronne and Fracastorius, bordering the remelted areas, were badly damaged on their seaward sides, and craters which had once existed on the collapsed regions were either badly reduced – as Stadius has been – or totally overwhelmed.

As the tremendous upheavals died down, smaller craters began to appear in the uplands and also on the solidifying floors of the maria. Some, such as Archimedes on the Mare Imbrium, were born before the surface had solidified enough for them to become very deep, so that their floors were rapidly remelted and became smooth and featureless; others, such as Copernicus and Eratosthenes, were not born until later, by which time the old collapse-areas had become about as solid as the original surface had been before the great seas came into existence.

Gradually the uplifts and collapses became smaller and less

frequent, as the inner magma cooled and the increasing distance between the Earth and Moon reduced the tidal effects, until at last crater formation virtually ceased.

I am well aware that this whole idea is speculative, and that it leaves much to be desired, but it does seem to explain most of the features observed on the Moon. There is no longer any difficulty about the non-random distribution; lines of weakness give the answer – and we can see why the great chains of craters line up with the central meridian, since the Earth's gravitational pull was responsible. On this basis I suggested, in 1952, that the reverse side of the Moon would contain fewer large chains and certainly fewer seas than the side we have always known. This has proved to be correct, though at the time I had no hope that the problem would be solved within a decade! If the crater-building process were relatively gentle, as I believe, we can also see why the craters which break into earlier formations have not ruined the walls of their victims, and the almost invariable 'overlapping rule' of smaller craters disturbing larger ones would be expected. Moreover, we put the seas into their proper place, either as outsize craters (Mare Imbrium) or lava-overflows (Mare Frigoris).

In passing, it should be added that N. S. Shaler, an American geologist and lunar student, suggested that the seas were meteoric in origin while the craters were volcanic, but there seems no reason for such a distinction. More logical is the idea that impacts from meteorites 'triggered off' volcanic action, though personally I see no reason to bring in two processes when one will do.

On the other hand there has recently been an important contribution from one of Japan's leading selenographers, S. Miyamoto. Miyamoto is one of a few authorities* who has tackled the problem as it really should be tackled – from the geological viewpoint – and he has suggested that the maria are due to the sorting-out of the light-coloured silicic mass from the heavy, darker, basaltic mass in the crust of the ancient Moon. This sounds very reasonable, particularly as much the same thing has happened on Earth. My main objection here is that I have never seen any reason to put the maria and the craters into different categories; but Miyamoto's sequence of events is very convincing, and I am quite ready to be proved wrong.

* Others are Spurr, Fielder, Firsoff and Green.

Finally, of course, there are those enigmatical features, the bright rays. All previous theories have had difficulty in explaining them. The impact idea fails completely, and neither is it easy to see how an outburst from the central peak of a ray-crater can have produced such long, regular lines – an idea which I used to support simply because I could think of no alternative.

In 1962 I wrote a short paper outlining a different theory. As we have seen, the rays are not continuous; they seem to be renewed all along their length – sometimes obviously, as with the Tycho-Bessel ray, but more often by craterlets which are too small to be prominent. This, it seems to me, may be the key. Suppose that almost at the end of the Moon's active life, there were explosions from the peaks of a few craters, such as Tycho, scattering ash for limited distances? Smaller craterlets lying along the lines of weakness emanating from the focal points might be 'triggered', and they too would send out material. If the area covered were very local, there would be no impression of a series of stars, and the result would be an apparently continuous line.

My paper was already in the post to the Secretary of the British Astronomical Association when I received the manuscript of a much more detailed paper on the same lines, written by the Indian astronomer P. Devadas. Devadas' work had been carried out earlier than mine, and was much more exhaustive. If therefore the idea proves to be correct, Devadas must take the credit; if it does not, I am willing to share the blame!

It is perhaps fitting to end by noting a modern development. We cannot doubt that although small meteoric pits must be formed now and then, the main crater-forming period of the Moon ended millions of years ago. Ever since life appeared on the lands of Earth, and perhaps before, the lunar world has been calm and almost inactive. We can no longer say 'quite inactive', however, since, in 1958, the Russian astronomer N. Kozirev observed what seems to have been an outbreak inside the crater Alphonsus.

Kozirev's observation will be dealt with in Chapter 12. It has caused strong arguments, and interpretations of it vary; but at least *something* happened – and if there is even a trace of vulcanism lingering on in one of the craters, it is not unreasonable to suppose that the central peak itself is volcanic.

That, for the moment, is as far as we can go. The problem of how the Moon's surface was moulded is a fascinating one, but now, for the first time, we have definite prospects of solving it. As soon as men from Earth land upon those barren rocks, we will find out once and for all whether the craters were produced by celestial bombardment, or whether they are the result of tremendous volcanic activity in the remote past.

Chapter 10

The Nature of the Surface

On a clear winter's night, the Moon shines down with a brilliant radiance which floods the landscape with light and throws long black shadows on the earth. The dazzling disk looks as if it were covered with ice or snow.

Once again, however, appearances are deceptive. Despite its apparent brilliance, the Moon is one of the poorest reflectors in the Solar System. On an average, it sends us only 7 per cent of the sunlight which it receives, so that it looks as though the surface must be made up of darkish rocks. If the Moon had the reflecting power of Venus, for instance, it would be glorious indeed; but Venus is covered with 'clouds', and there are no clouds on the Moon.

Not all the lunar surface has the same reflecting power or albedo. Some of the darkest areas have an albedo of only 5 per cent, which, significantly, is roughly the same as that of some volcanic lavæ. The uplands have a higher albedo, resembling that of granite, while a very few patches, notably the glittering crater-ring of Aristarchus, may reflect up to 35 or 40 per cent of the sunlight which falls upon them.

What, then, is the Moon's surface really like? We find that there is no general agreement. For instance, T. Gold believes that the maria are covered with dust-layers several miles deep, while other astronomers deny that there is any dust at all. Before going further into this sort of question, however, let us see what positive information is available.

Since the Moon sends us light, we may expect to receive a certain amount of heat as well. We cannot feel it, because it is too slight, and neither can we record it on an ordinary thermometer, but it may be measured easily enough by using a large telescope together with a special instrument known as a thermocouple. The first attempts were made by Lord Rosse in the nineteenth century, and were quite useful; nowadays the measurements are probably very accurate.

The principle of the thermocouple is straightforward enough. If we take two wires made of different metals and make a complete circuit by soldering their ends together, forming a ring, an electric current will flow through the circuit if the joins are at different temperatures. We can therefore produce a current by warming one join and keeping the other at a constant temperature; the current may be measured with a delicate device termed a galvanometer. Rosse concentrated the light (and therefore heat) of the Moon on to one join, and measured the strength of the current set up in the circuit. The total heat received could then be worked out.

There are many complications to be borne in mind, and the whole process is not nearly so simple as might be thought. Part of the heat received is merely reflected solar heat; the rest is heat which has been absorbed by the Moon's surface and then sent out again. The wheat has to be sifted from the chaff, and it is not always easy to tell which is which. Rosse's early results were naturally uncertain, but they did at least show that the Moon's equatorial zone becomes very hot indeed around lunar midday.

There is every reason why this should be so. The Moon, remember, has practically no atmosphere, so that there is nothing to shield its surface from the full force of the Sun's rays. On the other hand, neither is there anything to blanket in the heat during the hours of darkness, and so night on the Moon may be expected to be very cold. This is precisely what has been found. On the lunar equator, the temperature ranges from above 210 degrees F. at noon down to around − 250 degrees at midnight.

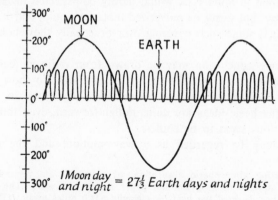

Diurnal variations of Temperature for the Earth and the Moon

More recent work, notably the series of measures carried out by E. Pettit and S. B. Nicolson with the 100-inch Hooker reflector at Mount Wilson Observatory, has led to reliable figures. Modern instruments of the thermocouple type are incredibly sensitive, and it is said that by using the Palomar reflector it would be possible to measure the heat sent out by an ordinary candle at a distance of 6,000 miles;* even the tiny amounts produced by stars such as Arcturus have been detected, so that the Moon presents no major problems at all. On the other hand, it would be wrong to suppose that temperatures are the same all over the Moon. At the poles, where the Sun is never very high up, the temperature never rises to as much as the freezing-point of water.

It is worth remembering that the temperatures on the 'other side of the Moon' will be of the same sort as those on the familiar face. The reverse side is always turned away from the Earth – but not from the Sun, so that day and night conditions there will be no different.

There is one way in which the temperature measures can help in studies of the nature of the Moon's surface. During a lunar eclipse, the Moon passes into the shadow cast by the Earth, and for a period all direct sunlight is cut off. Immediately, the temperatures drop. In 1927 and 1939, for instance, Pettit and Nicolson found that the temperature fell by well over 250 degrees in the course of an hour. It is clear, then, that the Moon is coated with some material which is extremely bad at keeping warm once the Sun has stopped shining upon it. Solid rock would hardly be expected to behave in such a way, but dusty or pulverized material would, and it may be that there is some such covering over practically the whole of the Moon.

The same conclusion may be drawn from radio studies of the Moon, begun soon after the end of the last war. To show what is meant, a little must be said about radio astronomy in general. Luckily the basic ideas are quite straightforward, even though the complications seem to be endless.

Light may be regarded as a wave-motion, and the distance

* Neglecting atmospheric absorption, of course. I am reminded of a delightful news item in a London paper some years ago: 'The Palomar telescope *has detected* the heat of a candle 6,000 miles away.' (The italics are mine!)

116

between two successive crests is known as the wavelength. The colour of light depends on its wavelength; red light, for instance, has a wavelength much longer than that of blue. By our everyday standards even red light has a very short wavelength, amounting to a minute fraction of a millimetre, but this is only part of the story.

Radiations of wavelength longer than that of red light cannot be seen, since they do not affect our eyes, but they can be measured; most people have come across the infra-red lamps used in hospitals, for instance. With still longer wavelengths we come to the so-called radio waves, which are of the same basic nature, and are studied by means of radio telescopes. Most famous of these instruments is the 250-foot 'dish' at Jodrell Bank, in Cheshire. The dish focuses the radio waves just as an optical reflector focuses visible light, but it does not produce a visible image of the object being studied, and one certainly cannot look through it. By no means all radio telescopes are built on the dish pattern, and special designs are developed for various special investigations.

The Earth's atmosphere is still a stumbling-block, because the shielding layers high above the ground block out many of the waves which we are so anxious to study. This is one reason why the Moon will be so suitable a site for observatories and laboratories of the future. To go more fully into the details of radio astronomy would be out of place here, and it is enough to say simply that all heated bodies, including the Moon, send out radio waves.

In 1946 micro-wave radiation from the Moon was detected by Dicke and Beringer, using a wavelength of 1·25 centimetres. Then, three years later, two Australian investigators, Piddington and Minnett, carried out an important piece of research. They used a four-foot metal reflector to focus the Moon's radio waves, and managed to obtain temperature values for the Moon by studying the waves received. The results were of tremendous interest. The temperatures were much more uniform than those obtained by the older methods; moreover, Piddington and Minnett found that maximum occurred not at lunar noon, but three days later.

More work has been done since, and it is found that as the wavelength is increased, so the temperature-range becomes less. In 1962 J. F. Denisse, working with the radio telescope at Nançay in France, announced that for wavelengths greater than 12 inches there was no variation at all, and that the temperature always remained

117

the same – well below freezing-point. During a lunar eclipse, too, the temperatures measured by radio do not drop in the same way as those measured with instruments of the thermocouple type.

There is a sound explanation for this curious state of affairs. When we use a thermocouple, we are naturally measuring the temperature at the surface of the Moon – the surface we can see. But the Moon's coating is partially transparent to radio waves, and so we are, in effect, studying radiations which are coming from below the lunar surface. Longer wavelengths penetrate deeper. Consequently, Denisse, working at wavelengths of one foot, was dealing with deeper layers than Piddington and Minnett had been at a mere centimetre and a quarter.

The results show that the Moon's coating is very poor at conducting heat. Even when the surface is raised to over 200 degrees, the temperature a foot or so down is still below freezing-point. Using all this information, we can make some speculations about the surface structure, as has been done by Jaeger and Harper among others. It seems that the most likely arrangement is of a shallow layer of dusty or pulverized material lying above solid rock.

Radio astronomy has certainly given us information which we could hardly have obtained in any other way – which is remarkable in view of the fact that it is only just over a quarter of a century since Karl Jansky, working with the Bell Telephone Company in America, first detected radio emissions from the sky and so laid the foundations of a whole new branch of astronomical science. But there is still sharp disagreement about the depth of the Moon's outer layer, and this brings us on to the dust-drift theory.

Whether the Moon's craters are volcanic or whether they are due to bombardment, there must be a good deal of material on the surface which may be termed 'dust'. We know that the Earth sweeps up cosmic matter regularly, in the form of very small particles spread about in the Solar System; no doubt the Moon does the same. Bearing this in mind, T. Gold, then of the Royal Greenwich Observatory, put forward a new and striking picture of the surface conditions, in 1955. He adopted the impact theory for the origin of craters, and suggested that the maria were covered with layers of dust many kilometres deep. Indeed, he later said that in his view 'space-travellers of the future will simply sink into the dust with their gear'.

118

On Gold's theory the dusty particles are very small, so that the various thermal and electrical effects will cause the surface to become agitated and to behave rather in the manner of a liquid. Wherever the dust is formed, it will flow downhill to the lowest point, and will therefore collect in the relatively low-lying maria to form tremendous drifts.

It is rather difficult to picture dust acting in such a way, and it has since been shown that the process could not happen unless the particles were improbably small. But there are a good many other weak links in the argument, too. To begin with, the dust might conceivably have buried various craters, but it could not have destroyed their walls; and the most casual glance at the great bays such as Fracastorius and Lemonnier shows that the seaward walls have most certainly been destroyed. The Sinus Iridum may well come into the same category. And the 'floors' of these bays are not very far below the level of the outer bright regions, which Gold does not believe to be dust-covered to anything like the same extent.

We must also consider the ghost rings on the maria. Stadius may be regarded as a ghost, but there are many others which can barely be traced; ten years ago I pointed out that most of the so-called ridges on the seas are really parts of the walls of ghost-rings, and this has since been confirmed by Fielder. The dust theory breaks down altogether here, since the ghosts cannot be accounted for. Moreover, we also find craters, such as Archimedes and Plato, whose floors are of the 'mare' type – or lunabase, to use Spurr's term. According to Gold, the dust would have had to flow uphill over the crater-walls before settling down inside, which does not seem very logical. It is also worth noting that cleft-floors are light, as Fielder has shown, whereas on Gold's theory they would have to be dark.

There is also the radio work, which indicates (though it does not prove) that the other coating cannot be deep. All things considered, Gold's theory fails to meet the facts. It is ingenious and original, but it does not stand up to analysis.

It has often been said that the Moon is picking up dust all the time, and that there must therefore be a deep layer by now. I am not so sure. We cannot, of course, be at all precise about the rate of dust-collection in the past, but there is observational evidence that no appreciable layer has been produced during the last five hundred million years or so. The lunar rays extending from Tycho, Copernicus and other craters may be mysterious, but we may be certain that they are surface deposits and nothing more. A relatively thin layer of cosmical dust would hide them completely, and yet they remain very conspicuous. Therefore, they must have been formed after the dust-fall on the Moon had dropped to negligible proportions.

The only possible quibble about this idea, so far as I can see, is that we do not know when the ray-systems were produced. They may be more recent than is generally thought. But this does not seem likely; and it is equally far-fetched to suppose that the dust-collection stopped suddenly after having been great enough to fill the huge maria to depths of several miles!

The disagreements are certainly very marked. At one end of the scale we have Gold and his supporters, who believe in a dusty Moon covered in places to a great depth; at the other, people such as myself, who incline to the view that the dust can be no more than a few centimetres deep at most. The only way to clear the matter up once and for all is to send a rocket to find out.

Dust-drifts being rejected, what then can we say about the Moon's surface rocks?

One characteristic is that they seem to show a certain amount of luminescence – a term which may need some explanation. Some materials have the power of absorbing short-wave radiation and then re-emitting it as visible light; there are minerals, for example, which can be made to glow when exposed to an ultra-violet lamp, which provides a good case of luminescence at work.

The Moon is being bombarded by short-wave radiations from the Sun, and various astronomers, notably F. Link in Czechoslovakia and J. Dubois in France, have reported luminescent effects which are strong enough to be unmistakable. Their work has been followed up by N. Kozirev, in Russia, who has compared the spectrum of the Moon with that of the Sun. Since the Moon shines by reflected sunlight, its spectrum should be an enfeebled copy of the Sun's, complete with the dark bands still known at Fraunhofer Lines in honour of the young German scientist who drew attention to them a century and a half ago. But if the Moon's rocks shine feebly on their own account, the dark lines should be less intense in the lunar

120

spectrum than they are in the spectrum of the Sun. This is what Kozirev has found. The luminescence disappears abruptly at the time of sunset over the Moon's rocks.

We could learn a great deal from the colours of the rocks – if any colours were to be seen. Unfortunately this is yet another point upon which there is no general agreement. Of course the surface is not of uniform hue; the pure tint of the Mare Imbrium, for instance, contrasts sharply with the lighter patches of the Mare Nubium or the Oceanus Procellarum. Yet violent reds, greens, blues and yellows simply do not exist.

Some observers say that the various maria have their own special colours – greenish for the Mare Crisium and Paulus Somnii, yellowish for the Mare Frigoris, and so on. Between 1830 and 1838 Mädler frequently recorded a reddish patch near the little crater Lichtenberg, which lies between Aristarchus and the limb, and this has been confirmed by D. P. Barcroft and R. M. Baum in modern times, while the shadow inside Philolaus, a noble crater in the far north, has been described as purplish. I am in no position to comment, because in thirty years of lunar observation I have never seen any distinct local colour anywhere on the Moon. Visually, I remain to be convinced that any local colours exist; but it must be added that on this point V. A. Firsoff, in particular, does not agree with me, and his eyes are much more colour-sensitive than mine. Russian observers also report faint hues.

In 1910 R. W. Wood, in the United States, took some photographs of the Moon in ultra-violet light. This work led him to believe that a small area not far from Aristarchus and Herodotus was covered by a sulphur deposit, or at any rate something quite unlike the surrounding regions. Sulphur would come as no surprise, since it is closely associated with volcanoes; in fact it is so often found around the craters of Earth volcanoes that it is still known as brimstone, and we can see the point of the old reference to 'fire and brimstone'.

Wood's experiments were carried out at East Hampton, New York State, with equipment which was made of odds and ends, as he himself wrote. He never followed up the work with more elaborate apparatus, but the existence of 'Wood's Spot', as it came to be called, was confirmed in 1926 by F. E. Wright at the Lick Observatory. Wright also found a few more areas of similar type, notably

121

in the area of the Sinus Roris. Meanwhile, A. Miethe and B. Seegert, in Germany, have carried out an extensive programme of research, and have even produced a colour picture of the Moon, which is admittedly a composite but is of great interest. The Mare Tranquillitatis, for example, comes out as strongly greenish.

Yet even if these hues are real, they are so faint and fugitive that they are very hard to detect in ordinary visual observation. Still, the fact that differences exist at all is another argument against the idea of a deep coating of dust, which would tend to make the surface uniform.

It may be that the surface layer is made up of crushed material. The Russian astronomer N. Barabashov believes it to consist of disintegrated tufa-like rock, with grains ranging in size from 3 to 10 millimetres in diameter, while the layer itself is no more than 3 centimetres deep. V. V. Sharonov and N. N. Sytinskaya, at Leningrad, have developed a theory that the surface is made up of slag-like material; a meteorite hitting the crust will cause a temporary 'hot spot' where the surface will be vapourized, and the vapour will condense and fall back to the ground, producing a slag coating. And according to Firsoff, 'all evidence points to bubbly pumice-like rock and substantial absence of large deposits of dust'. It is now easy enough to bounce radar waves off the Moon, and the lunar surface seems to act in the manner of a smooth mirror, though any glance through a telescope shows that it is anything but smooth; therefore the minor surface irregularities are small compared with the wavelengths of the radar pulses, which fits in quite well with the slag and pumice pictures.

Neither is it clear whether there is any real difference between lunarite and lunabase. There may be; on the other hand, the differences in appearance may be due only to differences in the depth of the outer coating. We have to confess that at present we do not know.

The idea of water-sheets on the Moon is so completely out of the question that we need waste no time on it; even if the Moon used to have moisture on its surface, it can have none now. Neither can we have the slightest faith in Fauth's ice theory, according to which the lunar surface is permanently frozen. Yet we have to be a little more cautious before saying baldly that the Moon is utterly without water in any form.

In 1961 Z. Kopal, of Manchester, made some suggestions which are as interesting as they are unexpected. If the young Moon contained a great deal of water, and if the globe never became really hot inside, this water would remain bound up in a solid form. It is quite on the cards that the Moon contains a great deal of radioactive material, just as the Earth does – and radioactivity means heat, so that the interior of the Moon is now at a temperature of at least 1,000 degrees. This is enough to break the water-molecules free, and drive them out in the form of superheated steam along any crack stretching toward the surface. Radio measures have shown that even a foot below the outer surface, the temperature is below freezing-point; according to Kopal, the steam therefore condenses into a liquid and then turns into ice before it reaches the actual surface.

If Kopal is right, there may be glaciers at a very shallow depth. Indeed, he suggests that some of the glaciers may be observable, and that the famous lunar domes are nothing more than glaciers coated with dust, so that the central pits of the domes represent the springs of geysers which occasionally break out. If the geyser became active during the night, the water would freeze, but Kopal believes that the ice would persist for a long time, and that there may even be areas of exposed ice in favourable positions near the poles.

On the whole it seems that the domes are too big to be coated glaciers, and the idea of geysers seems rather improbable, but this is a minor point. Two years before Kopal announced his theory, Firsoff had already suggested that the Moon might have extensive oceans below its crust. I admit to having serious doubts about the existence of either water or ice below the surface rocks, but these misgivings are probably founded more upon prejudice than upon scientific reasoning!

It has also been suggested that snow may persist on the Moon. W. H. Pickering, author of the photographic atlas of 1904, believed that the brilliance of certain regions – Aristarchus, Pico, Menelaus in the Hæmus Mountains, Proclus near the Mare Crisium, the central peaks of Theophilus, and others – was due to snowy deposits. Aristarchus, in particular, is a puzzling formation. It is definitely the brightest spot on the whole Moon, and is so brilliant that it shines prominently by earthshine. Unwary watchers have mistaken it for an erupting volcano, and it seems likely that even Sir William Herschel, father of stellar astronomy and one of the greatest observers of all time, fell into the same trap, though one hesitates to accuse him of it!

Pickering also thought that cracks in the Moon's surface sent out water vapour, which was at once re-deposited as snow and became conspicuous because of its greater reflecting power. Unfortunately, there are any number of serious objections.

For one thing, mountain-tops are the very last places where we might expect to find snow on the Moon. It would be far more likely to hide itself inside shadowed valleys and gorges, where it would be virtually unobservable. Moreover, the fierce heat of the lunar day seems to rule out the possibility, at least in regions anywhere near the Moon's equator. Aristarchus and similar formations are at their brightest under high light – and can we seriously believe in the existence of snow upon a world where there is no moisture and virtually no atmosphere? It seems utterly unreasonable. The true answer must lie in the nature of the surface material, whether it be pulverized rock, pumice or slag; Aristarchus simply happens to have an unusually high albedo.

But so far we have based all our conclusions on the blunt statement that 'the Moon is without atmosphere'. Before going any further, it will be wise to pause for a while to see whether this statement is true.

Chapter 11

The Lunar Atmosphere

The Moon is the Earth's companion-planet. As we have seen, it is much too large to be classed as a mere satellite, and in the Solar System its status is comparable with that of our own world.

Yet the Earth and Moon are as unlike as it is possible to be. It is not only a question of size; it is a matter of conditions and past history. Most of the differences spring from one vital fact which has been known for very many years. The Earth has a dense mantle of air, without which no life of the sort we know could have developed here; the Moon is virtually devoid of any atmosphere at all. If we say that the Moon is an 'airless world', few people will criticize us.*

Earlier astronomers, notably Schröter and Herschel, believed that the Moon must be a living world, with a relatively dense atmosphere. Yet it is easy to show that nothing of the kind can be true; a simple visual observation will suffice, and anyone who owns a moderate telescope can make it.

As the Moon travels across the sky, it often passes in front of stars, and hides or occults them. Occasionally a bright star (Aldebaran in Taurus, perhaps, or Antares in Scorpio) is occulted; but this does not happen frequently, since there are not many brilliant stars in the Zodiac, which explains why a telescope of some size is needed for really useful work. Occultations of fainter stars are very common indeed. Before an occultation, the star is seen shining steadily right up to the moment when it is hidden by the Moon's advancing limb, but the disappearance is as sudden as the flicking-out of a candle-flame in a gale. One moment the star is there; the next, it is not. Reappearance on the opposite side of the Moon is equally sudden.

---

* 'Air' and 'atmosphere' are words usually, but wrongly, regarded as interchangeable. The term 'air' really relates to the Earth's atmosphere, which is made up chiefly of oxygen and nitrogen. The point may be slightly pedantic, but it is probably worth making.

Now consider what would happen if the Moon were surrounded by a dense atmosphere. For some time before being hidden by the Moon's limb, the star's light would be passing through the lunar atmosphere, and the star would flicker and fade. This actually does happen on the all-too-rare occasions when the planet Venus occults a star. Venus has an atmosphere at least as deep as the Earth's, and a star will fade very obviously for a second or two before occultation. I had a good view of this in 1959, when, for the first time for centuries, Venus occulted a really brilliant star, Regulus in Leo. Observing with Henry Brinton's 12½-inch reflector at Selsey, I recorded a perceptible fading which was undoubtedly due to the dimming of the starlight by Venus' atmosphere, and all other observers who watched the occultation saw the same thing.

An occultation of a star by the Moon is an interesting phenomenon, particularly when the Moon is waxing – since the occultation then takes place at the dark limb, which cannot be seen unless lit up by earthshine. When the Moon passes through a star-cluster such as the Pleiades, half a dozen naked-eye stars may be occulted within a period of a few hours. Predictions are given in the annual Handbook of the British Astronomical Association, and accurate occultation timings are of value, since they serve to give a check of the Moon's exact position in the sky.

However, we can learn even more than might be thought. If a belt of atmosphere lay round the lunar limb, it should bend or refract the light-rays coming from the star just before immersion (we can see an example of refraction simply by shining a torch through a tank of water; the beam is obviously bent). The effect would be to keep the star in view for a little while longer than would otherwise be the case, so that the occultation would take place later than predicted.* Reappearance at the opposite limb would be slightly early, so that the whole occultation would last for a shorter time than that forecast by theory. The amount of the time-difference should give a reliable key to the density of the lunar atmosphere responsible for it.

* It is actually possible to see the Sun and Moon before they really rise, as refraction lifts them into view when they are still below the horizon. On some occasions the Sun and the full moon may be seen simultaneously, apparently just above opposite horizons. When the Sun or Moon is rising or setting, the bottom part of the disk is the more affected by refraction, which is why the disk appears to be flattened.

Unfortunately we have first to measure the time-differences, and this is what nobody has ever been able to do. Sir George Airy, who was Astronomer Royal between 1835 and 1881, believed that the effect was large enough to be detected, but later astronomers, using more sensitive equipment, do not agree. One trouble is that the Moon's limb is very rough. If a star passes behind a mountain, it will naturally vanish sooner than if it passes behind a valley. The difference is slight, but when we are considering tiny fractions of a second it is enough to wreck the accuracy of the method completely. There have even been reports of a star vanishing, reappearing, and then vanishing again in quick succession, presumably because it had been temporarily hidden by a mountain. It seems that the only positive result of the visual occultation method is to show that the density of the Moon's atmosphere cannot be greater than 1/10,000 of that of the Earth's air at sea-level.

In other words, the Moon's mantle is negligible by our ordinary standards. Even at a value of 1/10,000, it is no denser than the Earth's air at a height of about fifty miles above the ground, which is what we usually call a vacuum. There can be no chance that any terrestrial-type creature could breathe upon the Moon.

Occasionally the Moon occults a planet. W. H. Pickering, who was a great observer of the Moon even if he seems to have been less successful as a theorist, watched an occultation of Jupiter in 1892, and recorded a dark band crossing the planet's disk, tilted at an angle to the famous Jovian belts. Pickering believed this to be due to absorption in a lunar atmosphere, and confirmed it on other occasions. He stated that the dark band appeared only when the planet disappeared at the Moon's bright limb; when occultation took place at the dark limb it was not seen, and Pickering concluded that the atmosphere responsible for it was frozen during the lunar night. Others who recorded a dark band were two of Pickering's colleagues, Barnard and Douglass.

All this is very interesting, but we must be suspicious of it. For one thing, Pickering worked out a density for the lunar atmosphere of 1/1800, which is not only too great, but impossibly too great. Neither has the dark band been seen at recent planetary occultations, though plenty of people have looked for it. It has certainly never been photographed; and as we know to our cost, the human eye is very easily deceived.

Another visual proof concerns the absence of marked twilight effects on the Moon. Twilight has been reported from time to time, but never with anything approaching certainty. This, too, shows that the Moon's atmosphere cannot have a density greater than 1/10,000 of that of the Earth's air at sea-level.

There is no mystery about it. When I wrote the first edition of this book, more than ten years ago, the term 'escape velocity' was unfamiliar to most people apart from scientists, and I spent several pages in describing it. The situation is different today, and almost everyone knows what it means. Briefly, it is the speed at which a body would have to move if it were to break free from the gravitational pull of the world from which it started. In the case of the Earth, escape velocity is 7 miles per second, so that if I could throw a cricket-ball upward at 7 miles per second it would never come down; it would move off into space. At any lesser speed the ball would fall back to the ground.

Atmosphere is made up of atoms and molecules, moving about at high speeds. A particle moving outward at escape velocity would therefore be permanently lost. The Earth's air is safe, because the escape velocity is relatively high, but our mantle contains only traces of the quickest-moving gases, hydrogen and helium; Jupiter, with a much higher escape velocity (37 miles per second) has been able to retain virtually all its hydrogen, so that its atmosphere is unbreathable; Mars, with an escape velocity of a mere 3 miles per second, has lost much of its atmosphere, though by no means all.

On the Moon, escape velocity is only $1\frac{1}{2}$ miles per second. In the remote past there may have been a dense atmosphere, but the weak lunar pull was unable to retain it, and by now almost all the atmosphere has leaked away into space. We cannot be surprised, then, to find that there is no evidence of a dense mantle now; if there were, it would be very surprising indeed. Visual work has taken us as far as it can, and we have to turn to less direct methods.

Two Russian astronomers, Fesenkov and Lipski, attacked the problem in the 1940s. If there is any light coming from diffusion in a thin lunar atmosphere, it should have special qualities, and should be detectable with sensitive instruments. Fesenkov, in 1943, had no luck at all, and concluded that the Moon's atmosphere could not have a density greater than one-millionth of our own. Six years later Lipski made a new investigation, and obtained different results, announcing a value of 1/20,000. This was confirmed in 1952, and in 1953 Lipski published another paper in which he stated that the real density was as high as 1/12,000, which agreed quite well with earlier work carried out by Bernard Lyot in France.

It was not long before doubts crept in. Lyot and Dollfus, working at the Pic du Midi 10,000 feet up in the French Pyrénées, where conditions are exceptionally good, failed to confirm Lipski's value either in 1949 or 1952, and after Lyot's sudden and tragic death Dollfus concluded that the lunar atmosphere was too tenuous to be detected at all. This would mean that the density could not exceed one thousand-millionth, so that the old idea of an airless Moon would be substantially true.

Firsoff, however, has pointed out that the work was carried out photographically, with special safeguards to cut out effects due to light diffused in the Earth's atmosphere, so that the Moon's atmosphere would also be concealed. If so, then, according to Firsoff, Dollfus first suppressed the effects of the Moon's mantle and then concluded that it did not exist. It should be added, however, that by similar methods Dollfus has announced that a thin atmosphere surrounds the planet Mercury, which is not a great deal larger than the Moon and where the escape velocity is only one mile per second more.

Evidently there is no general agreement, and so far the last word has come from the radio astronomers. This is a new development, since it dates back only to 1956, but it is a very important one.

We have seen that certain objects in the sky send out strong radio waves. These are known as 'radio stars', but the term is a particularly unfortunate one, since in general they are not single stars at all; the only star known to be the source of radio waves is the Sun, simply because it is so close to us that its radiation is easy to detect. 'Radio sources' is a much better name for the more remote objects, which are of various types. One of the most powerful is the so-called Crab Nebula in Taurus, which we know to be the wreck of a star which was seen to explode in the year 1054. The modern Crab Nebula consists of a patch of violently agitated gas, in rapid expansion. A small telescope will show it, though photographs taken with large instruments are needed to reveal its full complexity.

Luckily, the Moon sometimes occults the Crab Nebula, and it is possible to study this 'radio occultation' to look for effects related to (though by no means identical with) those once expected with visual occultations. At Cambridge this has been done by Costain, Elsmore and Whitfield, who conclude that there may be very slight effects due possibly to an extremely tenuous lunar atmosphere. Radio astronomy is still in its infancy, and these first results may be of dubious accuracy, but at least they are better than nothing at all.

If there is a trace of atmosphere, it is presumably made up of heavy gases, whose atoms and molecules move relatively slowly. Harlow Shapley, in America, has suggested that the chief constituent is argon, produced by the decay of radioactive potassium in the lunar rocks, while, in 1958, W. F. Edwards and L. B. Borst suggested that two of the inert gases, krypton and xenon, were possibilities. We know that argon is quite plentiful in our own air, and there are traces of krypton and xenon; but all things considered it seems rather pointless to discuss the composition of the Moon's atmosphere until we can prove that the atmosphere itself exists – which at the moment we cannot.

So far we have been talking about a general atmospheric mantle, but this may not be the full story; it is possible that local, temporary atmospheres occur here and there – which brings us on to the vexed question of 'obscurations' on the Moon. They used to be called 'mists', but this is a bad term, since there is no analogy with an Earth-type mist.

First, there are the periodical reports of twilight effects round the horns of the crescent Moon. Schröter saw them a century and a half ago; so did Mädler; so have many modern observers. On 20th March 1912, for instance, W. S. Franks, a winner of the Gold Medal of the Royal Astronomical Society, was observing with a 6-inch refractor when he saw the south horn prolonged into the lunar mountains as a feeble line of light well into the dark hemisphere; on 14th April 1948 H. P. Wilkins saw star-like points of light, caused by mountains catching the solar rays, joined by feeble filaments of light much brighter than the earthshine; on 18th September 1949 W. H. Haas, in the United States, saw each cusp prolonged by four or five degrees – and so on. Most experienced observers have seen this sort of thing occasionally (though I admit

130

that I have not), and it is rather dangerous to dismiss all such reports as being due to errors of observation.

Secondly, there are the obscurations inside certain craters and in certain special areas. As a typical example, let us consider an observation made on 10th February 1949 by F. H. Thornton, using an 18-inch reflector of excellent quality. While examining the so-called 'Cobra-Head' of the Herodotus Valley, Thornton 'noticed what seemed to be a diffused patch of thin smoke or vapour, apparently originating from the Valley on the east side where the landslip is, and spread over the edge on to the plain for a short distance. Every detail of the edge of the Valley was perfectly clear and distinct except where this patch occurred, but there the definition was poor and very blurred'. This is by no means the only time that such phenomena have been recorded in the Aristarchus-Herodotus area.

There are many records of variations inside the 'Greater Black Lake', Plato, the dark-floored crater on the edge of the Mare Imbrium. In a small telescope the interior seems to be uniformly grey, but with larger instruments some tiny craters and white spots are seen, and the various maps and charts made of them during the last century or so are most interesting. Details sometimes recorded as 'conspicuous' may be unaccountably missed on other occasions, while previously faint objects show up well. There are also cases when the floor appears totally blank under good conditions, with telescopes which should certainly show considerable detail.

It is worth while to give a specific case. Under Plato's eastern wall, A. S. Williams, in 1892, recorded a white spot. W. R. Birt, who paid a great deal of attention to Plato, had drawn a chart sixteen years earlier, but had not shown it. To W. H. Steavenson, in 1920, it appeared as a definite crater with inner shadow, and one of the most conspicuous features of the floor; the telescope used was the 28-inch refractor at Greenwich Observatory (now at Herstmonceux), and the crater was recorded on several occasions. Yet to H. P. Wilkins and myself, just before midnight on 3rd April 1952, it was totally invisible, even though we made a special search for it with the largest refractor in Europe (the Meudon 33-inch). Four hours later T. A. Cragg, observing in the United States with a good 12½-inch reflector. was unable to see even the most prominent details on Plato's floor. It is tempting to suggest that the obscuration spread from the east, covering Steavenson's crater, so that by the time Cragg made his drawing the whole floor had been covered.

Plato is not the only formation to behave in such a way. Another is the great plain Schickard; in 1939 I saw what I still believe to have been a genuine obscuration there, since the whole interior seemed to be filled with what I described at the time as 'whitish mist'. Something similar was recorded by Wilkins on 31st August 1944. In 1892 E. E. Barnard, who was noted for his keen eyes and powers of observation, looked at the bright ray-crater Thales, in the far north, and saw it 'filled with pale luminous haze', though the surrounding features were perfectly sharp and clear-cut, while in 1902 the French astronomer Charbonneaux saw 'a small but unmistakable white cloud' form close to Theætetus, in the region of the Apennines. Charbonneaux was using the 33-inch Meudon refractor, the same instrument with which Wilkins and I made our observations of Plato half a century afterwards. The region of Picard, in the Mare Crisium, has also been said to be subject to obscurations.

To give one more example: on 29th March 1939 Wilkins was looking at Copernicus, then in shadow, when he saw that for fifteen minutes, around nineteen hours G.M.T., the central mountain group was seen distinctly as a diffused light spot, together with indications of the inner western terraces, even though sunrise on the central peaks did not begin until three hours later.

We can also learn something from studies of lunar shadows, which are not always as sharp as they are believed to be. Here, too, significant effects have been recorded.

As the Sun rises over a lunar crater, it will first strike the outer west rampart. With increasing altitude, the rays reach the inner east wall, and much of this inner wall is in full sunlight while the west wall still casts deep shadow over the crater-floor. The glare from the sunlit east wall is often strong enough to illuminate some of the interior features over which the Sun has not yet risen. W. R. Dawes, a well-known lunar observer of the last century, was the first to point this out; in 1952 W. H. Steavenson repeated the observation, and distinctly saw the central mountains of the twin craters Godwin and Agrippa by the reflected wall-light alone. He even detected the 'reversed shadows' cast by the peaks. He was, however, using a large telescope and a specially screened eyepiece, and even then the wall-lit mountains were not conspicuous.

A. C. Eliot Merlin, in Greece, had a different experience in 1909, when he was observing Mersenius, a large walled plain east of the Mare Humorum. He wrote: 'The broad, irregular and sharply indented shadows of the illuminated ridges, etc., in the neighbourhood could be distinguished, apparently projected on the dark, unilluminated portion of the lunar surface. . . . The interior of Mersenius itself was perfectly dark, but the shadow of the east wall, only the top of which was illuminated by the rising sun, could be seen projected on the unlighted surface beyond the terminator. The appearance was that of sharply defined, inky-black shadows projected on a rusty black background. This effect must almost certainly have been caused by a dimly lighted zone bordering the shadows. . . . The dimly lit regions on which the shadows were cast were those which would themselves be shortly illuminated by the rising sun, thus forming a kind of false dawn.' Eliot Merlin's telescope was an $8\frac{1}{2}$-inch reflector; I have used it myself, and can vouch for its excellence.

Unusual shadow effects have also been noticed elsewhere. For instance, W. H. Haas considers that the sunrise shadow inside Eudoxus, north of the Caucasus Mountains, is always much darker than that in its larger neighbour Aristoteles, and a curious brownish-black border to the shadow inside Philolaus, not far from Pythagoras in the north-east, has been seen by several observers.

We need not go into further examples; suffice to say that there are plenty of them. In fact, there are few lunar observers of many years' standing who have not seen at least a few obscurations of peculiar shadow effects. This leaves us with only two possibilities. Either we are dealing with gaseous emission from the Moon's crust, forming what may be termed a temporary and localized atmosphere either of gas or dust, or else all the observations are wrong.

Most of the reports come from amateurs. There is nothing surprising in this, because until recently there were not many professional astronomers who paid serious attention to the Moon, and those who did so – such as Barnard – also saw the effects. It has been stated that amateur work is unreliable, and that the failure of most professional scientists to see the obscurations is an indication that nothing of the sort takes place, but a moment's thought will show that this view is quite illogical. It is quite pointless to spend a few hours, a few days, or even a year or two in looking around the Moon with a large telescope and then dismissing all 'atmospheric' phenomena because none have been seen; one might as well stare up at the night sky for a minute or two and then deny the existence of shooting-stars simply because no meteor appeared during that particular period. Neither is photography of much help in detecting such feeble, elusive phenomena. Moreover, it is natural for even eminent theorists to be rank amateurs at practical lunar observing. Experience is really the only thing which counts for much in this kind of work, and no professional astronomer has enough spare time to spend night after night studying the features of the Moon with an adequate telescope.

Let us repeat that the few professionals of the past who have carried out really serious lunar observing have joined the amateurs in confirming the existence of obscurations. Barnard was one, Pickering another; there are several more.

One cannot hope to see obscurations very often, and it may be worth giving my own experience – not because I am keen-eyed or a skilful observer, which is not the case, but merely because I have studied the Moon's surface consistently for a long time. I began regular observations in 1933. I did not record any obscurations or peculiar shadows during my first five years, but I would not have included this period in any case, because I was still only a boy and lacked any sort of experience. My work therefore extends over 1938-1939 and from 1945 to the present, a total of nineteen years. I have seen two obscurations which I regard as definite, plus another two possibilities – and that is all. If this is typical, then a persistent observer may expect to see one obscuration every four or five years, provided that he is properly equipped. Anyone who spends less time in such work will never see one at all, except by sheer luck; and this is where some distinguished critics may have erred in their judgment.

Support for this view was forthcoming in 1958, when N. Kozirev, at the Crimean Astrophysical Observatory, saw what seems to have been an outbreak inside the crater Alphonsus. There was no luck about it; Kozirev was concentrating on the area, because of earlier reports of activity inside Alphonsus made by the American astronomer D. Alter. The whole story is fascinating, and an account of it is given in Chapter 12. At least it has shown that the amateur reports of obscurations here and there on the Moon cannot be dismissed as easily as some people had thought; on the other hand, neither does it prove that a tenuous atmosphere covers all the Moon.

There is one possible method which, if it could be used successfully, would show the existence of a lunar atmosphere. If we could record meteor trails across the Moon, the problem would be solved at once.

As we noted in Chapter 2, the Earth encounters vast numbers of meteors each day, together with much rarer objects of greater size. If the Moon has an atmosphere of reasonable density, there must be meteors there too. For the moment, let us base ourselves on the assumption that Lipski's value of 1/10,000 is fairly near the truth, and see what conclusions follow.

The Earth's atmosphere thins out rapidly with altitude, and it may be said that the density is about halved for every $3\frac{1}{2}$ miles increase in height. But on Lipski's figures, the atmosphere of the Moon would fall off by half only for every 21 miles' ascent, so that at an altitude of 50 miles the corresponding densities of the two atmospheres would be equal. Higher than this, the lunar mantle would actually be the denser of the two! Of course, this is only an approximation, and there are many factors which complicate the picture, but the general pattern is clear enough.

Terrestrial meteors become luminous far above a height of 50 miles. In fact, some at least burn out at this level. If therefore Lipski's value were correct, at least a fair number of lunar meteors should be seen. We are now sure that Lipski's value is too high; but it has been calculated that lunar meteors should still occur even with a density for the Moon's atmosphere of 1/100,000. If however there is no shielding atmosphere, then we ought to see occasional flashes as meteoric bodies strike the Moon.

In 1952 I had some correspondence about all this with E. J. Öpik, then of the Armagh Observatory. As Öpik is acknowledged to be one of the world's leading experts upon meteoric phenomena of all kinds, his views were clearly of exceptional value, and with his permission I quote from his letter:

'Lunar meteors are quite probable. Considering the surface gravity on the Moon, which leads to a six times slower decrease of atmospheric density with height, the length of path and duration of meteor trails on the Moon will be six times that on the Earth, if a lunar atmosphere about 1/20,000 to 1/100,000 of the density of the terrestrial atmosphere exists. At the same time, meteors the size of fireballs will penetrate the lunar atmosphere and hit the ground. The average duration of a meteor trail on the Moon would be 2 to 3 seconds (against half a second on Earth), and each trail should end with a flash when striking the ground, because all meteors which can be observed on the Moon from such a distance must be large fireballs. The average length of the trail would be 75 miles, about $\frac{1}{30}$ of the Moon's diameter, so that meteors would be very slow and short objects.'

Öpik added that with a 12-inch telescope it should be possible to record an average of one meteor for every eight hours' work.

Even though it now seems that the lunar atmosphere is less dense than was thought in 1952, Öpik's conclusions still hold good. We must, of course, beware of ordinary meteors in the Earth's air, which might by ill-chance happen to appear right in front of the Moon; but it should not be difficult to eliminate these. The chances that a terrestrial meteor will keep right in front of the Moon throughout its path are very slight, just as a bird flying towards us is unlikely to keep right in front of one small cloud. Besides, the rate of movement would be different.

What we must look for, therefore, is a faint streak passing over the Moon's disk, more or less constant in brightness until it ends in a minute flash. Energetic searches have been carried on in the United States by W. H. Haas and his colleagues of the Association of Lunar and Planetary Observers, and numerous trails have been recorded. The average length is 75 miles, agreeing excellently with the value given by Öpik. Haas worked out the probable diameter of such an object seen by him in 1941; assuming it to have been a genuine lunar meteor it would have been 600 feet across, which is probably much the same as that of the meteorite which landed in Siberia in 1908. In this case, an observer on the Moon itself would have seen it shining as brightly as the full moon does to us.

Unfortunately it cannot be said that any of this work is conclusive. There is no case of a lunar meteor being seen simultaneously by two observers at different sites; and until this is done, we are bound to keep an open mind. The search is both difficult and delicate, and it is only too easy to make mistakes. Lunar eclipses are good opportunities, and I have taken part in several co-operative searches at such times, but without result.

Every now and then reports are received of dark objects passing in front of the Moon. Bats and birds are often responsible, though moths, aeroplanes, meteorological balloons and leaves are other culprits. At any rate, all such objects are definitely terrestrial in origin.* I remember that on one occasion I was observing the Mare Serenitatis area with my 12½-inch reflector when I saw an extraordinary dark patch which shifted slowly but steadily. After a few minutes it moved clear of the Moon and began to glow brightly, revealing itself as a weather balloon catching the sunlight. Had I held different views, no doubt another Flying Saucer would have been added to the records!

Turning to actual flashes on the Moon's surface, we find a similar lack of positive information. Yet there are certain significant facts. In 1938 L. LaPaz, of the University of New Mexico, calculated that for an 'airless Moon' a meteor with a mass of 10 pounds should produce a flash bright enough to be seen from Earth with the naked eye – in which case there should be about 100 flashes each year visible without a telescope. It need hardly be stressed that nothing of the kind is seen. Flashes on the Moon are very rare indeed. However, some have been recorded, notably by the A.L.P.O. observers and by Tsuneo Saheki in Japan, who, on 25th August 1950, saw what he termed a stationary yellowish-white flare lasting for a quarter of a second. Perhaps the best example of all was seen by F. H. Thornton, using a 9-inch reflector, on 15th April 1948, inside the much-studied crater Plato. Thornton's own description of it runs as follows:

'While I was examining Plato, I saw at its western rim, just

---

* I was once sent a report by an earnest observer who had seen 'a curious dark object projected in front of the Moon', which he considered to be of great astronomical importance. Tactful questioning brought out the additional fact that 'it appeared to be flapping', after which there was really little more to be said.

inside the wall, a minute but brilliant flash of light. The nearest approach to a description of this is to say that it resembled the flash of an A.A. shell exploding in the air at a distance of about ten miles. In colour it was on the orange side of yellow. . . . My first thought was that it was due to a large fall of rock, but I changed my opinion when I realized that close as it seemed to be to the mountain wall, it was possibly over half a mile away.'

Was this a lunar meteorite? At any rate it is a plausible theory; it cannot have been anything in the nature of a volcanic outbreak, since it was so brief. After all, the Siberian Meteorite of 1908 blew down trees over twenty miles away, and if it had not fallen in marshy, uninhabited tundra the death-roll would have been colossal. The meteorite which Thornton saw landing in Plato was probably no larger than this.

Thornton's observation was exceptional. Other flashes have been recorded now and then, but most of them are dubious, and none have been seen by two or more observers simultaneously. It seems, then, that the observed number is not only less than might have been expected from LaPaz' estimate, but strikingly less. On the other hand there may be complicating factors, and if we could see only meteorites of 'Siberian' size we could expect no more than one or two per century, so that we would be very lucky to catch them in the act of landing.

In December 1961 a systematic search for flashes was started in America by observers of the Martin-Marietta Corporation, using electronic equipment together with a $12\frac{1}{2}$-inch reflector used at a magnification of 600. It is too early to say whether any positive results will be obtained, but at least it is likely that before long we will find out for certain whether meteoric impacts on the Moon can or cannot be traced.

All things considered, it seems then that we may expect the Moon to have a very thin atmosphere, made up possibly of argon and various heavy gases, with a ground density of much less than 1/10,000 of that of our own air; but we have no proof. There is observational evidence in favour of temporary and local atmospheric patches, probably gaseous but possibly due to disturbed dust. The most we can hope for is that the Moon's mantle will prove to be dense enough to act as a meteor-screen, but even this is doubtful, and in every other way the lunar atmosphere is likely to be useless to the explorers of the future.

It is worth adding that the Russian rocket experiments of 1959 gave indications of very tenuous gas at a height of some 6,000 miles above the Moon. More will be said about this later. In any case, it is only an offshoot of our main problem; and it is becoming more and more clear that even if we are not strictly correct in saying that the Moon is an 'airless world', we are certainly not very far wrong.

Chapter 12

Changes on the Surface

The appearance of the Moon changes from night to night, almost from hour to hour. As the shadows shift, new features are brought into view and old ones vanish, so that a crater which juts out strikingly from the terminator one evening may be difficult to find at all twenty-four hours later. To know any one formation really well, an observer must study it under all possible angles of illumination – and not merely look at a couple of photographs, as is often done.

Obviously, these rapid changes are not real. By working out the position of the terminator beforehand, an observer can predict more or less what he is going to see when he begins work at the telescope. He is not likely to be much in error, since the Moon is almost changeless; practically all activity ceased there many millions of years ago, long before animal life spread widely over the lands of our own world.

Limited activity may still go on. We have already discussed the reported obscurations in Plato and elsewhere, and it is certainly difficult to dismiss them. Then there are cases of apparent long-term changes of brilliancy in a few areas; for instance a blackish patch on the floor of the great crater Petavius, seen by all the early observers up to the time of Beer and Mädler, cannot now be traced, while there is at least a chance that a very bright spot on the floor of a smaller crater, Werner – the northern member of the Aliacensis-Werner 'twins' outside the west wall of Regiomontanus – has faded during the last century and a half, since Beer and Mädler deliberately rated it as equal to Aristarchus and it is now far inferior. We must also consider the so-called 'moving patches' in Eratosthenes, which W. H. Pickering believed to be due to either plants or insects; and there are the famous dark bands inside Aristarchus, which, whatever their nature, are certainly most peculiar objects.

For the moment, let us postpone the question of dark and bright patches, and concentrate upon more radical changes on the lunar surface. In particular, are there any cases of newly formed craters, or craters which have disappeared since astronomers first began to make accurate telescopic studies of the Moon?

The classical case is that of Linné, on the Mare Serenitatis, one of the most famous and probably the most-studied object on the whole Moon. Lunar observers in general have every reason to be grateful to it, since it was the direct cause of the reawakening of interest in the Moon from 1866 onwards.

Linné is easy to find. It lies fairly near the centre of the disc, so that there are no important libration effects to confuse the issue; moreover it lies in relatively flat country, with nothing near it apart from the usual low ridges and mounds. Lohrmann, in 1834, described it as 'the second most conspicuous crater on the plain . . . it has a diameter of about 6 miles,* is very deep, and can be seen under all angles of illumination'. Mädler, at about the same time, wrote: 'The deepness of the crater must be considerable, for I have found an interior shadow when the Sun had attained 30 degrees. I have never seen a central mountain on the floor.' Both observers drew it, measured it, and used it as a reference point. It also appears as a conspicuous crater on six drawings made by Julius Schmidt between 1841 and 1843.

All this seemed definite enough. Yet on 16th October 1866, Schmidt was examining the Mare Serenitatis when he suddenly realized that Linné had disappeared. Where the old crater had stood, all that remained was a small whitish patch. It was a startling discovery, but Schmidt had no doubts about it.

His announcement caused a tremendous sensation. Up to then, Mädler's view of the Moon as a dead, changeless world had been accepted without question, and astronomers were not inclined to change their opinions. Hundreds of telescopes were pointed at Linné, and during the next few years a great many drawings were made of it. The results were not in full agreement, but at least it was clear that the deep crater described by the old observers had utterly gone – if, of course, it had ever existed! In its place was a

---

* Lohrmann actually said 'somewhat more than one mile', but the old German mile is equal to 4½ of ours. Madler gave 1·4 German miles, thus agreeing with Lohrmann. The most conspicuous crater on the whole Mare Serenitatis is, of course, Bessel, 12 modern miles in diameter and over 3,000 feet deep.

small whitish patch, containing a tiny feature which was sometimes described as a craterpit and sometimes as a hill.

Minor changes have been reported since 1866; for instance a shallow depression some 6 miles across, described by several observers soon after Schmidt's announcement, is no longer to be seen, and it has been suggested that the whitish patch surrounding the central feature is variable in extent, so that it increases slightly in size when a wave of cold sweeps over the Moon at the time of a lunar eclipse. Yet all this is very uncertain, and the main problem is to decide whether a major alteration took place between 1843 and 1866. So let us examine the evidence, putting the prosecution first.

(1) *Evidence in favour of change.* Linné, remember, does not lie in a crowded part of the Moon; it is very much on its own, and is excellently placed for study. To suppose that Lohrmann and Mädler. the two best lunar workers of the pre-1850 period, both drew and measured a deep crater which did not really exist is surely improbable. In addition, Schmidt, who spent a lifetime in studying the Moon, looked at Linné both before and after the reported change, and had not the slightest hesitation in saying that something had happened.

The earlier charts are not helpful. Cassini's map of 1692 shows a feature in the right position, but the chart is very rough. Most unfortunately, only one of Schröter's sketches has come down to us – there must have been others, but all his notebooks were burned with his observatory at Lilienthal. The one surviving drawing was made only to show the bright rays which cross the Mare Serenitatis. The other details are only roughed in; and although both Linné and Bessel are shown as spots, the sketch cannot be said to prove anything either way.

If no change occurred, we can only suppose that Lohrmann. Mädler and Schmidt made the same remarkable mistake, quite independently of each other. The odds against this are undeniably strong.

(2) *Evidence against change.* On the other hand, we have to remember that although Mädler was a superb observer, he was using a very small telescope. His 3·75-inch refractor had obvious limitations, and since he explored every part of the Moon it is probable that he made occasional slips. We depend, therefore, only upon

142

Lohrmann and Schmidt. Lohrmann had to give up his work early, because of failing eyesight, while when Schmidt recorded Linné as a deep crater he was still very young and inexperienced.

When I first studied the problem, I collected all the literature I could, and spent a great deal of time looking at Linné from my own observatory. I came to the conclusion that the evidence in favour of change was conclusive; and I said so. More recent results have, however, made me think that I was falling into the all-too-common trap of jumping to conclusions. The whole question hinges upon what Linné looks like at the present time.

In 1952 F. H. Thornton, using an 18-inch reflector, described it as a small pit standing on top of a low dome. I confirmed this in 1953, using the Meudon 33-inch refractor. My drawings showed the pit displaced slightly to the west of the centre of the dome or mound; H. P. Wilkins, who was with me, showed it as symmetrical. In any case, the pit has been photographed, so that its existence cannot be denied. W. H. Steavenson, using his 30-inch reflector in 1954, wrote that Linné showed up as 'a small deep crater a little over one mile in diameter, having a west wall considerably higher than the east, and giving the appearance of a hemispherical dome when seen under a very low light'. Steavenson made the mound about 4 miles in diameter, which agreed well with Thornton's estimate and my work at Meudon. At various times between 1951 and the present I have seen the same appearance, both with my $12\frac{1}{2}$-inch reflector and with various larger telescopes.

This does not correspond at all with the deep, conspicuous crater of Mädler and Lohrmann, which is why I was so strongly prejudiced in favour of change. Occasional reports had come in of a more crater-like appearance, but I dismissed them more summarily than I should have done. Then, on 23rd March 1961, using using my $8\frac{1}{2}$-inch reflector, I saw the same thing myself, and wrote in my notebook that 'Linné appeared as a distinct crater, with interior shadow and strong outer shadow cast by the east wall'. I telephoned a colleague, P. J. Cattermole, who at once looked at Linné with his $6\frac{1}{2}$-inch reflector and confirmed my description. An hour later, when the Moon had come round an inconvenient tree which blocks part of the sky from my observatory, I used my $12\frac{1}{2}$-inch reflector, with the same result.

It was only later that I found that Fielder, with an 18-inch reflector, had seen Linné as 'a normal craterlet' on 8th September 1955. And E. Hill had similar experiences on 15th December 1961 and 2nd January 1962, though admittedly he made the diameter of the crater smaller than I had done.

There is no chance that Linné really suffers abrupt changes in form. In any case, I looked at it again on 25th March 1961, two days after I had recorded it as a crater (the intervening night was cloudy) and saw that it was back to normal. We have to deal with peculiar lighting effects, together with some unusual ground-slopes in the Linné area, and it seems that under some conditions Linné really can give the false impression of a crater. This may have been what Mädler saw, since the usual central craterpit must have been far beyond the reach of his modest telescope.

If Linné really altered between 1843 and 1866, some activity in the Moon's crust must have been responsible, causing the walls of the old crater to collapse and probably raising the modern dome. But to me, at least, the evidence is much less convincing than it seemed to be ten years ago. All we can do is to consider the facts, weigh them up, and come to our own personal conclusions. It is probably safest to say simply that the case is 'not proven'.

There is one other similar report. On the western border of the Mare Crisium, Schröter described 'a large distinct crater, with bright walls and a dusky floor, visible under all lighting conditions'. He named at Alhazen, measured its diameter as 23 miles, and used it as a reference-point. Yet Mädler could not find it at all; all that he could make out was an ill-defined depression between two mountain peaks, and he transferred the name to a completely different crater away to the south, so that the modern Alhazen is not the same object as Schröter's.

We know that Schröter was not a good draughtsman, but he made few bad mistakes, and it is hard to see how he can have been so definite about a crater which did not exist. (It certainly does not exist now; even if the floor and walls of the old formation have changed in colour, merging with the outer country, the crater would still be shown up by its shadow under a low sun.) Moreover, Tobias Mayer, over twenty years before, had drawn a well-marked crater in the same position. Yet the evidence is not clear-cut, and this also applies to our next case – Alpetragius.

Alpetragius itself is very prominent. It lies closely outside the

144

1. The Full Moon

This photograph was taken on December 11, 1951, at 20 hours 59 minutes, by E. A. Whitaker, F.R.A.S., using the 36-inch reflector at Greenwich Observatory, and is reproduced by kind permission of the Astronomer Royal. It shows the Moon very shortly before full, and the various features can be identified by comparison with the maps given in the Appendix. The rays from the brilliant crater Tycho dominate the southern part of the Moon; the rays from Copernicus and Kepler are also well shown. The vast ring-plain, Bailly, appears on the rough limb near the top of the plate, and other ringed formations well displayed are Schickard (in the south-east) and Grimaldi (right on the terminator, due east), while the dark-floored Plato and the glittering Aristarchus are also very easy to identify.

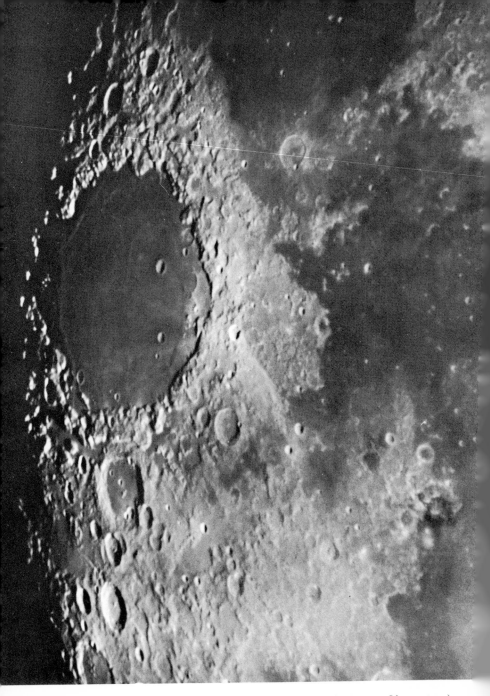

2. The Mare Crisium area (photograph by M. Matsui, Kwasan Observatory)

3. Clavius (photograph taken with the 200-inch Hale reflector at Palomar)

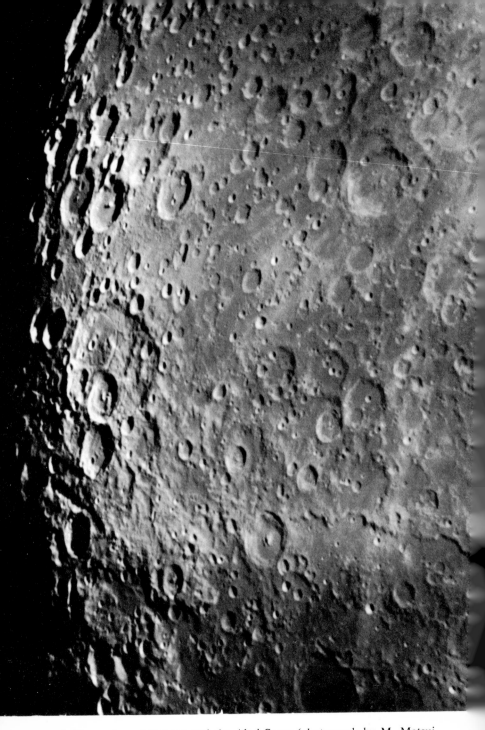

4. The region of Janssen and the Altai Scarp (photograph by M. Matsui, Kwasan Observatory)

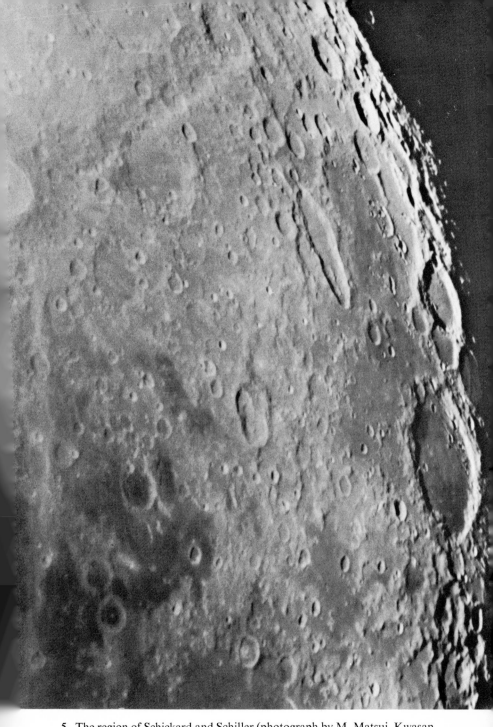

5. The region of Schickard and Schiller (photograph by M. Matsui, Kwasan Observatory)

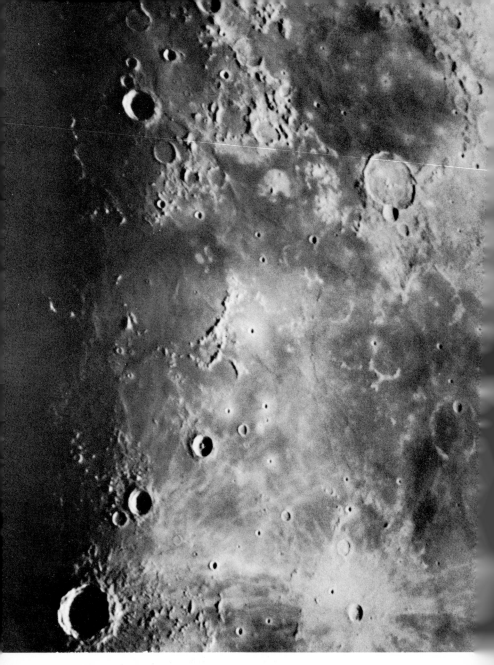

6. The area from Copernicus and Kepler to the Mare Humorum (photograph by M. Matsui, Kwasan Observatory)

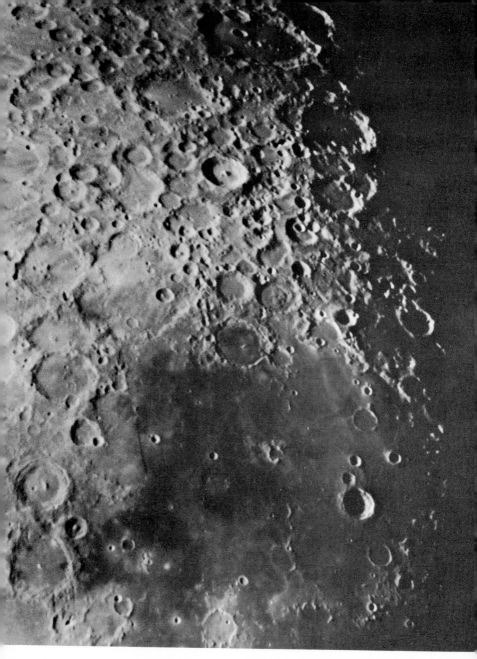

7. The area of Ptolemæus and Alphonsus, the Straight Wall, Tycho and
   Clavius (photograph by M. Matsui, Kwasan Observatory)

8. Pythagoras to the Sinus Iridum (photograph by M. Matsui, Kwasan Observatory)

9. The area of Langrenus, Petavius and Messier (photograph by M. Matsui, Kwasan Observatory)

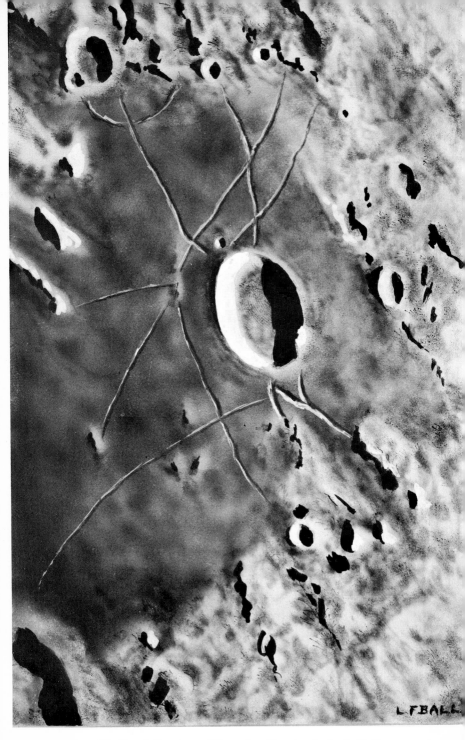

10. The cleft system of Ramsden (drawing by L. F. Ball)

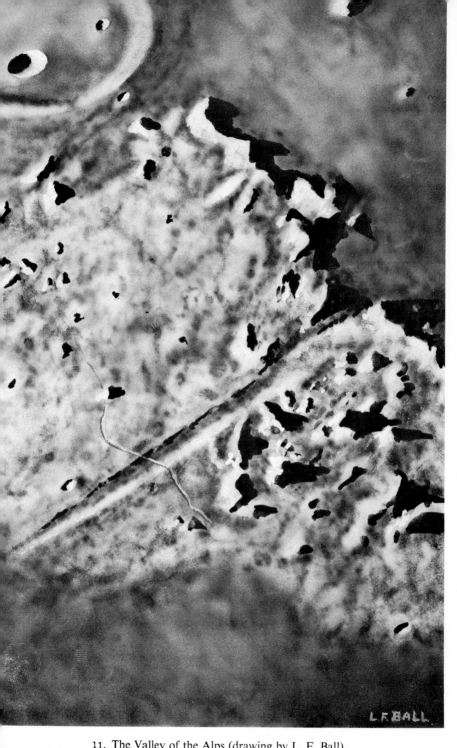

11. The Valley of the Alps (drawing by L. F. Ball)

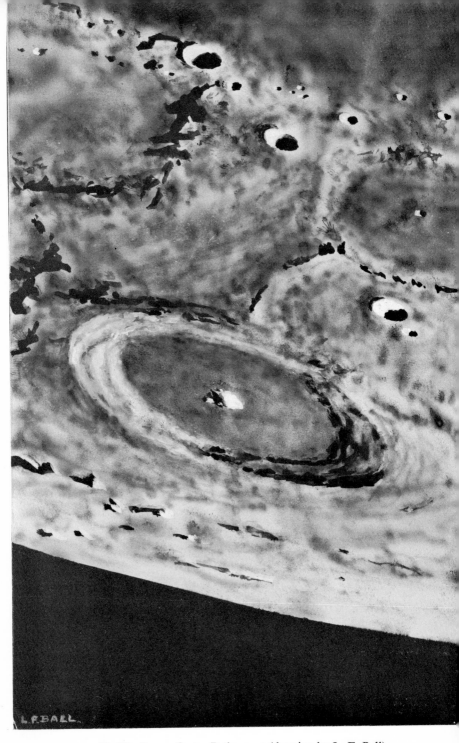

12. The Lunar Crater Pythagoras (drawing by L. F. Ball)

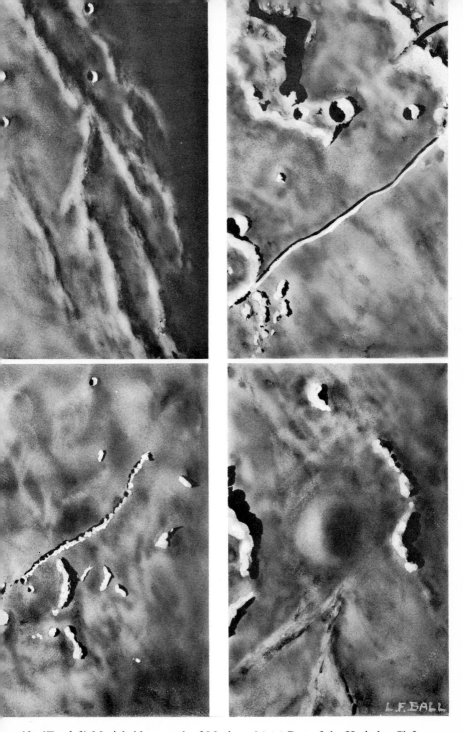

13. (*Top left*) Marial ridges south of Marius (*right*) Part of the Hesiodus Cleft
(*Lower left*) Crater chain west of Bullialdus (*right*) Dome east of Kies
(drawings by L. F. Ball)

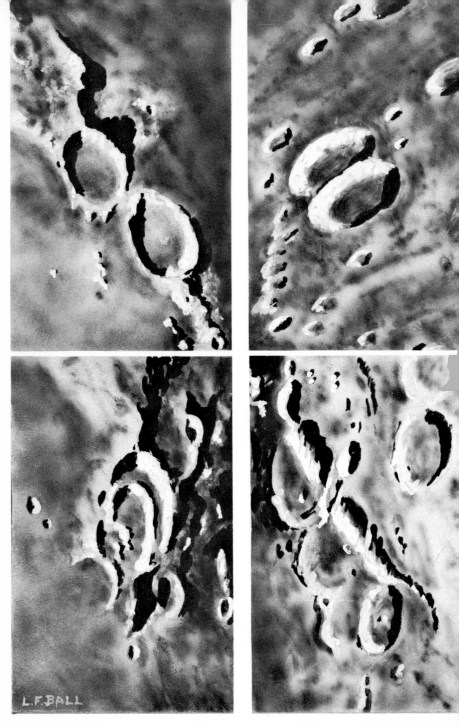

14. (*Top left*) Twin craters Mercator and Campanus (*right*) Twin craters Steinheil and Wa
(*Lower left*) The complex crater Damoiseau (*right*) The Rheita Valley
(drawings by L. F. Ball)

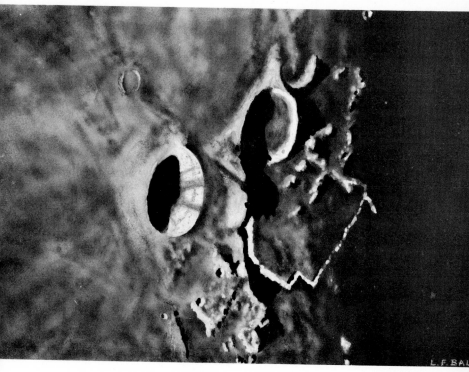

15. The craters Aristarchus and Herodotus (drawing by L. F. Ball)

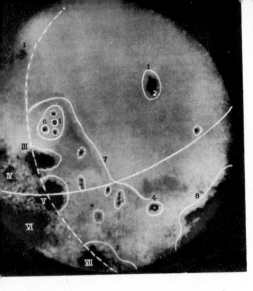

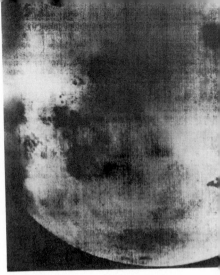

16. The far side of the Moon

(*Top left*) The historic first picture received from Lunik III

(*Top right*) Part of the reverse hemisphere photographed on a larger scale. *The Mare Crisium* (*lower left*), *Mare Moscoviæ* (*upper right*) *and the crater of Tsiolkovskii* (*lower right*) *are easy to identify.*

(*Lower left*) Photograph of a lunar globe, made in the U.S.S.R. and sent to the autho by the Soviet Academy of Sciences in 1961. To the right shown the familiar part of the disk; to the left, part of the region photographed from Lunik III. The white area between represents the zone n photographed from Lunik III and which therefore remains unknown.

wall of Alphonsus, in the Ptolemæus chain, and has a particularly large central peak. Near it Beer and Mädler showed two small craters; one, lettered *d*, was said to be five miles across, and the other somewhat smaller. The smaller crater is still there, but the larger is not. Once again, Schmidt was responsible for noting the apparent change. In 1868 he reported that the former crater had become a bright white spot, not unlike the modern Linné, and this is how it appears today. We must remember, however, that only Beer and Mädler had recorded the crater *d*, and it was always a small feature, so that a mistake is probable. It would be unwise to place too much reliance upon observations of delicate detail made with a small refractor.

So much for vanishing craters; in only one case – Linné – is the evidence at all strong. Next let us turn to cases of craters said to have been formed during the last two centuries.

The ring-plain near the Alps known as Cassini was strangely left out of the early maps, and was first drawn in 1692 by J. D. Cassini, after whom it has been named. Yet there seems no chance that it is new; it is low-walled, and could easily be overlooked, quite apart from the fact that it appears to be decidedly ancient even by lunar standards.

The large walled plain Cleomedes, just north of the Mare Crisium, contains a small crater considered by Schröter to have been formed about October 1789 – since he had missed it previously, and saw it quite clearly afterwards. Judging from the general look of the formation, any such thing seems to be wildly improbable, and as the crater is not at all prominent we may conclude that Schröter had merely missed it.

A similar case concerns Halley, a crater on the borders of the great walled plain Hipparchus (its twin, closely to the north-west, is named Hind). No floor detail is shown by Lohrmann or Mädler. A photograph taken by Lewis Rutherfurd in 1865 shows one distinct crater. At the present time, there are two; and it has been suggested that the second, not shown on the Rutherfurd photograph, has been formed since 1865. Yet such a view is very difficult to maintain.

Slightly more convincing is a report which concerns not a true crater, but a rimless depression close to the famous crater-cleft of Hyginus, and known as Hyginus N. It was first seen on 27th May 1878 by a German observer, H. Klein, who described it as being

3 miles across and filled with shadow under oblique lighting. This agrees well with the modern appearance. Klein had observed the region frequently during the previous twelve years without seeing a trace of it, and as it was also absent from all the maps Klein concluded that it was definitely new. Schmidt also had drawn the region over thirty times during the preceding thirty years, and in the position of Klein's N he had sometimes recorded a small dark spot, sometimes a bright spot and sometimes nothing at all, so that he too was certain of a real change.

A smaller depression, not far from N, was also thought to be of recent origin. It is certainly rather strange that both features had been missed – not only by Schmidt and Klein, but also by Beer, Mädler and Lohrmann – but both are small. Probably nothing whatsoever has happened there, but it is just possible that there is another explanation. Obscurations in the Hyginus area have been reported from time to time, and seem to be as well-authenticated as these fleeting phenomena ever are, so that there is a chance that

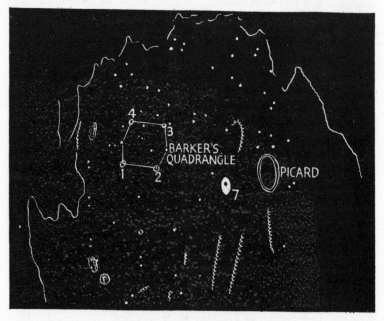

Mare Crisium: Picard area

once more we are dealing with occasional 'veiling', though personally I have grave doubts.

This brings us on to the region of Picard, in the Mare Crisium. The Mare surface here is fairly level; on the whole plain there are only three craters of any size – Picard itself, Peirce to the north, and Graham, a smaller formation north of Peirce. The region south and south-west of Picard was shown more or less featureless by all observers up to the beginning of the present century; Neison, author of the first good British lunar map, recorded only a few low ridges, and Goodacre, in 1912 and 1930, showed only three white spots. In the 1930s, however, Robert Barker, using a 12½-inch reflector, discovered a conspicuous 'quadrangle' made up of craterlets connected by ridges, where Mädler had drawn absolutely nothing. Examination of old drawings showed that parts of Barker's quadrangle had been seen from time to time, but never so prominently or so completely. Nowadays it can be seen with a very small telescope, and the whole region is dotted with craterlets and white spots. In 1949 I published a chart showing over seventy of them, even though most of the work was done with a 3-inch refractor.

Normally it would be logical to say simply that the spots had been overlooked, and this is probably the right answer, but it may be significant that once more we are dealing with one of those parts of the Moon which have been regarded as subject to obscurations. W. R. Birt, in the late nineteenth century, sometimes found that Graham, the crater near Peirce, was totally invisible when it should have been obvious. This has also been the case more recently; for instance Wilkins could see no trace of it on 12th May 1927, though it had been normal on 11th May and had reappeared faintly by 13th May. Three times in 1948 I saw the whole area 'misty grey and devoid of detail', with the surrounding surface sharp and clear-cut.

One object, a white spot closely west of Picard,* is particularly interesting. Most white spots are really craterpits too small to be seen as such, but this one was thought by Birt to be not a crater at all; he believed it to be some sort of surface deposit. Now and then it showed haziness and abnormal brilliance, not only to Birt but also to other observers of the time. Much more recently, Thornton has examined it with his 18-inch reflector and has found that it is

---

* Numbered 7 in my chart, *Journal of the British Astronomical Association*, Vol. 59, page 250 (1949).

in fact a low dome crowned with a summit crater, so that it is very similar to Linné in its modern guise. I have been able to confirm this appearance.

Here too the whole question remains open. The craterlets Barker's quadrangle and the rest – are unlikely to be new; it may be that they are periodically obscured, or it may be that they were merely missed. I hold the latter view, but I may be wrong.

Different again is the case of Messier, on the Mare Fœcunditatis. It is the western member of a pair of small craters, noteworthy because two curious streamers extend from them toward the Mare coast. The eastern 'twin' used to be called Messier A, but has now been renamed Pickering. The two can always be recognized without difficulty owing to the double ray, which gives them a strange resemblance to a comet.

Between 1829 and 1837 Beer and Mädler made over 300 drawings of the area, and they described Messier and Pickering as being exactly alike. In their own words: 'To the east of Messier there appears an identical formation. Diameter, shape height and depth, colour of interior are the same, even the positions of the peaks; everything points to the fact that here we have either a most remarkable coincidence, or that some as yet unknown law of nature has been at work.' The situation now is not the same. Pickering is the deeper and more distinct of the two, and generally appears triangular, whereas Messier is elliptical.

However, both craters show marked changes due to the varying illumination. I have made at least 500 observations of them, and have found that although Pickering generally looks larger than its companion, it is sometimes smaller; often the two are equal, and under high light both appear as white spots. Walter Goodacre measured their diameters in 1932, giving a value of 8 miles for Messier and only 7 for Pickering, despite the fact that Messier so often looks the smaller of the two. Probably Beer and Mädler concentrated on the comet-like rays, and any radical change is most improbable. K. W. Abineri believes that the apparent changes in shape occur because Pickering has a double west wall, and my own work tends to confirm this idea – though it is worth noting that here, too, obscurations have been reported from time to time, and on one occasion Klein described Messier as being 'filled with mist'.

H. H. Nininger, the American authority upon meteorites, has

suggested that the twin craters were formed by a meteor plunging through a ridge, leaving a hole on each side and producing a sort of tunnel. This seems as unlikely as any idea could be – it would indeed be a remarkable meteorite which could slice clean through a rocky wall and leave a couple of eight-mile holes!

If we reject the lunar tunnel, we need spend little time on the so-called lunar bridge which caused an amazing amount of discussion some years ago. In 1953 J. J. O'Neill, in the United States, reported that a 'tremendous arch' existed between the two capes Olivium and Lavinium, bordering the Mare Crisium (it is remarkable how often we have to come back to the Mare Crisium area). O'Neill's sketch was hopelessly inaccurate, but later observations made by Wilkins indicated that some sort of arch did in fact exist nearby. This may be so: but at best it is a tiny natural feature of no interest or importance whatsoever.

Closely west of the crater Fontenelle, on the border of the Mare Frigoris, Mädler drew a regular square enclosure with high mountainous walls. Neison, in 1876, wrote that it was 'a perfect square, enclosed by long straight walls about 65 miles in length and one mile in breadth, from 250 to 300 feet in height'. Today, the enclosure is incomplete. The south-east wall, drawn definitely by both Mädler and Neison, is no longer there, but there is a conspicuous mountain mass some twenty miles south-west of Fontenelle which Mädler and Neison considerably misplaced.

Strangely enough, the difference between Mädler's representation and the modern aspect passed unnoticed for many years, and it was only in 1950 that J. C. Bartlett, of Baltimore, directed attention to it. He suggested that definite change had taken place, and this led to a lively discussion between Bartlett, W. H. Haas, D. P. Barcroft and myself, from which some interesting facts emerged – as follows:

Mädler's map appeared in 1837. After a long search, I discovered a good photograph taken by Draper in 1863, which shows the Square as it is now; so if there has been any change, it must have taken place between 1837 and 1863. Neison's book did not appear until 1876; and as he still showed the complete Square thirteen years after it had ceased to exist, his evidence is quite unreliable, and in this area his map is not much more than a copy of Mädler's. The final evidence comes from Schröter. On a drawing made as long ago as 1809, the Square is shown as it is at the present time, with

Beer & Mädler. 1837

Moore. 1951

Bartlett (Madler's Square)

its south-east wall missing; moreover, the mountain mass south-west of Fontenelle is shown in its modern position.

Why should Mädler have drawn in a definite wall? The answer seems to be that there is a low ridge there, and the land to the west is slightly darker than that to the east, so that in a small telescope – such as Mädler used – the Square looks complete. Schröter, with his larger instrument, did not fall into a similar trap. I have experimented with two telescopes, a 3-inch refractor (probably almost as good as Mädler's) and a 12½-inch reflector, and have found the Square much more prominent with the small telescope. With a higher magnification, its true nature is revealed.

Various other features in or near the Square have also been suspected of alteration, but the evidence is very slender, and it seems much more likely that the Square has remained unchanged for thousands of millions of years. Yet Bartlett's work has raised many interesting issues, and it is fitting that the Square has been re-named in his honour.

One thing must be clear from what has been said above: all our 'evidence' in favour of these changes on the Moon depends upon a few observers – Schröter, Lohrmann, Mädler and Schmidt – who lived long ago. Unless we include the highly dubious cases of Hyginus N and the craterlets near Picard, we have to draw upon work carried out in the early days of lunar study, usually with inadequate telescopes, and even then only Linné seems worthy of really serious consideration. In any case, alterations of form in lunar craters are so rare and so uncertain that it is tempting to dismiss them all as due to nothing more than observational mistakes. This was the general view until the end of 1958, but then the situation changed with dramatic suddenness. For the first time, activity was not only seen visually, but also confirmed by means of photography; and this brings us on to the famous (or, according to some astronomers, notorious) case of Alphonsus.

Alphonsus is one of the most majestic walled plains on the Moon. It is not far from the centre of the disk, and is a member of the Ptolemæus chain, with Arzachel to the south and Ptolemæus itself to the north. Alphonsus has a diameter of over 70 miles, and its walls reach a maximum of 7,000 feet above the floor. There is a pronounced central mountain, and a great amount of interior detail, including some remarkable dark patches as well as clefts.

Mild activity in the crater had often been suspected. As long ago as 1882, for instance, Klein had described it as 'one of the most consistently active regions of the Moon'. Yet there was no proof, and Alphonsus was not studied so intently as – for instance – Plato. Then, in 1956, Dinsmore Alter, using the 60-inch reflector at Mount Wilson in California, took some photographs which proved to be of great importance, and showed traces of what might be a slight 'veiling' of the crater-floor.

Infra-red light is very penetrative, and will slice through haze; ultra-violet light is much more easily blocked. This is shown excellently in the case of Mars, where infra-red photographs record the surface details and ultra-violet pictures merely show the upper layers of the Martian atmosphere.* Alter reasoned that the same should apply to the Moon, though of course any lunar atmosphere, either temporary or permanent, would be far less dense than in the case of Mars. He therefore photographed various areas, including Alphonsus and Arzachel, in both ultra-violet and infra-red.

The first positive results were obtained on 26th October 1956. With ultra-violet, the cleft-ridden area in the western part of the floor of Alphonsus seemed to be veiled; nothing of the kind was seen with Arzachel, which was included in the photograph. Alter suggested that the cause was a slight discharge of gas from the tiny, very black spots lying along the clefts in Alphonsus, forming a local and possibly short-lived atmosphere; he added, significantly, that on two occasions the same sort of thing had been recorded in Linné.

Alter's work came to the attention of Nikolai Kozirev, in Russia.

* Or generally so; sometimes the atmosphere of Mars becomes unusually transparent to ultra-violet. I have dealt with this more fully in the Mars chapter of my book *The Planets*.

Using the 50-inch reflector at the Crimean Astrophysical Observatory, Kozirev started to make a careful study of the area. His method was to take regular spectrograms (i.e. photographic spectra), and since the Crimean reflector has no separate guiding telescope he had to watch during the exposure time to make sure that there was no drift of the image. While doing this, at 01.00 hours G.M.T. on 3rd November 1958, he noticed that the central peak of Alphonsus had become blurred, and was apparently engulfed in a reddish 'cloud'. Another spectrogram, obtained between 03.00 and 03.30 hours G.M.T., proved to be remarkably interesting when it was developed later. While guiding the telescope, Kozirev kept his eyes on Alphonsus, and noticed that the central peak had become abnormally bright. Suddenly the brilliance began to fade; Kozirev immediately stopped the exposure and started a new one, which was completed at 03.45 G.M.T. By the time it was finished, everything was normal once more, and Alphonsus looked just the same as it usually does.

When an announcement was made, some time later, astronomers all over the world were taken aback; it was so utterly unexpected. I was probably less surprised than most, because I had always been convinced that minor outbreaks on the Moon were by no means out of the question, but I wanted to be sure that there were no mistakes in translation, so I wrote to Kozirev at the Crimea. He replied immediately,* sending me copies of his spectrograms and a full account of what had happened. He said that in his view the red cloud was seen because 'at that time the peak was being illuminated by the Sun through the dust and ashes thrown up by the eruption', and that his spectrograms showed that 'hot carbon gas had been sent out, causing a rise in temperature of perhaps 2,000 degrees'.

The hot carbon gas and the marked rise in temperature have been questioned by other astronomers, but at least one thing was evident; there had been a disturbance of some sort. 'Eruption' is a misleading term, because the outbreak was minor by Earth standards, but the spectrograms appeared to be conclusive; the only

---

* Kozirev does not speak English or French, so the quotes given here have been translated for me from his Russian. He does speak German, but I do not, which meant that when I met him at the Crimean Astrophysical Observatory some time later we had to talk via an interpreter.

alternative would be to suppose that Kozirev had deliberately faked them, which is so utterly ludicrous that nobody in their senses would give it a moment's consideration. Moreover, the focal point of the activity had been the central peak, which seemed therefore to show traces of vulcanism even if it could not be compared with an Earth volcano.

The next step was to see whether there had been any permanent change in the area. During the next few weeks and months, various observers reported that a red patch had appeared near the site of the outbreak, presumably representing coloured material thrown out on 3rd November. Among those who saw it were H. P. Wilkins, G. A. Hole and B. Warner in England, P. Hédervári and L. Botha in Hungary, and several observers in the United States. According to Wilkins, using at $15\frac{1}{4}$-inch reflector on 29th November 1958, the patch was roughly circular, with a black pit-like spot in the centre and rounded masses of red-coloured material all round; in the following January Hole, with his 24-inch reflector, said that the appearance was 'very clear and obvious', while Warner made use of the 18-inch refractor at the University of London Observatory and described the spot as 'bright red'.

On the other hand, some observers could not see the spot at all. I have searched for it in vain; on one occasion I was at Hole's observatory and failed to see any red colour even though Hole told me that it was too conspicuous for him to overlook. At the Pic du Midi, Fielder has been similarly unsuccessful. Yet this may not be significant; in my own case I am fairly sure that my eyes are rather insensitive to slight colour-tones, though I admit that I will be more satisfied about the reality of the patch once I have been able to catch a glimpse of it.

On 23rd October 1959 there came a report that Kozirev had made another observation of activity in Alphonsus. I had been observing at the same time (01.00 to 03.00 G.M.T.) with my $8\frac{1}{2}$-inch reflector in Sussex, and had seen nothing, so I was frankly doubtful. The mystery was cleared up when I discussed it with Kozirev in the following year. Apparently he had made no visual observation, and the evidence for activity rested only upon one uncertain spectrogram.

Arguments are still going on, and will continue for a long time. Yet it seems that the Moon is not so inert as used to be thought;

and even if Kozirev's interpretations can be challenged, his observation cannot. It is tempting to say that it adds force to the volcanic theory of crater-formation and weakens the bombardment hypothesis, but this may be putting matters too strongly.

One thing is certain, however. Now that the lunar surface has been so thoroughly mapped, any changes which may take place in the future will have no chance of passing undetected. The face of the Moon is known well enough for us to be sure that the disappearance of a crater five or six miles across would be noticed, while even a smaller formation would probably be missed if it lay, as Linné does, upon a relatively featureless plain.

Chapter 13
Eclipses of the Moon

A total eclipse of the Sun is regarded as a most important event. Astronomers are quite ready to travel thousands of miles over the Earth's surface to take full advantage of the few minutes when the Sun is hidden, since only then is the solar atmosphere visible at its glorious best.

Because the Moon appears only just large enough to cover the Sun, the belt of totality is always narrow – no more than 170 miles. For instance, the eclipse of February 1961 was total in South France, but not in England; observers from the British Isles saw an incomplete or partial eclipse instead (or, rather, they would have done if the skies had not been cloudy). With an eclipse of the Moon, the whole situation is different. When it occurs, it is visible from a complete hemisphere of the Earth, because it is due to the Earth's shadow and not to any solid body blocking out the lunar disc.

Consequently, eclipses of the Moon are more often seen, from

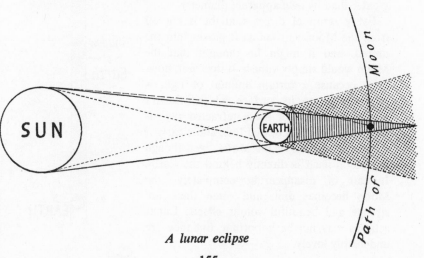

A lunar eclipse

155

any particular point on the Earth, than eclipses of the Sun. On the other hand they are much less spectacular, and are not nearly so important. All that really happens, from the viewpoint of the casual observer, is that the Moon becomes dim and changes colour during its passage through the shadow.

A diagram of a lunar eclipse is given on page 155. The principle cone of shadow cast by the Earth is known as the umbra; on an average it is about 860,000 miles long, which is more than three times the distance of the Moon from the Earth, so that at the mean distance of the Moon (239,000 miles) the cone has a diameter of about 5,700 miles. In the second diagram I have made an attempt to show this to a more accurate scale. In any case, it is obvious that the umbra is extensive enough to cover the Moon completely, and totality may last for as much as an hour and three-quarters, remembering that in the course of an hour the Moon moves across the sky by an amount which is slightly greater than its own apparent diameter.

Every scrap of direct sunlight is cut off from the Moon as soon as it passes into the umbra, and it might be thought that the Moon would simply vanish. It does not, however, because a certain amount of light is refracted on to its surface by the Earth's atmosphere. One of these refracted rays is shown (p. 155) as a dotted line, and clearly it strikes the surface of the Moon, even though the Moon itself is directly behind the Earth. Instead of disappearing completely, the Moon becomes dim, and often there are strange and beautiful colour effects. Lunar eclipses may not be important, but they are undeniably lovely.

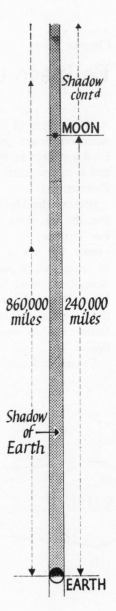

Shadow cont'd

MOON

860,000 miles   240,000 miles

Shadow of Earth

EARTH

Because the Sun is a disk, and not a mere point of light, the umbra of the Earth's shadow is bordered by what is termed the penumbra. This, too, causes a dimming of the Moon, but the effect is not nearly so marked. Since the Moon has to pass through the penumbra before it enters the umbra, an experienced observer will be able to detect the falling-off of light before the main eclipse begins, but the casual onlooker will probably notice nothing at all until the umbra reaches the Moon's disk.

Not all lunar eclipses are total; sometimes they are partial, and on other occasions penumbral, when the Moon avoids the main shadow-cone altogether. As we have seen in Chapter 3, it all depends on whether full moon occurs near a node. On an average, at least one lunar eclipse can be seen from any point on Earth each year, but not all of them are total. A list of forthcoming lunar eclipses is given in the Appendix.

Eclipses may be predicted for centuries ahead, because the movements of the Sun, Earth and Moon are so accurately known. As long ago as 600 B.C., Thales of Miletus, first of the great Greek astronomers, was able to forecast eclipses fairly well by using a much rougher method. He knew that the Sun, Moon and node return to almost the same relative positions after a period of 18 years 10¼ days, the so-called Saros, and that any solar or lunar eclipse will be followed by a very similar eclipse 18 years 10¼ days later. (This is according to our modern calendar, and allows for five leap-years in the meantime.) The method is only approximate, because the relative positions are not exactly the same, but it is better than nothing. For instance, the table in the Appendix shows that there was a total lunar eclipse on 29th January 1953, visible in Britain. Add on one complete Saros period, and we reach February 1971 – and sure enough we find another total eclipse; but this time it is only partly visible in Britain, because the Moon sets before the eclipse is over.

In this way Thales was able to make some useful predictions, even though he had no idea of how eclipses were produced. In those early times it was not even known that the Earth is a globe. Yet by 450 B.C. Anaxagoras of Clazomenæ was well aware of what happened, and he also saw that because the Earth's shadow on the Moon is curved, the Earth itself must be spherical.

Eclipse records go back almost as far as history itself, but most of them refer to the Sun, and the oldest lunar eclipse on record seems to have been that observed by the Chinese in 1136 B.C. Two later eclipses should also be mentioned, as they have a place in history, and one of them even had marked effects upon the whole sequence of events in the Classical period.

In 413 B.C. the Peloponnesian War was raging; the two chief Greek states, Athens and Sparta, were fighting for supremacy, and the Athenian army which had invaded Sicily was in serious trouble. In fact, things were so bad that Nicias, the Athenian commander, decided to evacuate the island altogether, and if he had done so at once all might have been well. Unfortunately, there was a total lunar eclipse on the night before the evacuation was due to begin, and Nicias believed that it had been sent as a warning. The astrologers were called in, and advised that the army should stay where it was 'for thrice nine days'. Nothing could have suited Gylippus, the enemy commander, better, He attacked the waiting Athenian fleet, destroyed most of it and blockaded the rest of it in harbour. The trapped Athenian army was utterly wiped out, and eight years later Athens itself lay at the mercy of Sparta.

The story of the 1504 eclipse is not only more modern, but also more cheerful. At that time Christopher Columbus was in the island of Jamaica, and difficulties arose when the local inhabitants refused to supply him and his men with food. Unlike Nicias, Columbus knew a great deal about lunar eclipses, and he remembered that one was due on 1st March. He therefore told the Jamaicans that unless they mended their ways he would make the Moon 'change her colour, and lose her light'. The eclipse duly took place, so terrifying the natives that they immediately raised Columbus to the rank of a god. No further trouble was experienced with food supplies!

The effect on the Jamaicans would probably have been even greater if the Moon had disappeared completely, as has been known to happen. There were two total eclipses in 1620, the first of which was watched by Kepler, and each time the Moon became utterly invisible; Hevelius noted the same thing in 1642, while in 1761 the Swedish astronomer Per Wargentin (after whom the famous lunar plateau is named) observed an eclipse in which the Moon vanished so thoroughly that it could not be found even with a telescope, though nearby faint stars shone out quite normally. Beer and Mädler saw a very dark eclipse in 1816, and in 1884 the shadowed

Moon could only just be made out. On the other hand, the eclipse of 1848 was so bright that it was hard to tell that an eclipse was in progress at all, though the Moon is said to have turned a curious shade of blood-red.

These differences are due mainly to conditions in the Earth's atmosphere; remember that all the sunlight reaching the eclipsed Moon has to be refracted on to the lunar surface. It may well be, for instance, that the tremendous volcanic explosion of Krakatoa in 1883, which scattered so much dust in the upper atmosphere that its effects were visible for months afterwards, had something to do with the darkness of the 1884 eclipse. It is also possible that dust from Canadian forest fires made the eclipse of 22nd September 1950 rather darker than normal.

My observations of three recent eclipses show that on 29th January 1953 the predominant colour was coppery-pink, with some glorious bluish hues and also what can only be termed 'flame-colour'; at the partial eclipse of 15th July 1954 there were reds and blues, though not so vividly; and on 24th March 1959, another partial eclipse, the shadow was a rusty red.

It has been suggested that the luminescence of lunar rocks may affect the colour and appearance during eclipse. Since the luminescence is connected with radiation from the Sun, we might therefore be able to link 'bright' and 'dark' eclipses with the state of the Sun. I have tried to do so, but without success, and I am frankly doubtful whether the luminescence would be enough to make the Moon's rocks glow visibly.

The most important fact about a lunar eclipse, to the selenographer, is that it results in an abrupt cut-off of sunlight. Since the Moon is almost without atmosphere, and the surface rocks are very poor at retaining heat, the result is that a sudden wave of cold sweeps across the Moon, and the temperatures fall quickly. During the 1939 eclipse, Pettit and Nicolson, at Mount Wilson, found that the temperature dropped from $+160°$ F. to $-110°$ F. in the course of only an hour. The temperatures measured at radio wavelengths do not show anything of the kind – because here we are dealing with regions slightly below the Moon's surface, where the temperature-range is much less because the outer rocks are such excellent insulators.

Sudden cold of this sort might well be expected to produce

obvious changes on the Moon's surface if any ice or snow existed there. Half a century ago, W. H. Pickering carried out some work along these lines. He was not unprejudiced; he believed the white spots such as Linné to be due to hoar-frost, and he expected that the spots would increase in size during an eclipse. Linné does admittedly look at its largest when it has only just emerged from the lunar night, but this is probably due to contrast. The same is true of the peculiar white spot near Picard in the Mare Crisium.

Pickering and Douglass in America and S. A. Saunder in Britain made careful measurements of Linné during successive eclipses, and came to the conclusion that there was a definite growth of the white nimbus. I admit that I am not convinced; I have studied Linné at four eclipses with completely negative results, and now that we can reject Pickering's hoar-frost a change of this kind would be very difficult to explain. I have been equally unsuccessful in finding eclipse-changes in dark-floored plains such as Grimaldi and Plato. Yet the question is still open, and amateur observers with adequate telescopes can do valuable research here during coming lunar eclipses.

There is no glare from the full moon during an eclipse, and occultations of stars can be well seen. Unfortunately, very bright stars are seldom in the right place at the right time, and the only recorded case of a brilliant planet (Jupiter) being occulted by a totally eclipsed Moon dates back as far as the year 755. It should also be added that a total eclipse is the best time to search for 'lunar meteors'. Several careful searches have been made, and I have taken part in some of them myself, but so far without result.

A lunar eclipse may not be so exciting as a total eclipse of the Sun; there are no prominences or coronal rays, and everything happens much more slowly. Yet it cannot be denied that the passing of the Moon through the dark cone of shadow thrown by our own world has a quiet fascination all its own.

Chapter 14

The Way to the Moon

From the earliest days of mankind, we have had to look at the Moon from a respectful distance. A quarter of a million miles is not much to an astronomer, but it is a long way judged by our everyday experience, and the idea of travelling to the Moon seemed to be out of the question. Space-travel dreams, of course, go back a long way, and the first science-fiction story of a lunar voyage was written by a Greek, Lucian of Samosata, in the second century A.D.; but until recently ideas of this kind remained dreams and nothing more.

The situation now is very different. Rockets have been sent into space; men have made journeys round the Earth, above the top of the main layers of atmosphere; Governments are spending huge sums of money in the general research programme. Few scientists doubt that the Moon will be reached well before the end of the century, and that the nearer planets, Mars and Venus, will be next on the list in due course.

The swing of scientific opinion has been as rapid as it has been remarkable. When R. H. Goddard launched the first liquid-fuel rocket, in 1926, nobody paid much attention, partly because Goddard himself disliked publicity but mainly because space research was generally believed to be the idle hobby of a few cranks. The improved rockets built in Germany during the early 1930s, before Hitler came to power, were looked at with tolerant (or sometimes intolerant) amusement, and even the V2's which fell on London near the end of the war failed to persuade many people that the rocket age was close at hand. Even as late as 1950 the amateur interplanetary societies flourishing in various parts of the world were commonly ranked with the 'fringe' of flat-earthers, astrologers, flying saucerers and the like.*

* During casual conversation at an astronomical meeting before the war – it must have been in 1937 or 1938 – I made the remark that I thought I would live long enough to see men reach the Moon. An eminent scientist was heard to comment: 'These schoolboys get wild ideas, don't they?'

What really caused the change was the American announcement that plans were afoot to send up an artificial earth satellite, using rocket power. When the Russians successfully launched their Sputnik I, on 4th October 1957, all but the diehards had to realize that science fiction was turning rapidly into science fact; and even the diehards were largely converted in 1961, when first Yuri Gagarin and then Herman Titov made orbital flights in rocket vehicles. Not long ago I was talking to Gagarin, and asked him whether he thought he would ever make a personal trip to the Moon. He replied, with absolute confidence: 'If I am selected, there will be no difficulty.' I have not met the first American astronaut, Colonel Glenn, but I have no reason to suppose that his reply would be any different.

One point is often overlooked, however. The plan to send a man to the Moon is only one branch of the general space research programme, and it may not even be the most important one; there are few things which an automatic scientific laboratory cannot do better than a man. Now and then we still hear the old parrot-cry: 'Why waste money on space-ships when there is so much still to be done on Earth?' The only answer is to suggest that the questioners should read a few technical books on science, and see how greatly mankind can benefit from the results of studies carried out from beyond the atmosphere. It is also worth noting that a space-probe costs less than a battleship.

This is a book about the Moon, and to go into details about space research would take many pages, so it may be best to give a very bare summary of the basic ideas. First, we cannot use any conventional flying machines, such as aeroplanes, because no such machines will function without a surrounding atmosphere, and above a height of only a few miles the Earth's air is too thin for aircraft to be of the slightest use. Jules Verne's fictional space-gun is equally out of the question. To reach the Moon, a projectile fired in the manner of Verne's *Columbiad* would have to start off at approximately escape velocity, 7 miles per second, but any solid object moving through the dense bottom part of the atmosphere at this speed would create violent friction, so that it would be

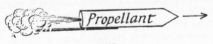

162

destroyed in the same way as a meteor. There is also the point that the shock of blast-off would not only reduce a human passenger to jelly, but would also wreck any scientific instruments. It is too early to say much about 'anti-gravity', and so our only really practicable method is to use the rocket.

The firework rocket of the sort let off on Guy Fawkes' Night consists of a tube, filled with explosive (usually gunpowder) and with a hole or exhaust at one end. When you light the gunpowder, it starts to burn, and gives off hot gas. The gas tends to expand; it can break free only by way of the exhaust, and so it escapes through the exhaust in a concentrated stream, so 'kicking' the rocket body in the opposite direction. So long as the gas goes on escaping, the rocket will continue to fly.

This means that the rocket would work just as well in the absence of any surrounding air. It depends on what Newton called the principle of reaction: every action has an equal and opposite reaction. Indeed, surrounding air is actually a nuisance, because it sets up friction and has to be pushed out of the way.

There are many solid fuels which are more effective than gunpowder, but as much as sixty years ago the Russian pioneer Konstantin Eduardovich Tsiolkovskii, who really laid the foundations of the science we now call astronautics, realized that it would be better to use liquid fuels. This is what Goddard, in America, did on 16th March 1926. His first liquid-fuel rocket was small enough by modern standards, but it marked the beginning of a new era. Instead of being a mere powder-filled tube, it had to have a firing chamber for burning to take place; pumps; ignition mechanism; and storage tanks for the liquid oxygen and whatever else was used (petrol, in Goddard's case). The 'rocket' was obsolete, and the 'rocket motor' had been born. The vast rockets of today are basically of the same sort, different though they are in scale and complexity.

Yet fuel is always a real problem. Even the best liquid propellants fall short of what is needed, and solid fuels have severe limitations, even though they have proved to be more useful than was expected. Goddard's solution – and Tsiolkovskii's – was to use a step-rocket. Here, several rockets are mounted one on top of the other. At blast-off, the bottom rocket does all the work; when it has exhausted its supply of propellant it breaks away and falls back to Earth, leaving

163

the second rocket to continue under its own power with the double advantage of being above the densest part of the air and provided with a 'running start'. Theoretically you can add as many steps as you like, though each involves extra problems of engineering. The first step-rocket went up from White Sands, in the United States, in February 1949, and proved to be very encouraging, since the upper stage attained a height of 244 miles – a record up to that time. All the modern earth satellites and space-probes are launched by means of step-vehicles.

The trouble, of course, is that it takes a very large launching rocket to cope with a very small 'payload'. If you want to take a kitten from London to Glasgow, it would be annoying to have to hire a ten-ton truck, but that, in effect, is what space-research planners have to do. Nuclear motors will presumably come to the rescue in due course, but that lies far in the future as yet, and meanwhile the only course is to make liquid and solid fuels as efficient as possible.

An ordinary rocket has its disadvantages. It may rise to the top of the atmosphere, or even beyond, but if it is not moving at escape velocity it will soon fall back, destroying itself and often with the loss of its instruments as well. If, however, a vehicle can be taken up by rocket and set in a stable orbit round the Earth, it will not come down – provided that it is above the atmosphere, so that there is no air-resistance to worry about. The information gained can be sent back by radio, and the observations can be carried on for long periods instead of only a few minutes. As soon as the satellite has entered a stable orbit, it will move in just the same way as a natural astronomical body would do. The real Moon is in no danger of falling on to the Earth, because it is in motion; the same is true of an artificial satellite. Only if part (or all) of its orbit is low enough for air-resistance to become appreciable will the satellite come back into the lower layers and be destroyed in the manner of a shooting-star.

The satellite launchings carried out from 1957 onward showed that the possibilities were endless, and there seemed no reason to doubt that rockets could be sent even further – certainly as far as the Moon. The first to try anything of the sort were the United States workers, with their Pioneer vehicles of 1958. It cannot be said that the Pioneers failed, because two of them did at least go up

164

to 70,000 miles, providing a tremendous amount of information; but they were not successful in reaching the Moon, and once again the Russians were first in the field.

On 2nd January 1959 the Soviet team launched the first of its moon-probes, Lunik I. Starting at a velocity slightly greater than 7 miles per second, the top stage of the rocket by-passed the Moon at a distance of about 4,600 miles, sending back signals, and then went its way into space. By 8th January it was 750,000 miles from the Earth, and to all intents and purposes it had entered an orbit round the Sun, so that it had become an artificial planet. It had taken 34 hours to travel from Earth to its nearest point of approach to the Moon, and of course its velocity relative to the Earth had become less all the time.

We do not know where Lunik I is now. Radio contact with it was lost after 62 hours, and probably we will never find it again, but there is every reason to think that it will go on circling the Sun for many millions of years to come.

Lunik I was an outstanding first attempt. Signals received from it showed, for instance, that the Moon has no appreciable magnetic field. The next step was inevitable; it was taken on 12th September 1959, when the Russians sent up Lunik II with the object of scoring a direct hit on the Moon.

When a space-probe is launched, every effort is made to use it to the full. With Lunik II, for instance, the programme included studies of cosmic rays, investigations of particles sent out by the Sun, possible magnetic fields in space, the numbers of meteoric particles, and methods of rocket control and guidance. At a distance of thousands of miles from the Earth, the Lunik sent out a cloud of sodium vapour which was both seen and photographed by Russian observers, showing that the rocket was following its predicted course.

Particularly interesting were the measures made by the Lunik's instruments as the vehicle neared the Moon. Atoms which are incomplete, because they have lost one or more of their electrons, are said to be ionized, and can be detected. At about 6,000 miles from the Moon, the Lunik showed that the number of particles increased, and the Russians suggested that a region of ionized gas might be responsible, forming a sort of lunar ionosphere similar

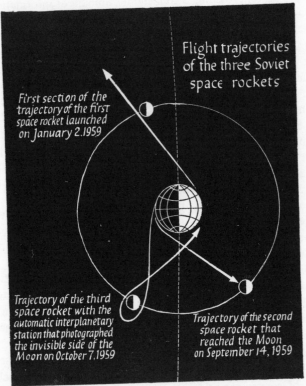

Flight trajectories
of the three Soviet
space rockets

First section of the
trajectory of the first
space rocket launched
on January 2.1959

Trajectory of the third
space rocket with the
automatic interplanetary
station that photographed
the invisible side of the
Moon on October 7,1959

Trajectory of the second
space rocket that
reached the Moon
on September 14, 1959

to that of the Earth. This may or may not be correct, but the measures themselves seemed fairly definite.

The absence of any marked lunar magnetic field was confirmed. Such a result was only to be expected; but there seems little doubt that if the Moon really did possess strong or even moderate magnetism, the instruments in Lunik II would have recorded it.

Before hitting the Moon, the last stage of the rocket separated from the container carrying the scientific equipment. Presumably no effort was made to bring either component down gently; a crash-landing was as much as could be hoped for. The predicted time of impact was 21h. 01m. G.M.T., and observers all over the world were at their telescopes, hoping to see some sign of a flash as the Lunik reached the end of its journey. More reliable were the results from the Jodrell Bank 250-foot 'dish'; even as it neared its goal, the rocket was still sending back signals which could be picked up unmistakably. At 21h. 02m. 23s. the signals ceased abruptly. This, then, was the moment of landing.

I was using the 12½-inch reflector at my own observatory, and since the Russians had given an approximate landing-area I had risked a reasonably high magnification. Suddenly I saw, or thought I saw, a minute spark, so faint as to be at the limit of visibility. The time was 21h. 02m. 23s. – though I did not then know what was happening, and all I had to work on was the original estimate of 21h. 01m. When I checked up and found that H. P. Wilkins at Bexleyheath had recorded the same sort of spark at the same moment and in the same position, I wondered whether I had in fact seen the landing of the carrier-rocket. On the whole, however, I am more inclined to dismiss it as a trick of the eye; various other observers in Europe recorded phenomena in different places, and there is no general agreement. It seems unlikely that any of the reports are reliable, and we must admit that the exact impact-point of Lunik II is not known, though the Russians believe it to have been not very far from the great crater Archimedes.*

The question is not really important; we may at least be quite sure that Lunik II did hit the Moon not far from where the Russians had expected. Of course it destroyed itself, since it landed at a speed relative to the Moon of about 2 miles per second, but it had done even, more than its makers could have hoped. For the first time, a vehicle had been sent direct from one world to another.

Less than a month later, the Russians achieved an even more spectacular triumph; with their new vehicle, Lunik III, they managed to photograph the far side of the Moon, which can never be seen from the Earth because it is always turned away from us. In doing so, they showed once and for all that the ancient science of astronomy has now merged with the new science of astronautics. The frontiers were down, and the way to the Moon was open.

---

* Other reports also came in – notably from an earnest lady who had been watching the impact with binoculars, and told me that at the vital moment she had seen the Moon split in half.

Chapter 15

The Other Side of the Moon

'What lies on the other side of the Moon?' Astronomers over the centuries have been asking themselves that question. It seemed so infuriating not to know; the Moon is our nearest neighbour in space, but until 1959 our knowledge of its surface was restricted to the 59 per cent which can be studied from Earth.

The various librations have been described in Chapter 4, but a chart will help to show their effects. In the left-hand drawing, the large crater Gerard is shown, together with the lunar limb, at mean libration. The same area is shown in the right-hand sketch, but this time with the most favourable libration for that region; Gerard is much better placed, and new details, actually on the far hemisphere, have come into view. Yet one inescapable fact remained: 41 per cent of the Moon was absolutely inaccessible to observation, and nobody really knew what it was like.

Speculation was not lacking, and it seems worth mentioning a strange theory put forward by a nineteenth-century Danish astronomer, Hansen. Hansen was a famous mathematician, and was engaged in studying the movements of the Moon when he found

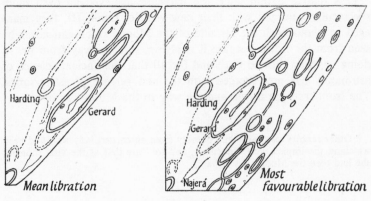

Mean libration

Most favourable libration

The Gerard area
168

some tiny discrepancies which he could not explain. They led him to suggest that the Moon was not uniform in density, but that one hemisphere was slightly more massive than the other. This would result in the centre of gravity being some way from the centre of figure, and he worked out that it was 33 miles further from the Earth. He concluded that all the Moon's atmosphere and water had been drawn round to the far side, which might well be inhabited!

It was an attractive idea, but few people took it seriously, and a little thought will show that it is quite untenable. For one thing, the effect of a displaced centre of gravity would certainly not be to draw all the atmosphere round to one side, even if the Moon were capable of retaining a dense mantle. Later, Hansen's discrepancies were satisfactorily cleared up without resort to lop-sidedness, and the theory was definitely relegated to the scientific museum. The position was summed up rather neatly by a famous poem which has been handed down to posterity, written, I believe, by a house-maid in the service of a well-known poet. There seem to be several versions of it, and I have chosen the most-quoted one:

> *O Moon, lovely Moon with the beautiful face,*
> *Careering throughout the bound'ries of space,*
> *Whenever I see you, I think in my mind—*
> *Shall I ever, O ever, behold thy behind?*

All that could really be said was that the far side was likely to be just as barren, just as hostile, and just as 'airless' as the side which we have always known. When it came to the question of the arrangement of craters and mountains, or the frequency of maria, one could do little more than guess.

One interesting investigation was carried out in the last century by the American geologist and astronomer, N. S. Shaler. Shaler considered the ray craters on the visible side, and realized that their positions could be plotted from their rays even if the craters themselves could not be seen. He therefore started to examine the limb regions to see whether he could trace any rays which came

Disk of Moon

Ray-centre
on averted side

169

from the far side, and which might give a clue as to the positions of the craters responsible for them. As he had expected, there were a few, and eventually he plotted six possible centres, all well on the hidden hemisphere and thus permanently invisible from Earth.

Unluckily he mislaid his notebooks, and when he returned to the problem, thirty years later, he could remember only the rough positions of three of his ray-centres. Neither could he reobserve the rays, since his eyesight was no longer sufficiently keen. For some time the problem was neglected, but in the 1930s a British observer, E. F. Emley, returned to it, with results very similar to Shaler's. Later still, H. P. Wilkins used Emley's observations, together with his own and some of mine, to locate eight ray-centres on the averted part of the Moon. It now seems that the positions given were not so very wide of the mark, but at the time there seemed little prospect of finding out.

In 1952 I made some comments about the possible features of the hidden side, based upon my own ideas as to the origin of the craters. There is now no point in giving them in detail, but I forecast a lack of large Maria and a less marked lining-up of large craters. This was because the lines of weakness in the lunar crust due to the pull of the Earth would be less pronounced, assuming that the Moon's rotation had been 'captured' at a fairly early stage in the history of the Earth-Moon system. I then wrote that 'It is probable than there are no formations on the far side so vast as the Mare Imbrium, for instance. . . . Great chains of walled plains are probably less frequent. On the whole, it seems likely that the hidden side of the Moon is very like the side we can see; there may be no large Maria, but there are certainly mountains, and the usual medley of craters, ridges and clefts. In fact, the landscape is probably similar to that of the rough southern uplands in the third and fourth quadrants.' On the impact theory of crater formation, of course, no marked difference between the visible and averted hemispheres would have been expected.

I added that 'before the first Moon-voyage is accomplished, it is likely that the hidden side will have been photographed by a rocket-carried camera'; but at that time I had no hope that anything of the kind would be possible for many years. Actually it took less than eight, and this brings us on to the most important of all the Russian space-vehicles up to the present time: Lunik III.

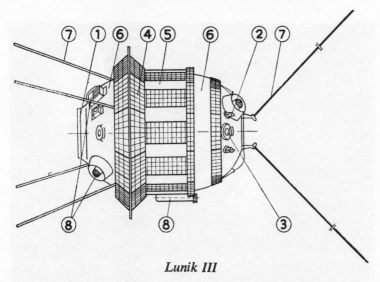

Lunik III

1. photographic objectives; 2. motor used for orientation of vehicle; 3. photo-electric cells; 4. solar batteries; 5. shutters of the temperature control system; 6. heat screens; 7. antennæ; 8. other apparatus

Lunik III, like its forerunners, was given a full research programme, but its main task was to pass beyond the Moon and photograph the far side. It was launched on 4th October 1959, exactly two years after the first Russian success with Sputnik I. The launcher used was, of course, a step-vehicle; it had to be powerful, owing to the weight of its load, called by the Soviet team 'the automatic interplanetary station'. Without fuel, the upper stage of the rocket weighed about a ton and a half, while the weight of the 'station' itself amounted to nearly nine hundredweight.

It is not easy to grasp the difficulties of sending a vehicle of this type into a pre-planned orbit. The slightest mistake would have caused the Lunik to miss its target not by a few miles, but by thousands. However, all went well. By 4.30 G.M.T. on 7th October the rocket had passed by the Moon, and lay well beyond it, at a distance of under 40,000 miles from the lunar surface. The positions at this moment are shown in the diagram on page 172; it will be seen that from the Earth, the Moon is almost new, which means

*Position of Lunik III, during the photography
of the far side of the Moon*

that the averted side is in full sunlight. It will also be seen that the
Lunik was not within range of the whole of the far hemisphere,
but only about 70 per cent of it.

All was ready, and the Russian remote control turned the vehicle
until the camera lenses were trained on to the Moon. Then the
photographic apparatus was switched on, and for the next forty
minutes the pictures were taken. Two cameras were used, giving
photographs on different scales. After the programme had been
finished, the films were automatically developed and fixed ready for
transmission back to Earth.

Delay was inevitable, because the Lunik was still receding from
us. It reached its apogee, or furthest point, on 10th October, when it
was 292,000 miles away, and then it started to swing in once more,
reaching perigee (29,000 miles) on 18th October. It was then that
the pictures were sent back. They were scanned by a miniature
television camera, and the transmissions were picked up by the

172

waiting Russians. Late on 24th October, the photographs were given to the world.*

Under the circumstances, the pictures were of remarkable quality, but of course it would be absurd to hope for anything comparable with photographs of the familiar side taken from the comfort of a home observatory. At first sight much of the disk appeared blank, but the dark Mare-areas stood out well; the western limb of the Moon as seen from Earth – the region of the Mare Crisium and the Mare Australe – was included, which made interpretation a good deal easier. On the new areas there were only two important dark patches. One was the feature now known as the Mare Moscoviæ, or Moscow Sea; the other, at the very edge of the photograph, was the Mare Desiderii or Dream Sea. Later measures showed that the Mare Moscoviæ is less than 190 miles in diameter, so that it may turn out to be a dark-floored crater of the Grimaldi type rather than a mare; the smaller area named in honour of Tsiolkovskii, the Russian space-flight pioneer, is definitely not large enough to be classed as a sea. This leaves us with the Mare Desiderii, which is not well shown and which may not be one continuous sheet; probably it extends on to the thirty per cent of the hidden side not covered by the Lunik photographs, and which is therefore still unknown. At least, however, it is clear that sea-areas really are much less extensive than on the familiar hemisphere.

At the time some people suggested that craters also were scarce, because few were shown unmistakably. This is quite untrue. The photographs were taken under the equivalent of full-moon lighting, and the most casual glance at a rather blurred full-moon picture is enough to show that normal craters cannot be seen as such; only those with exceptionally bright walls or exceptionally dark floors stand out. For instance, Plato and Tycho can always be found, but larger formations such as Maginus and Hipparchus are very difficult to locate under high light. The Lunik pictures are, at best, comparable with bad full-moon photographs of the familiar face, and so ordinary craters are not detectable easily.

* They were first seen in Britain at 10.15 p.m., during my monthly 'Sky at Night' programme on B.B.C. television. The photograph came through exactly one minutes before transmission was due to begin, which did not give me much time to think out a suitable commentary – but it was a moment not to be forgotten! Luckily the Mare Crisium was shown so clearly that I was able to recognize it at once, which enabled me to get my bearings.

For correlating the photographs with details on the known hemisphere, the Russians made extensive use of H. P. Wilkins' charts of the lunar limb. Wilkins, unhappily, died early in 1960; but as I had collaborated with him in his book, and had done a certain amount of work on the charts, I was invited to Russia later in the year. When I reached the Sternberg Institute, in Moscow, I was able to see the remaining thirty Lunik photographs, which were much more informative. Y. N. Lipski and his colleagues have since used them to draw up a map of the new regions, showing almost 500 separate objects, and this map is reproduced in the Appendix.

Naturally, it is hard to be certain about the nature of some of the features. Tsiolkovskii, for example, is probably a dark-floored crater with a bright wall and a central mountain, but this may not be its true form; we can only wait for clearer pictures of it. The Soviet Range may really be more like a scarp than a towering line of peaks, while the Mare Desiderii is possibly made up of numerous dark patches and craters which have blurred together in the photographs. Yet the general theme is definite enough, and we can prove what astronomers have always believed: the averted part of the Moon is basically just the same as the part which we can see from Earth. There are differences in detail, but that is all.

Lunik III had done its work well, but its fate is unknown. Radio contact with it was lost abruptly, and was never regained. It may be still moving round the Earth, but more probably it fell back into the atmosphere and was destroyed. A fault in the transmitters may have developed, but the general view in Russia is that the vehicle was hit by a meteor, so that its instruments were put out of action. The truth will never be known now.

So far, about one-eighth of the whole surface of the Moon remains unseen and unphotographed. There is still a blank area, as is shown by the photographs of the lunar globe produced in Russia in 1961. No doubt it will be filled in before long; indeed, the United States vehicle Ranger III, launched on 26th January 1962, was expected to complete the story. Ranger should have landed on the Moon gently enough to avoid damaging its instruments, and before impact it was hoped that pictures would be sent back by television, showing objects down to a dozen feet in diameter. Unfortunately the first stage of the launcher proved to be slightly too effective, and the second stage, carrying the instruments, went into the wrong orbit. It was then hoped to send the vehicle past the Moon at a distance of 25,000 miles, and to obtain photographs of the area not covered by Lunik III, but further troubles developed, and no worthwhile pictures were obtained before the Ranger departed into space to join the increasing company of tiny artificial planets now in orbit round the Sun. Another Ranger, launched later in the year, was even less successful; it missed the Moon, and in addition its instrumentation failed.

Yet failures are only to be expected in a research programme which is so difficult, so delicate and so new. Before long further rockets will land on the Moon; before long, too, we will see further flights of the Lunik and Ranger type, so that it should not be many years now before we have really accurate maps of the tantalizing 'other side of the Moon'.

Chapter 16
Life on the Moon

The Earth upon which we live is an unimportant planet, moving round an equally unimportant star. To suppose that we are the only intelligent beings in the whole universe is surely the height of conceit; if we agree (as most astronomers do) that planetary systems are very common, then life must be common too.

Proof, however, is lacking – and may always be lacking. The only bodies close enough to be studied in any detail are those of the Solar System, and the prospects of finding advanced life-forms on any of them seem to be painfully slim. Only the Earth is suitable for beings of our type.

Of course our knowledge is incomplete, because basically we still know very little about 'life'; and it is often suggested that there may well be creatures of entirely alien pattern – made of gold, perhaps, and breathing pure hydrogen. Beings of this interesting type are well known to story-tellers, who generally term then B.E.M.'s (=Bug-Eyed Monsters) and scatter them indiscriminately upon Mars, Venus, Jupiter and even the Moon. Let us admit at once that we cannot rule out the possibility of B.E.M.s. Shakespeare's lines 'There are more things in Heaven and earth, Horatio . . .' hold good in science, as in everything else. A friend of mine once said that he could not deny the possibility of an intelligent Martian who looked like a cabbage and squeaked like a mouse. He did not think that it was probable, but it was not absolutely out of the question – and of course he was right. Yet when we start to consider totally alien forms, speculation becomes pointless. We know a good deal about the way in which living matter is built up, and all available evidence indicates that B.E.M.s do not exist on Mars, the Moon or anywhere else, so that until (and if!) new evidence comes to hand it will be best to leave matters there and confine ourselves to discussing life *as we know it*.

Let us begin by summarizing the conditions necessary for our sort of life. There must be a reasonably even temperature, an atmo-
176

sphere which contains oxygen, and a reasonable amount of moisture. In the Solar System, there are very few worlds which fulfil all three qualifications. The giant outer planets, with their low temperatures and poisonous atmospheres, are most uninviting; Pluto is too cold; Mercury is almost devoid of atmosphere, and has numerous other disadvantages into the bargain. Venus and Mars are less hostile. We know little about Venus, and the tremendous quantity of carbon dioxide in its atmosphere seems to argue against the existence of animals or men, but it may be that there are broad oceans in which primitive marine life flourishes. Mars has a relatively thin atmosphere, and it is becoming more and more probable that the famous dark areas are due to living organisms of some kind, but there seems to be insufficient oxygen to support Earth-type creatures, apart possibly from microscopic ones.

The Moon is less hospitable still. As we have seen, the temperature range on the surface is enormous, and atmosphere and moisture are lacking. It is safe to say that advanced life-forms are out of the question. This seems so obvious today that we tend to forget that less than two centuries ago, leading astronomers were quite ready to believe the Moon to be an earth-like world peopled with men.

The idea of a habitable Moon is very old. Indeed, once it was realized that the Moon is a rocky globe, it was tacitly assumed to be the dwelling-place of human beings.* Even the invention of the telescope did not cause a general change of view. It was thought that the bright areas were lands, while the dark patches were seas of open water; and although Galileo apparently had doubts, Kepler believed that the telescope had revealed a living world, with extensive oceans and a dense mantle of air.

By 1800 the idea of oceans had been abandoned, but it was still thought that there must be air and water, and that life survived on the surface. This was the opinion of Schröter, and he was supported by the most famous astronomer of the day, William Herschel.

Herschel, the Hanoverian musician who became official astronomer to King George III, is best remembered for his discovery of the planet Uranus, in 1781, but his most important contributions were in stellar astronomy. As an observer it is possible that he has

* It is not certain who first realized that the Moon is a non-luminous globe. Anaxagoras, friend of Pericles of Athens, certainly knew it as long ago as 450 B.C.

never been equalled, and between 1781 and his death, over forty years later, every honour that the scientific world could bestow came his way. His views about life in the Solar System, were, however, rather surprising. He thought it possible that there was a region below the Sun's fiery surface where men might live, and he regarded the existence of life on the Moon as 'an absolute certainty'. In 1780 he wrote to the then Astronomer Royal, Nevil Maskelyne, as follows:

'Perhaps conclusions from the analogy of things may be exceedingly different from truth; but seeing that our Earth is inhabited, and comparing the Moon with this planet; finding that in such a satellite there is a provision of light and heat; also, in all appearance, a soil proper for habitation fully as good as ours, if not perhaps better – who can say that it is not extremely probable, nay beyond doubt, that there must be inhabitants on the Moon of some kind or another?'

Maskelyne was not in the least convinced, and it is on record that later, when Herschel said much the same thing in a paper about lunar mountains, the Astronomer Royal deleted the offending paragraph before passing it for publication. Yet the idea of moon-men was certainly not dismissed out of hand.

Schröter's views were not so extreme, but he, too, was sure that the Moon must be populated. He knew that the lunar atmosphere is thin, but he grossly over-estimated its density, and even considered that some of the features visible on the Moon were artificial. This last idea was supported by another German astronomer, Gruithuisen (originator of the meteor theory of crater formation), who announced in 1822 that he had discovered a real 'lunar city' on the borders of the Sinus Medii, not far from the centre of the disc.

Gruithuisen, as we have noted, was a keen-eyed observer who did some excellent work, but unfortunately his vivid imagination tended to bring ridicule upon him even during his lifetime. His 'lunar city' was a case in point. He described it as 'a collection of dark gigantic ramparts . . . extending about 23 miles either way, and arranged on either side of a principal rampart down the centre . . . a work of art'. Actually, his 'dark gigantic ramparts' turn out to be no more than low, haphazard ridges. Two of them are vaguely parallel for some distance, but there is nothing in the least like an artificial structure, and in any case the ridges are so low that they are difficult to see at all except when near the terminator. There can be no question of any change here, as Schröter, years before Gruithuisen, and Mädler, ten years afterwards, drew the region just as it is today.

Beer and Mädler showed that the Moon is definitely unable to support higher life-forms, and after the publication of their great book, in 1838, the moon-men were more or less handed over to the story-tellers, who have certainly used them to the full. Bug-eyed monsters, however, are newcomers to the literary scene, and up to the time of Herschel it was thought more probable that the 'Selenites' were as human as ourselves.

Even so, the people of 130 years ago were quite ready to believe in a habitable Moon. This led to the famous Lunar Hoax, the biggest scientific practical joke of all time (apart possibly from the Piltdown Man), and which is certainly worth describing.

Sir William Herschel had explored the northern skies with his great telescopes, discovering vast numbers of double stars, clusters and nebulæ, and probing the depths of space as no man before him had ever done. However, the southernmost stars, which never rise in Britain, remained comparatively unknown. Catalogues of the brighter ones were drawn up from time to time; Halley, the second Astronomer Royal, actually spent the year 1677 in St. Helena specially for the purpose, but by the nineteenth century it had become clear that there was an urgent need for a more detailed survey.

Fittingly enough, the task was undertaken by William Herschel's son, John. On 13th November 1833 he set out for the Cape of Good Hope, taking with him his own telescopes and equipment. He remained at the Cape for four years, and when he finally left, in 1838, his work had been well done. It took him over ten years to collect and sort all the observations.

Herschel did not mean to pay any particular attention to the Moon or planets, which can be seen just as well from the northern hemisphere as from the Cape. He was concerned with the stellar heavens, and there was more than enough to occupy him. However, Richard Locke, a graceless reporter of the New York *Sun*, had a bright idea. Herschel was on the other side of the world; communications in those days were slow and uncertain; who was there to check any statements he might care to make?

Locke saw his chance, and took it. On 25th August, 1835, therefore, the *Sun* came out with a headline about 'Great Astronomical Discoveries', and an account of how Herschel had built a new telescope powerful enough to show the Moon in amazing detail. Locke's tongue must have been very much in his cheek, but the article was so cleverly worded that it sounded almost plausible. It was well-known, Locke wrote, that the chief limitation of any telescope is that it cannot collect enough light for extreme magnification, but Herschel had overcome this by effecting 'a transfusion of artificial light through the focal object of vision' – in other words, by using the telescope to form an image, and then reinforcing the image by means of a light-source in the observatory itself!

The way was open, and the *Sun* kept up the good work for the next six days. Herschel, evidently, had seen all manner of strange creatures. There were bluish goat-like animals, brown quadrupeds, and even 'a strange amphibious creature, of a spherical form, rolling with great velocity across a pebbly beach'. The climax was reached on 28th August, with Locke's priceless account of lunar bat-men:

> Certainly they were human beings. . . . They averaged four feet in height, were covered, except on the face, with short, glossy, copper-coloured hair, and had wings composed of a thin membrane. . . . The face, which was of a yellowish flesh colour, was a slight improvement upon that of a large orang-outang, being much more open and intelligent in expression. The mouth, however, was very prominent, though somewhat relieved by a thick beard upon the lower jaw. . . .

Locke was clever enough to bring in 'science' now and then. Sometimes a higher-powered eyepiece had to be used, sometimes conditions were unsuitable for observing, and sometimes it was necessary to turn up the hydro-oxygen burners to light up the faint image by the method of 'artificial transfusion'. The series was brought to an end by an account of how the astronomers forgot to cover up the main mirror, so that when the Sun shone on it it acted as a vast burning-glass and set light to the observatory.

The articles met with a mixed reception, but some eminent critics swallowed the bait completely. 'These new discoveries are both probable and plausible,' declared the New York *Times*, while the *New Yorker* thought that the observations 'had created a new era in astronomy and science generally'. A women's club in Massachusetts is said to have written to Herschel asking his views upon how to get in touch with the bat-men and convert them to Christianity, while even the Academy of Sciences in Paris held a debate when the news spread across to Europe, though it must be added that the French astronomers were highly suspicious!

The hoax was exposed by a rival paper within a few weeks, and the *Sun* itself confessed on 16th September. Even then, however, lingering doubts remained, and not for some months was the whole absurd business finally killed.

It is easy to laugh; but can we afford to? It is as well to remember the 1938 panic, when a misleading broadcast of H. G. Wells' *War of the Worlds* led some people in the United States to believe that the Earth was being attacked by monsters from Mars; and even more recently, alarm and despondency was spread by a radio announcer who became bored with the lack of news, and told his listeners that the Moon was about to fall on to the Earth. (I understand that the broadcasting company subsequently dispensed with his services.) Then, too, there are flying saucers. I do not propose to enter into a discussion about space crockery, but I cannot resist mentioning the occasion in 1958 when I interviewed Mr. George Adamski, co-author of the classic Saucer book, on the B.B.C. television programme 'Panorama'. Mr. Adamski told me that he had been beyond the Moon, and had seen some dog-like creatures running about on the far side. Strangely enough, these interesting animals have not been confirmed by the photographs taken from Lunik III.*

All this is most entertaining, but it is hardly science, so it is time to turn back to the work of true astronomers.

Although the idea of intelligent life on the Moon died more than

* He also told me that the inhabitants of Saturn play table tennis. I was once a County table tennis player myself, and I would dearly like to play against a Saturnian, but so far it has not been possible to arrange a fixture.

a century ago, animals and plants were still considered possible. In fact, the last serious advocate of animal life on the lunar surface was none other than W. H. Pickering, author of the 1904 photographic atlas as well as a great number of papers about all branches of lunar study.

Between 1919 and 1924 Pickering, observing from the clear air of Jamaica, carried out a detailed study of the noble crater Eratosthenes, which lies at the southern end of the Apennine chain. He found some strange dark patches which seemed to show regular variations over each lunation, and although he was sure that tracts of vegetation existed on the Moon he thought it more likely that the Eratosthenes patches, which moved about and did not merely spread, were due to swarms of insects.

This startling idea was put forward in Pickering's final paper on the subject, published in 1924. He pointed out that a lunar astronomer of a century earlier would have seen similar moving patches on the plains of North America, due to herds of buffalo, and that the Eratosthenes patches were about of this size; on the other hand they moved more slowly – only a few feet per minute – and it was therefore reasonable to suppose that the individual creatures making them up were smaller than buffalo. Although insects were considered the most likely answer, Pickering's paper contains the following remarkable paragraph:

> While this suggestion of a round of lunar life may seem a little fanciful, and the evidence on which it is founded frail, yet it is based strictly on the analogy of the migration of the fur-bearing seals of the Pribiloff Islands. . . . The distance involved is about 20 miles, and is completed in 12 days. This involves an average speed of 6 feet a minute, which, as we have seen, implies small animals.

Pickering's idea was that the creatures, animal or insect, travelled regularly between their breeding-grounds and the dark 'vegetation' tracts near by. His reputation ensured that due attention would be paid to his theory, but nobody nowadays is likely to take it seriously. The supposed creatures would have to put up with a total lack of oxygen or moisture, coupled with appalling temperature variations. Moreover they would have to be extraordinarily regular in their habits, moving almost to the nearest hour. It is clearly a waste of time to discuss the idea further.

There is another point to be considered, however. If we reject animals and insects, as we are bound to do, what is the explanation of Pickering's 'moving patches'? My own studies of them, carried out between 1954 and the present time, indicate that although the patches exist, they do not move. Certain parts of the crater-floor brighten under a high sun, while others become less obvious; but this is a very different matter from a patch in actual motion. I have never seen the slightest sign of anything of the sort, even though I have made hundreds of drawings of the area under every conceivable angle of illumination. The same is true of rather similar patches reported by Pickering inside the crater Aristillus, not far from Archimedes in the Mare Imbrium.

Aristillus shows other features of interest. For instance, there is Pickering's 'double canal', made up of two strange parallel streaks which he believed to develop as the Sun rose over them. Here, too, simple brightening of parts of the area seems to give an answer which is both logical and straightforward.

Insects and animals having been relegated to the pages of science-fiction novels, let us turn to possible plant life. Here we should be more cautious. Microscopic organisms, at least, can survive in very unexpected places, and even lowly plants of the moss variety are amazingly durable.

There are several craters which seem to show regular changes over each lunation. Most, such as Endymion, Grimaldi and Riccioli, have dark lunabase floors. Endymion, for instance, contains patches which are greyer than the general tone of the floor, and which seem to alter in shape as sunrise progresses; some expand, others are said to contract or even vanish. Pickering naturally attributed them to vegetation, but it seems much more probable that they are due to some unusual feature of the surface coating material.

Last, but certainly not least, we come to the celebrated banded craters, of which the most prominent example is Aristarchus.

Even when it is illuminated by nothing more powerful than earth-shine, Aristarchus is clearly visible; its central peak is definitely the brightest spot on the whole Moon. The great Herodotus Valley lies near by, and so does Wood's Spot, where sulphur deposits have been suspected. As we have seen, this is one of the areas where occasional obscurations have been reported. Yet in form Aristarchus is normal enough; it is 23 miles in diameter, with walls rising to 6,000 feet above the floor, while the brilliant central peak is by no means exceptional in height. It is the interior details which are so unusual.

As soon as the Sun has risen sufficiently for the east wall of Aristarchus to be free from shadow, faint dark patches come into view. As the lunar morning progresses, these shadings are seen to be really parts of well-defined dusky bands, which radiate from the central mountain, cross the floor, and run up the inner slopes of the walls. By noon, some of them appear to pass right over the wall crest and on to the outer country. In moderate telescopes they appear continuous, but in 1952 Wilkins and myself, using the Meudon 33-inch refractor, found that the main bands could be broken down into fine detail. As the Sun sinks, the bands become less conspicuous, and by nightfall they are hard to make out at all.

Rather strangely, early observers made no mention of the bands. Beer and Mädler said nothing about them; neither did Lohrmann, and an early Schmidt drawing, which shows Aristarchus on a large scale, also omits them. They were first described by Phillips in 1868, though I have found a drawing made five years before by Lord Rosse, using his 72-inch reflector at Birr Castle in Ireland, which shows them unmistakably.

Phillips' observation does not seem to have become known, and Neison's book, published in 1876, makes no mention of the bands, even though Aristarchus is described in considerable detail. Nothing more of them was heard until 1884, when Sheldon recorded two. Today they are easy objects with any 3-inch telescope under suitable conditions.

It is tempting to suggest that the bands have developed during the last half-century or so, and this was the idea put forward some years ago by Robert Barker. Yet we must be very wary of jumping to conclusions, and work carried out recently seems to show that nothing of the sort has happened.

In 1949 I became interested in the Aristarchus problem, and started looking for other formations showing bands of the same type. I soon found one; a small crater not far from Agatharchides, in the Mare Humorum area, where there were two distinct bands running up the inner east wall. I published a short paper about it, and the search was taken up by others, notable by A. P. Lenham and K. W. Abineri in England. Dozens of small banded craters are now known. Generally the bands run up the east walls, but not always, and there seems little doubt that they are genuine features, though it is not easy to decide whether we are dealing with dark bands against a light background or with lighter streaks against a less reflective background.

Lenham, in 1951, suggested that the bands might be produced by clusters of crystals, which during the night-time absorbed moisture oozing from the ground, losing their moisture and darkening when the Sun rose over them. This does not seem at all probable in the light of recent studies, and it is even less likely that the bands are due to vegetation – as did not seem out of the question even a decade ago. Again the most probable explanation lies in differences of surface coating, and the apparent development over each luna-tion may be accounted for by the changing illumination. However, the bands are interesting features, and are well worth studying.

All things considered, we have to agree that there is no evidence in favour of any observable life on the Moon, and that all the evidence is very much to the contrary. If life exists, it must presum-ably be underground. In 1961 the Russian astronomer A. Deutsch, of Leningrad, suggested that in view of the constant temperature below the outer coating, gases might exist there to support plants or even animals; in the United States, C. Sagan has expressed the view that a layer of organic matter may exist some tens of metres below the surface. Yet here, too, there is no evidence whatsoever in favour of anything of the kind, and it is logical to conclude that at present the Moon supports no living thing.

We cannot tell whether life ever existed on the Moon. My own view is that conditions were never suitable for it, and that lunar explorers of the future are unlikely to find even the most elementary fossils in the rocks; but others disagree, and the problem will not be cleared up until the first expeditions land. Meanwhile, a novel idea due to J. J. Gilvarry is worth mentioning.

According to Gilvarry, the lunar maria used to be true seas of water, and contained small marine creatures. The rocks making up the maria floors are, therefore, sedimentary; and Gilvarry points out that their hue can be explained if we suppose that they once supported living organisms – since even a small quantity of organic carbon will produce a darkish rock. He goes on to suggest that as the seas dried up, the organisms tended to recede from the bases of the encircling mountains, resulting in a lighter border to the maria. A light border is indeed seen in most of the circular seas, such as the Mare Imbrium and the Mare Nectaris.

Gilvarry's theory does not seem to have met with much support, and on the whole it seems to be more ingenious than probable; we can only wait and see. We should not have to wait for too long. The space age has begun, and well before the end of the present century the coming of the first men from another planet will bring life at last to the barren, silent Moon.

Chapter 17

Into the Future

The Moon has assumed a new importance for all of us. It is no longer out of our reach, and so let us look around and see where lunar research is likely to lead us.

Everything depends, of course, upon whether or not we act in the manner of rational beings. A third world war would end not only all studies of the Moon, but would also end civilization on Earth – a fact which Governments admit while still pouring endless money and effort into the senseless 'arms race' which has menaced us all ever since the last shots of Hitler's war were fired. It is tragic that a rocket which can launch a space-probe can also carry an atomic bomb, because it means that science and politics are hopelessly intermixed. It is true, of course, that rockets might not yet have reached their present state had not the Germans developed them for world conquest, but even if there had been no war the rockets would have been produced peacefully sooner or later.

At present there is only limited co-operation between East and West. The remedy here is in our own hands, and nobody will deny that a joint Russian, American and British space programme would be of the utmost value to all mankind. In a few centuries' time, humanity will – we hope – have grown up sufficiently not to care whether the first man to reach the Moon carried a hammer and sickle, the Stars and Stripes, or the Union Jack. Meanwhile, it seems that any idea of using the Moon as a base for military operations is as childish as it is perverted. If we really want to destroy ourselves, we can do so quite competently by using nuclear bombs carried in ground-to-ground missiles.

There have, however, been suggestions of sending nuclear warheads to the Moon for a quite different purpose. A tremendous explosion there would certainly provide useful information, particularly with regard to the depth of the surface layer, but it would be a great mistake. At present the Moon is uncontaminated, and we do not really know what the surface is like; once radiations are introduced artificially, the work of future scientists will be badly hampered. Biological contamination must also be watched. It seems unlikely that any Earth-type organism, even of microscopic size, could survive on the Moon's surface, but a micro-organism which landed and was then buried in débris, so being shielded from solar radiation, might conceivably be able to do so, and under certain conditions it might even multiply. We need have no fear of upsetting the Moon-men, but we want to study the Moon in its 'pure' state, which is why all lunar probes designed for landing are carefully sterilized.

One interesting piece of work will certainly be carried out. The Moon is under constant meteoric bombardment, and once a meteorite has landed it will remain utterly undisturbed. This is not the case on Earth, where we have to reckon with all sorts of factors as well as the weather. Recently, it has been suggested that the famous Orgueil Meteorite, which fell in France not far short of a century ago, contains traces of organic matter, in which case it might represent a fragment of an old life-bearing planet which met with some disaster in the remote past (though personally I have the gravest doubts). Once we can study meteorites which have lain on the Moon for thousands or even millions of years, we will be able to decide whether any of them do in fact contain such traces. This in turn will give us invaluable clues as to the history of the Solar System.

We may not even have to wait for the first manned flight, since it is quite on the cards that samples of the lunar crust will be obtained before then. Plans are already afoot for landing a vehicle gently on the Moon, so providing us with a true lunar transmitting station; Ranger III, launched in 1962, was the first attempt, and even though it failed it was by no means discouraging. If samples of the crust are drawn inside the vehicle, analyzed spectroscopically, and the results sent back to the Earth by television, much will be learned. The programme will be difficult, but not nearly so difficult as landing a rocket on the Moon would have seemed twenty years ago.

There will be many other tasks for our automatic lunar station. Because the Moon has no appreciable atmosphere, it is not shielded from the radiations from the Sun and stars, whereas on Earth our ionosphere acts as an effective blanket. The whole of the electromagnetic spectrum, from the far ultra-violet to the extreme infra-red, will be available, together with the puzzling, high-speed particles known as cosmic rays. Medical men in particular are very anxious to learn all they can about radiation, and the lunar station will be a real boon to them.

Another plan is to land a seismograph or earthquake-recorder on the Moon, and then create a mild shock some distance away. The resulting earthquake (or moonquake!) waves will provide information about the Moon's material, just as natural shocks do on Earth. This also was part of the Ranger project, together with the measurements of lunar temperatures, recording of meteorite hits, and detection of any natural radioactivity on the Moon. The next attempts will not be long delayed, and may have taken place before these words appear in print. More difficult still will be to land a vehicle on the Moon, obtain samples of the crust, and bring the vehicle back to Earth; but this too will be done in time.

It is hardly necessary to add that new vehicles of the Lunik III type will continue exploring the hidden side of the Moon, and will fill in the area not already covered by the photographs. Lunar satellite vehicles have also been suggested, notably by the Soviet astronomer Nikolai Vavarov, and seem to be perfectly practicable. One of their rôles would be to give us an improved value for the Moon's mass, which could be worked out by studies of how the lunar satellites moved.

Automatic stations have many uses, but there are some ways in which no machine can take the place of a man – and as a site for a full-scale scientific laboratory the Moon would be eminently suit-able. There would be limitless 'hard vacuum', and a complete absence of any shielding atmosphere, which would please both the physicists and the astronomers. On the Moon, even a modest telescope would be just as effective as the 200-inch Hale reflector can ever be at its site on Palomar Mountain.

What we are aiming at, then, is a proper Lunar Base, consisting of a research laboratory and – possibly – an advance station for journeys to Mars and Venus. But though it is easy enough to talk about a Lunar Base, it is quite another thing to build one, and tremendous problems lie in the way, some of which cannot be solved until unmanned vehicles have told us more about what the Moon's surface is like.

It is too early to say much about the form of the Base. The popular idea of a plastic hemispherical dome, kept inflated by the pressure inside it and equipped with airlocks for entry and exit, may or may not prove to be practicable; it may be necessary to 'go underground', either by using a natural cave or by making an artificial one. We do not yet know whether we are likely to find materials which will be of any help in construction, and neither do we know whether it will be possible to extract water from the lunar rocks, but clearly it will be essential to make the Moon help us as much as we can. Ferrying supplies from Earth will be most inconvenient, to put it mildly, though it will have to be done. Remember, too, that radiations from space will affect materials as well as human beings. Anyone who doubts this has only to look at a piece of indiarubber which has been exposed to the full force of an ultra-violet lamp. Materials for a surface Base will have to be very carefully chosen.

The idea of making Earth-type plants grow on the open surface of the Moon is pure science fiction, and the only answer, for a permanent Base, is to have a 'closed system', in which an atmosphere is maintained and in which plants can flourish. On Earth, plants absorb carbon dioxide and give off oxygen, and they could do the same in a Lunar Base if they could be persuaded to co-operate. The tiny seaweed-plants or algæ are particularly good at making oxygen, and algæ such as chlorella are theoretically edible, though even the most intrepid astronaut is likely to wince at the thought of living on green slime.

It has been said that if it is necessary to breed animals for food the best choice is the slug, all of which can be eaten – since it has no hair or bone. Slug jam is actually made in some parts of our world, but many people will join me in expressing preference for the algæ.

Hydroponic farming, in which the plants are suspended in nets and fed by liquid nutrients circulated below them, may provide a good answer to many of the food problems, but it would be wishful thinking to suppose that a lunar diet will be tasty. How long an average man could endure it remains to be seen, particularly since he will also have many other difficulties to face.

The harsh light will be a severe strain on human eyes, and space-suits will naturally have to be worn by those who venture outside the rockets or pressurized Bases. Problems of transport will also have to be considered. Wheeled vehicles will be limited (caterpillar treads may be better), and no ordinary flying-machines can function, because of the lack of atmosphere. The rocket is not a good answer so far as short-range journeys are concerned, since nothing will make it efficient at low speeds and over a limited range. Incidentally. Hermann Oberth, the Roumanian mathematician who wrote one of the earliest books dealing with space research in a properly scientific way, has designed a 'moon car' which can hop over clefts. Despite the low lunar gravity, it will be a distinctly hair-raising experience to attempt a leap over, say, the Herodotus Valley!

There is also the question of communication. From the visible hemisphere it will be easy to keep in touch with the Earth, since we can use wavelengths to which the terrestrial atmosphere is no barrier; but oddly enough it will be impossible to use wireless on the Moon itself, except over a very short range. Ordinary radios will be limited to the distance of the horizon, and even a 100-foot mast would not increase the range to more than a dozen miles or so. Radio waves travel in straight lines; on Earth, the layers in the ionosphere reflect them back to the ground and make it possible to communicate over long distances, but there is not likely to be a suitable ionosphere round the Moon, and so the transmissions will simply go off into space. A lunar operator wishing to call up a colleague beyond the horizon will have to route his message by way of the Earth, so that his signal will cover half a million miles. Even this will be impossible on the far side of the Moon, from which the Earth can never be seen, so that an operator there will be hopelessly out of touch.

In 1962 I suggested that it might be possible to create an 'artificial reflecting layer' round the Moon in the form of a belt of small copper needles. An experiment on these lines, involving the creation of a needle belt round the Earth, has actually been tried by United States workers, though it might well interfere with radio-astronomy studies, and scientists all over the world were vastly relieved when it failed. The idea was later supported, with regard to the Moon, by Z. Kopal and others, but whether it will prove wise or practicable remains to be seen. On the whole, a chain of lunar communications-satellites of the Telstar type may be a better answer.

Speculation could be carried on endlessly, but at any rate it is clear that the Lunar Base will be of the utmost use to doctors, astronomers, physicists, chemists and indeed to all scientists. It will be set up one day; just when construction will begin must depend, unfortunately, upon politics rather than upon science.

Meanwhile, it is very probable that the 'first man on the Moon' has already been born. Indeed, he may have completed his school career by now. Developments in space-science have become so rapid that it is dangerous to make hard-and-fast predictions, and I do not propose to attempt anything of the kind. Instead, it may be fitting to end with an imaginary trip to the Moon; if we can go there, even in imagination, what will we see?

Suppose we land at night-time, perhaps in the region of Aristarchus. Probably the first thing to be noticed will be the strange quality of the darkness. There is no air to diffuse any traces of light; we have to depend entirely upon the Earth, which is truly a glorious object, and the stars. If we have torches with us, we can use them – but there will be no beams of light, since there is no air to light up.

Let us take a more careful look at the stars. Probably the most striking difference about them will be the lack of twinkling; twinkling is another atmospheric effect, and does not occur on the Moon, so that the stars appear as hard, steely points of light. Moreover, there seem to be a great many of them. We are no longer looking through an extensive blanket of air, and our view of the sky is unrestricted.

The next unfamiliar thing is that the stars seem to move very slowly. The Earth turns on its axis once in twenty-four hours, so that a star on the celestial equator takes only twelve hours to shift across the sky from horizon to horizon, but on the slower-spinning Moon the corresponding period is about a fortnight. We could see this even more clearly by watching the progress of sunrise. There is no friendly dawn; the light of the Sun is seen only when the first part of the disk comes into view, and it takes more than an hour for the complete Sun to rise above the skyline.

Our Pole Star, too, is not the pole star of the Moon. The lunar celestial pole shifts more quickly than ours, and describes a small circle in the sky every eighteen years; the nearest bright star to the average north polar point is Zeta Draconis, of the third magnitude. If we are standing on the Moon in the Aristarchus region, the pole will be about twenty degrees above the horizon.

We are of course wearing vacuum-suits; otherwise we could not survive for a moment, partly because of the lack of air and partly because of the intensely low temperature. But though the Moon's rocks are cold, they are not damp, as with rocks in familiar caves such as Cheddar, Wookey Hole or the Grotto of Han. Dampness means water, and there is no liquid water anywhere on the Moon.

If we want to see the Earth at its best, a suitable observing site will be the Sinus Medii or Central Bay, at the time of lunar midnight. It is then new moon on the Earth, and consequently full earth on the Moon; our world is a magnificent orb, shining down from overhead with startling brilliance. Its light is far superior to that of full moonlight at home, since not only is the Earth much larger than the Moon, but it is also a much better reflector of sunlight. Remember that the albedo of the lunar rocks is, on an average, less than ten per cent.

One of the craters on the Sinus Medii is Bruce, six miles across and with walls rising to perhaps 1,000 feet above the floor. If we stand in the middle of it we will find it hard to realize that we are in a crater at all; it is more like a shallow dish, with ramparts sloping very gently up to their crests. There is no difficulty in climbing them, particularly since we have only one-sixth of our Earth weight, but even when this has been done we find that we are not far above the outer level of the Central Bay. Here and there are mounds, and everywhere we see tiny craterlets and pits, while in the distance mountain-tops gleam in the earthlight.

It will take a week for full earth to wane to half earth, and yet another week before the Sun rises over the Sinus Medii, so let us move across to the vast crater Pythagoras, 350 miles from the North Pole. If we arrive just after the Sun has appeared over the horizon, so that Pythagoras' inner east wall is fully lit, we will be able to see the central elevation – a massive mountain rising to 5,000 feet above the floor, though here too the slopes are gentle and present no mountaineering difficulties apart from the loose, crumbly nature of the surface in places. We find that the top does not rise to a sharp crest, but is broad and without any main summit; near its centre is a hill-top crater, with a rim rising only slightly above the level of the surrounding rocks, and with a saucer-like interior. It is not the highest point of the mountain mass, as there is a peak to the east of it, but as it is a full mile in diameter it is quite conspicuous, and it will take us some time to walk across it.

We cross the top of the low rim, and walk down into the crater itself. There is no need to scramble, though now and then we have to jump over tangled rocks, and when we are right inside it is clear that we are standing in a circular depression, even though the walls are low.

We will have a better view if we scale the summit on the far side of the craterlet, and this we can easily do. We are now at the highest point of the mountain, and we can look right down into Pythagoras, but at first sight we are rather puzzled.

Pythagoras is not far short of 100 miles in diameter, with walls 17,000 feet above the floor, but there seems nothing cavernous or precipitous about it. The central heights slope gently down to the floor, with broken rocks and débris; two other mountain-masses, almost as high as the one we are on, can be seen to the south-west, catching the rays of the rising sun; but the main peaks of the eastern wall, lofty though they may be, appear very inconspicuous and low over the horizon. We do not seem to be inside a walled plain at all.

The explanation is quite simple, as we noted earlier. The Moon's small size means that its surface curves more sharply than that of the Earth, and the horizon is much nearer. If we could stand on a perfectly level plain, the horizon at eye-level would be less than two miles away.

From Pythagoras, the Earth is low in the sky; it, the Sun and the stars could be seen at the same time if we cared to shield our eyes from the glare of the lunar rocks. The Sun, too, is unfamiliar; unless we wear protective filters its rays will damage our eyes, and even without optical aid we can see the solar 'atmosphere', visible to the naked eye from Earth only at the time of a total eclipse.

If we venture on to the far side of the Moon – to the Soviet Mountains, perhaps, or the crater-ring of Lomonosov – we will lose the Earth; we will also lose our direct lines of communication, since the obvious way to maintain radio contact beyond the horizon is to use the Earth as a relay-point. But for our final journey in imagination let us come back to more familiar regions, and suppose that we are standing inside Ptolemæus at lunar midday.

Ptolemæus is a tremendous crater, fully the equal of Pythagoras, and with a darker floor. At noon the Sun is almost overhead, and the temperature is high, since the rocks are heated to well over 200 degrees F. To travellers in space-suits the problem is not how to keep warm, but how to keep cool. The sunlight is harsh and glaring, and yet as soon as we pass into the shadow of a peak we step into blackness; the Moon is a world of contrasts, and there are no soft half-tones.

Some way off we can see a low rim which proves to belong to a crater five miles in diameter, with a bowl-shaped interior and gently sloping walls, together with mounds and ridges, and saucer-like depressions so shallow that it is difficult for us to tell whether we are in one or not. It comes as a surprise to learn that we are standing right in the amphitheatre of Ptolemæus. The main walls, which seem so prominent when viewed from Earth, cannot be seen at all – the horizon is too close; and even if we walk across the floor until we reach the rampart, we will be able to pass through to the outer surface without doing any mountaineering. Broad valleys pass through the broken wall, and everywhere there is débris. Ptolemæus is neither a ruin, as Janssen is, nor a ghost-crater such as Stadius; but it has had a troubled and disturbed history since it first came into being, many millions of years before the first land-creatures made their appearance on the bleak continents of Earth.

It is tempting to continue our journey in imagination, but men should reach the Moon before many years are past, and truth is always at least a hundred times as exciting as speculation. Meanwhile, I hope that I have managed to convey some impression of what the lunar world is like – strange, forbidding and hostile, but also overwhelmingly fascinating. It holds out a challenge for us; and if we choose civilized progress rather than barbarous warfare, the challenge of the Moon will not be ignored.

Appendix I
Observing the Moon

It is often believed that useful astronomical work can be done only at a great observatory, and that in consequence the modestly equipped amateur is wasting his time. This view has even been expressed recently by some professional astronomers, but it is significant that professional astronomers of the first rank do not agree. So far as the Moon and planets are concerned, the amateur still has an important rôle to play. He must recognize his limitations, but there is much that he can do.

For lunar work, at least something can be done with a moderate aperture. Even a 3-inch refractor is not to be despised, though it cannot show fine detail. A 6-inch reflector or 4-inch refractor is better; and with a 6-inch refractor or an 8-inch reflector, a full programme can be carried out. This naturally assumes good optical quality, and also a really firm mount. Telescopes mounted on shaky stands are quite useless, since only low magnifications can be employed. In particular, the notorious pillar-and-claw stand often supplied with small refractors is about as steady as a blancmange, and the only solution is to re-mount the telescope upon a firm tripod or pillar.

Clock drive, which compensates for the rotation of the Earth and keeps the Moon (or whatever is being observed) in the field of view, is very convenient, but is not absolutely necessary unless photographic work is to be carried out. Manual slow motions are, however, needed for telescopes of fair size.

Town-dwellers are at a grave disadvantage compared with those who live in the country. Railway stations, smoking chimneys and street-lights are no help to astronomers, and this is why Greenwich Observatory has been shifted from its old site to the remote peacefulness of Herstmonceux in Sussex. Smoke and lights have to be tolerated if they cannot be avoided, but the fatal thing is to try to observe through a window. Apart from the difficulty of keeping the telescope rigid, the temperature change between the room and the outer air causes so much local atmospheric turbulence that the Moon generally looks as though it is shining through several layers of water. Sharpness of image is essential, but can never be obtained from indoors.

Neither is it much good trying to observe a low moon, as the light then reaching the observer is shining through a thick layer of unsteady atmosphere. Twilight, however, is no handicap on its own, and neither is slight mist harmful in the usual way, though even the thinnest layer of cloud is usually fatal. Often a very brilliant starlight night (such as occurs after heavy rain) will prove to be hopelessly unsteady, with the Moon's limb shimmering and rippling, and under such conditions there is nothing to be done except stop observing until matters improve.

Beginners often make the mistake of using too high a power. On a really good night, of course, high magnifications may be used to advantage, but it is hopeless to put in a powerful eyepiece unless the image obtained is really sharp. Whenever a low power will do equally well, it should be preferred. For a 3-inch refractor, a magnification of 100 is usually adequate; powers of over 150 or so are useful only to finish off drawings which are already more or less complete. On my 12½-inch reflector, 350 is a good working power on clear, steady nights, though higher magnifications can of course be used when necessary. Using very large telescopes, I have found that powers as low as 300 show much detail which has not yet found its way on to any maps, visual or photographic. Pure magnification, in fact, is by no means the most important factor. Steadiness and good definition are much more vital in the long run.

When making a sketch of a lunar formation, the general procedure should be more or less as follows. Select the formation to be drawn. Survey it, and decide just what area is to be covered. Then, using a fairly low power, sketch in the main outlines (unless they have been prepared before hand from a photograph, in which case allowance for libration must be made for a crater anywhere near the limb). Also indicate the shadows and coarser details. Then change to a higher power, and put in the fine details. If the night is really good, maximum possible magnification should be used to check each tiny feature, but details which are doubtful or suspected should be carefully distinguished; on the whole it is better to make a written note of doubtful objects rather than insert them on the actual drawing.

Some observers make their 'final' drawings actually at the telescope. Others such as myself, less artistically gifted, make their drawings and then transfer them at once into an observing book. It is most important to make the fair copy immediately, and then check it at the telescope, since the temptation to 'leave it till tomorrow' will almost certainly result in mistakes in interpretation. This may seem a lengthy procedure, and indeed it is, but one really good drawing is worth a hundred fairly good ones.

When the drawing is complete, add the following data: year, date, time (using the twenty-four hour clock, and never using Summer Time), telescope, magnification, name of observer, position of the terminator, and any other relevant information, such as seeing conditions. If any of this is missing, the drawing will lose most of its value.

Another common fault is that of using too small a scale, which involves drawing too large an area at once. Twenty miles to the inch is a convenient scale, and it is better to be over-generous than parsimonious. I remember that on one occasion I was sent a sketch of the complete Mare Imbrium, made with a 5-inch refractor, in which the Mare itself was about four inches across and Plato perhaps a centimetre. Even if the sketch had been accurate (which it was not) it would still have been useless.

Drawings are of two main types, line drawings and shaded sketches of various kinds. Despite the difference in appearance, an indifferent artist should probably keep to line drawings, which can be made just as accurate even if they are far less attractive to the eye.

There are many formations on the Moon, and to learn the names of even the main ones takes a certain amount of time; but even if no conscious effort is made to memorize them, it will be found that the chief features will be recognized quite easily. When I started serious lunar observing, using a 3-inch refractor, I adopted a definite system. In a large observing book, each named formation was allotted a separate page, and within two years one or more drawings of each formation had been secured. The drawings themselves were of no value at all, but by the time I had finished I did at least know my way about the Moon, and the trouble taken proved to be well worth while in the end. Naturally, a map is needed. I used Elger's; but there are others.

Aimless sketches of lunar features are of limited value, and the amateur who intends to do something useful should choose a definite observing porgramme. The best plan here is to work with the Lunar Section of the British Astronomical Association (see Appendix II). Efforts are being made to chart various special features, such as domes, ghost-craters, ridges and crater-chains, in order to investigate their forms and their distribution. Much can be done with a modest aperture, and collaborating with other workers is invaluable. My own personal programme includes studies of domes and ghost-craters; I have also been measuring crater-depths by estimating the interior shadows, and keeping a watchful eye upon any areas suspected of variability, such as Linné, Alphonsus, the Messier twins, the Picard area, and the floors of dark craters such as Grimaldi, Riccioli, Endymion and Atlas. I observe these on every possible occasion, since there is always the chance of picking up something new.

It is probably true to say that the main trend in lunar observation has altered during the past half-dozen years. Formerly, great attention was – justifiably – paid to the exact charting of specific features. This phase is now more or less complete, and the serious amateur has turned to studies of rather different type, such as the distribution of the domes and ghost-craters, height measurements, and determination of crater depths by the shadow method. However, detailed drawings of interesting features are still useful.

It is clear, then, that the range is very extensive. The Moon is full of surprises, and the owner of even a small telescope will find more than enough to occupy him, provided that he possesses the two essential qualities of a true amateur astronomer – enthusiasm and patience.

Lunar Literature and
Lunar Maps

So much has been written about the Moon that it would be difficult to give a complete list, and I do not propose to attempt it; all
I have done is to select some books and maps which are of obvious
value.

(1) *Material out of print, but still obtainable for reference in
astronomical libraries*

THE MOON, by E. Neison (London, 1876). This was the first of the
English classics, and contains a complete map based on Mädler's.

THE MOON, by T. G. Elger (London, 1895). A clear, concise description of the surface, together with an outline map. The map, luckily,
has been revised by Wilkins and is still obtainable.

THE MOON, by R. A. Proctor (Manchester, 1873). Deals mainly,
though not entirely, with the Moon's movements.

PHOTOGRAPHIC ATLAS OF THE MOON, by W. H. Pickering (Annals of
the Harvard College Observatory, 1904). This has the advantage
of showing each area of the surface under five different conditions
of illumination.

(2) *Modern works, still in print*

FEATURES OF THE MOON, LUNAR CATASTROPHIC HISTORY, and THE
SHRUNKEN MOON, by J. E. Spurr (Lancaster Press, Pennsylvania,
1944-1949). Devoted to Spurr's volcanic theory, and intended for
the serious student.

THE FACE OF THE MOON, by R. B. Baldwin (University of Chicago
Press, 1949). Concerned mainly with the bombardment theory of
crater formation, but also containing much additional information.

STRANGE WORLD OF THE MOON, by V. A. Firsoff (Hutchinson, 1959).
A general account, containing many original ideas based on observational as well as theoretical researches by the author.

OUR MOON, by H. P. Wilkins (Muller, 1959). A popular introduction.

THE MOON, by H. P. Wilkins and Patrick Moore (Faber & Faber, 1960). A detailed description of the surface, with a reduced edition of Wilkins' map.

SURFACE OF THE MOON, by V. A. Firsoff (Hutchinson, 1961). An important book dealing mainly with the origin of the surface features.

STRUCTURE OF THE MOON'S SURFACE, by G. Fielder (Pergamon Press, 1961). A technical work by a professional astronomer; Dr. Fielder is I.C.I. Research Fellow at the University of London Observatory, and has specialized in selenography. This is probably the most important of the technical books about the Moon, and covers all aspects. It also contains lengthy lists of references. I had originally meant to give reference-lists here, but this seems to be unnecessary, since Fielder's book will provide the serious researcher with all the references needed.

THE MOON – A RUSSIAN VIEW. Edited by A. V. Markov (University of Chicago Press, 1962.) A collection of articles by distinguished Soviet lunar specialists; of great value, but too technical for the beginner.

PHYSICS AND ASTRONOMY OF THE MOON. Edited by Z. Kopal (Academic Press, 1962). An important collection of technical lunar papers; contributors include Dollfus, Urey, Sinton and Kozirev.

Among useful little books for younger readers may be mentioned TRUE BOOK ABOUT THE MOON, by H. P. Wilkins (Muller, 1960); THE MOON – OUR NEAREST CELESTIAL NEIGHBOUR, by Z. Kopal (Chapman & Hall, 1960) and THE MOON – EARTH'S NATURAL SATELLITE, by Franklyn M. Bramley (Faber & Faber, 1962).

(3) *Maps*

Various maps are obtainable. An excellent outline chart is Elger's, revised in 1959 by Wilkins (Geo. Philip & Son). Wilkins' own map is much more detailed, and is published separately by Faber & Faber under the title of MOON MAPS (1961). It must, however be added that it is probably too detailed to be useful to the beginner. The I.A.U. Map of 1935 is out of print, but had little to recommend it in any case.

There have been two recent photographic atlases. One has been edited by G. P. Kuiper (Yerkes Observatory publication, 1960) and is very ambitious. The second is No. 95 of the Contributions from the Institute of Astrophysics and Kwasan Observatory, University of Kyoto. It has been prepared by S. Miyamoto and M. Matsui from photographs taken with the Kwasan refractor, and is entirely admirable; there are eighty-five plates, and the whole atlas is of convenient reference size, so that the photographs are not ruined by over-enlargement.

The Russian ATLAS OF THE OTHER SIDE OF THE MOON has been published in English by Pergamon Press (1961).

(4) *Societies and Periodicals.*

In Britain, the British Astronomical Association (secretarial address 303 Bath Road, Hounslow West, Middlesex) has an energetic Lunar Section which issues papers and reports in the Association's Journal, as well as a quarterly periodical, THE MOON, formerly edited by F. H. Thornton and now by W. L. Rae. The American counterpart is the Association of Lunar and Planetary Observers, directed by W. H. Haas (secretarial address Box 26, University Park, New Mexico, where the official publication is THE STROLLING ASTRONOMER. Here too there is a lively Lunar Section. There are other publications which contain lunar material, such as the PUBLICATIONS of the Astronomical Society of the Pacific, the monthly SKY AND TELESCOPE magazine (Cambridge 38, Mass., U.S.A.), and, in Britain, journals such as NEW SCIENTIST. Younger enthusiasts are recommended to join the Junior Astronomical Society (secretarial address 44 Cedar Way, Basingstoke, Hampshire).

Appendix III
The Moon: Numerical Data

Mean distance from Earth: 238,840 miles
Maximum distance from Earth: 252,700 miles
Minimum distance from Earth: 221,460 miles.
Sidereal period: 27d·32166=27d. 7h. 43m. 11·5s.
Synodic period: 29d·53=29d. 12h. 44m. 2·8s.
Orbital eccentricity: 0·0549
Inclination of orbit to ecliptic: 5° 09′
Mass: 1/81·3 Earth=0·0123 Earth=3·7 × 10^{-8} Sun
Volume: 0·0203 Earth
Escape velocity: 1·5 miles per second
Diameter: 2,160 miles=3,476 Km.
Density: 3·3 water=0·60 Earth
Orbital velocity (mean): 2,287 m.p.h.=0·63 mi/sec.=3,350 ft/sec
Inclination of equatorial plane to ecliptic: 1° 32′
Magnitude of full moon, at mean distance: − 12·5
Apparent diameter: max. 33′31″, mean 31′5″, min. 29′22′

Appendix IV

Forthcoming Lunar Eclipses

The following list of eclipses may be found useful. The first four columns need no explanation. The fifth column, headed 'Mag.', is the magnitude of the eclipse, 1·0 or greater being total, anything less than 1·0 partial; for instance, 0·5 means that the Earth's shadow reaches half-way across the Moon at mid-eclipse. Column 6 gaves the geographical latitude and longitude where the Moon is overhead at mid-eclipse. Columns 7 and 8 indicate whether the eclipse can be seen from England or from the United States. 'Partly' may mean that the whole eclipse may be visible, but very low in the sky, or that the Moon rises or sets while the eclipse is in progress.

Yr. Mth. Day	Time, GMT, mid-eclipse h. m.		Mag.	Moon overhead: Long. Lat.	Visible in England	U.S.A.
1963 July 6	22	0	0·7	31 E, 22 S	Yes	No
„ Dec. 30	11	7	1·4	166 W, 23 N	No	Yes
1964 June 25	1	7	1·6	16 W, 23 S	Yes	Partly
„ Dec. 19	2	35	1·2	40 W, 23 N	Yes	Partly
1965 June 14	1	51	0·2	28 W, 23 S	Yes	Partly
1967 Apr. 24	12	7	1·3	178 E, 13 S	No	Partly
„ Oct. 18	10	16	1·1	158 W, 10 N	No	Partly
1968 Apr. 13	4	49	1·1	72 W, 8 S	Partly	Yes
„ Oct. 6	11	41	1·2	178 W, 5 N	No	Partly
1970 Feb. 21	8	31	0·05	124 W, 11 N	No	Yes
„ Aug. 17	3	25	0·4	50 W, 14 S	Partly	Yes
1971 Feb. 10	7	42	1·3	112 W, 14 N	Partly	Yes
„ Aug. 6	19	44	1·7	65 E, 17 S	Partly	Yes
1972 Jan. 30	10	53	1·1	160 W, 18 N	No	Yes
„ July 26	7	18	0·6	108 W, 20 S	No	Yes
1973 Dec. 10	1	48	0·1	29 W, 23 N	Yes	Yes
1974 June 4	22	14	0·8	26 E, 22 S	Yes	No
„ Nov. 29	15	16	1·3	128 E, 21 N	No	No
1975 May 25	5	46	1·5	87 W, 21 S	No	Yes
„ Nov. 18	22	24	1·1	20 E, 19 N	Yes	Partly
1976 May 13	19	50	0·1	62 E, 18 S	Partly	No
1977 Apr. 4	4	21	0·2	64 W, 6 S	Partly	Yes
1978 Mar. 24	16	25	1·5	115 E, 2 S	No	No
„ Sept. 16	19	3	1·3	73 E, 3 S	Partly	No
1979 Mar. 13	21	10	0·9	45 E, 3 N	Yes	No
„ Sept. 6	10	54	1·1	164 W, 7 S	No	Partly
1981 July 17	4	48	0·6	71 W, 21 S	Partly	Yes
1982 Jan. 9	19	56	1·4	63 E, 22 N	Yes	No
„ July 6	7	30	1·7	112 W, 23 S	No	Yes
„ Dec. 30	11	26	1·2	171 W, 23 N	No	Yes
1983 June 25	8	25	0·3	126 W, 23 S	No	Yes
1985 May 4	19	57	1·2	60 E, 16 S	Partly	No
„ Oct. 28	17	43	1·1	90 E, 13 N	Partly	No
1986 Apr. 24	12	44	1·2	168 E, 13 S	No	Partly
„ Oct. 17	19	19	1·3	67 E, 10 N	Yes	No
1987 Oct. 7	3	59	0·01	63 W, 5 N	Yes	Yes

Appendix V

Description of the Surface and Map

In my earlier *Guide to the Moon* I included a folded map of the Moon, together with a short description of the main surface features. Quite a number of people wrote to me saying that they would prefer a more detailed map, and accordingly I have prepared one, but several points should be made in connection with it.

First and most important of all, this does not set out to be a precision chart of the Moon. It is intended merely to act as a guide for those who are trying to find their way about, and this aspect has also influenced me in selecting the features to be named on it; to give all the names in, say Wilkins' large map would make these pages hopelessly crowded. I hope, however, that when the observer has identified all the features which I have given, he will find things easier when he changes to a really good and accurate map.

There are sixteen sections: one to four include the first quadrant, five to eight the second, nine to twelve the third, and thirteen to sixteen the fourth. There are bound to be some awkward divisions; for instance Archimedes, in the great Mare Imbrium group, is in Section 5 while its companion Aristillus and Autolycus are in Section 4 – it is a pity that the boundary happened to come just there! However, I have linked each separate map with the sections which adjoin it. The descriptions, too, are very short, and have had to be condensed almost to the point of dehydration, but again will act as a general guide. The depth and diameter measures are based on recent work; not all authorities agree, but the values given here are as accurate as I can make them, and it does not really matter much whether the diameter of – say – Ptolemæus is 92 miles or 93.

The map is drawn to about mean libration, so that it is impossible to draw in formations such as Thornton and Arthur, in the second quadrant, which lie partly or wholly on the far hemisphere, and may be seen only under favourable conditions of libration. Wilkins' map, however, gives special limb charts, and the observer who wants to make serious, detailed observations of difficult regions, will in any case need a map larger than that given in the following pages.

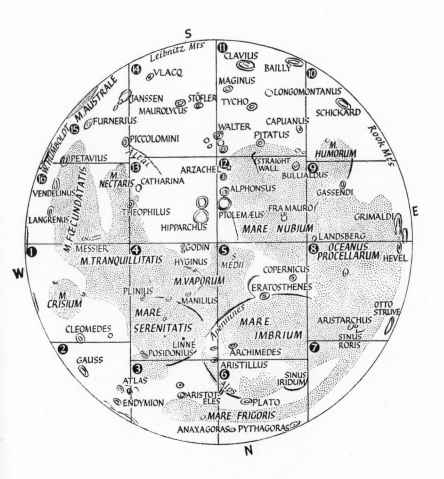

FIRST (NORTH-WEST) QUADRANT

This quadrant is dominated by sea-areas, and includes all the Mare Crisium and Mare Serenitatis, as well as the Mare Humboldtianum, Lacus Somniorum, part of the Mare Frigoris, and practically all of the Mare Tranquillitatis, Mare Vaporum and Mare Smythii. The western extensions of the Mare Imbrium – the Palus Nebularum and Palus Putredinis – stretch into Sections 3 and 4. Mountain ranges include the Hæmus and Caucasus, as well as part of the Alps, and the northern extension of the Apennines.

Of craters and associated formations, special note should be made of the dark-floored Julius Cæsar and Boscovich, the brilliant Proclus, Manilius and Menelaus, and the large enclosure of Cleomedes, Aristoteles and Eudoxus form a noble pair; here too are Autolycus and Aristillus, though the third member of the trio, Archimedes, lies in the second quadrant (Section 5). The Mare Vaporum is rich in clefts; as well as Hyginus and Ariadæus, there is the complex system associated with Triesnecker. Last, but certainly not least, the famous (or notorious!) Linné lies in Section 4, on the grey plain of the Mare Serenitatis.

Section

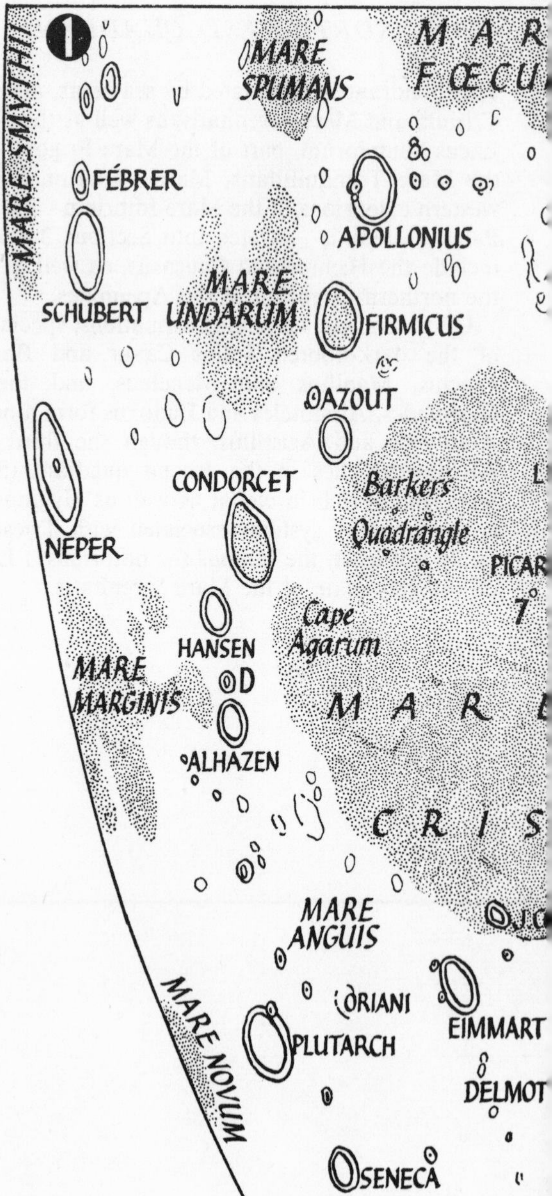
1
MARE SMYTHII
MARE SPUMANS
M A R
F ŒCU
FÉBRER
APOLLONIUS
SCHUBERT
MARE UNDARUM
FIRMICUS
AZOUT
CONDORCET
Barker's Quadrangle
NEPER
PICAR
7
Cape Agarum
HANSEN
D
MARE MARGINIS
M A R
ALHAZEN
C R I S
MARE ANGUIS
ORIANI
EIMMART
PLUTARCH
DELMOT
MARE NOVUM
SENECA

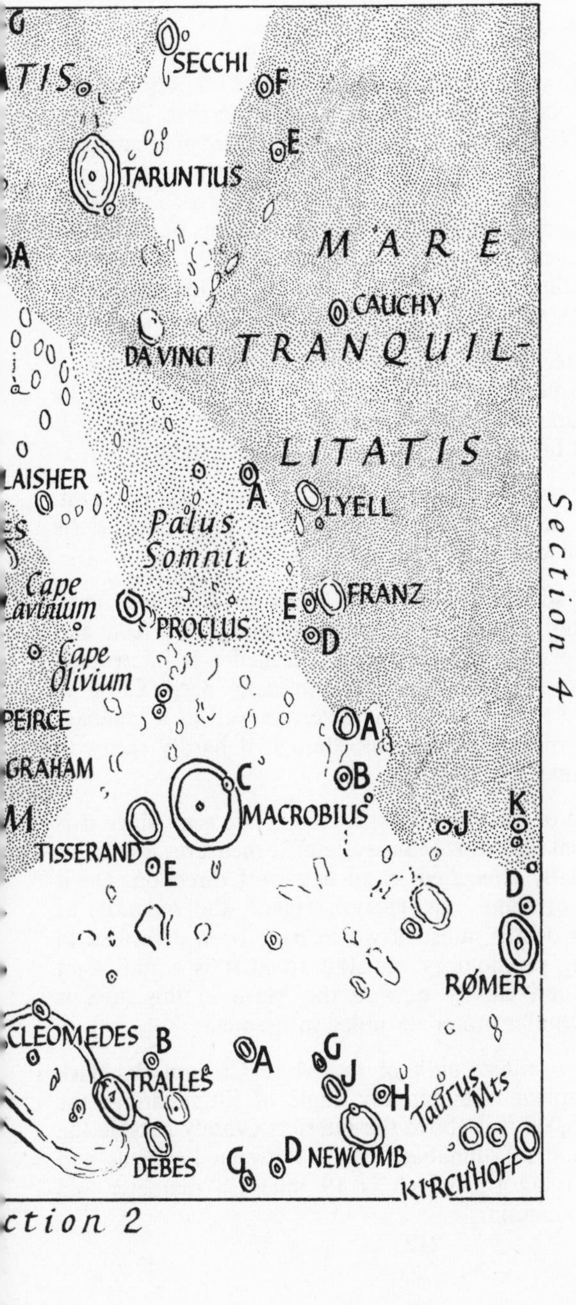

G

ATIS

SECCHI

◎F

TARUNTIUS

◎E

DA

M A R E

◎ CAUCHY

DA VINCI T R A N Q U I L -

L I T A T I S

LAISHER

ES

Palus
Somnii

◎ A ◎ LYELL

Cape
Lavinium

PROCLUS

E ◎ ◎ FRANZ

◎D

Cape
Olivium

PEIRCE

◎ A

GRAHAM

◎ B

M

C

MACROBIUS

◎ J ◎ K

TISSERAND ◎ E

◎ D

RØMER

CLEOMEDES B

◎ A ◎ G

◎ J

TRALLES

◎ H

Taurus
Mts

DEBES G D NEWCOMB

KIRCHHOFF

SECTION 1

ALHAZEN. This is the Alhazen of Beer and Mädler – not Schröter's, which cannot now be identified. It is a small crater, 20 miles in diameter, on the border of the Mare Crisium. Roughly south of it lies a similar but rather larger crater, HANSEN. Right on the limb, west of Alhazen and Hansen, lies the limb-sea known as the MARE MARGINIS, not fully shown on the chart because – as has been pointed out – the chart has been drawn to mean libration. The Mare Marginis extends on to the far side of the Moon, and is identifiable on the Lunik III photographs.

APOLLONIUS. A crater 30 miles in diameter, with walls rising to 5,000 feet above the floor; two craters lie on the western crest of its wall. It lies in the uplands south of Mare Crisium, and south of it is the patchy area of lunabase known as the MARE SPUMANS.

CAUCHY. An 8-mile crater on the Mare Tranquillitatis; it is bright, and is conspicuous at full moon. There are two fairly long clefts near by, one to either side of Cauchy.

CLEOMEDES. A magnificent enclosure 78 miles in diameter, north of the Mare Crisium. The walls average at least 9,000 feet, and there are peaks of even greater altitude. Cleomedes is interrupted by a 28-mile crater, TRALLES, which is extremely deep. Close to Cleomedes is EIMMART, 26 miles in diameter, as well as a lunabase patch which is known as MARE ANGUIS, though it hardly seems to merit a separate name.

CRISIUM, MARE. One of the most conspicuous of the seas, since it is entirely separate from the main Mare-system. It measures 280 miles by 350, and is actually elongated in an east-west direction. On it are three craterlets of some size (PICARD, PEIRCE and GRAHAM) as well as many minor details, most of which have been described in the text. The jutting promontory of CAPE AGARUM is a fine sight when well placed, and closely outside the Mare in this area is CONDORCET, a fine regular crater 45 miles in diameter.

FIRMICUS. A 35-mile crater south of the Mare Crisium. Its dark floor makes it conspicuous under any angle of illumination; the walls reach almost 5,000 feet above the interior. Closely outside the north-east wall is a small 'lunabase lake'. Between Firmicus and the Mare Crisium is AZOUT, which is 19 miles in diameter and has a low central mountain.

MACROBIUS. A fine walled plain, 42 miles in diameter and with walls reaching 13,000 feet. There is a compound central mountain mass of moderate height. Between Macrobius and the Mare Crisium is a smaller crater, TISSERAND.

MARGINIS, MARE. One of the limb-seas; it has been described with Alhazen.

NEPER. A deep crater, 70 miles in diameter, which would be a noble object if it lay further from the limb. It lies between the Mare Marginis and the Mare Smythii, and is probably the same type of formation.

NEWCOMB. A crater 32 miles in diameter, and of considerable depth, east of Cleomedes. West of Newcomb is a smaller but well-formed crater, KIRCHHOFF.

PICARD. The largest crater on the Mare Crisium; it is 21 miles in diameter, with walls rising to 8,000 feet. There is a central hill. The interesting area to the west of Picard has been described in the text. To the east, on the border of the Mare, lie the two capes LAVINIUM and OLIVIUM, together with rather imperfect craters such as LICK and YERKES.

PEIRCE. The second largest crater on the Mare Crisium; it is 12 miles in diameter, and the walls attain about 7,000 feet. North of it is the smaller but probably rather deeper crater GRAHAM.

PLUTARCH. A 40-mile crater with a central mountain. On the limb, to the north-west, is the small dark plain known as the MARE NOVUM. Near Plutarch lies a rather smaller crater, SENECA, while between Plutarch and Eimmart is the very ill-defined enclosure of ORIANI.

PROCLUS. A brilliant crater east of the Mare Crisium, 18 miles in diameter and 8,000 feet deep. Proclus is one of the brightest points on the Moon, and is the centre of a ray-system; there is a low central mountain. The rays cross the Mare Crisium, but not the Palus Somnii, which is bounded on either side by rays. In 1948 F. H. Thornton found bright and dusky bands inside Proclus, since confirmed by other observers including Wilkins, D. C. Brown and myself.

RØMER. A fine crater, 35 miles in diameter, with high terraced walls rising to over 11,000 feet. The floor contains a particularly large and massive central mountain, on the top of which is a summit pit. Well to the south, on the Mare Tranquillitatis, is the dark-floored, low-walled ring MARALDI (Section 4). From Rømer the so-called TAURUS MOUNTAINS extend north-west, towards Newcomb and Geminus, but must be regarded as a hilly upland rather than a mountain range.

SMYTHII, MARE. A small Mare, right on the limb and shown on the Lunik III photographs. It is not unlike the Mare Marginis. A good guide to it is the 46-mile crater SCHUBERT, which is not difficult to identify.

SOMNII, PALUS. Really an extension of the Mare Tranquillitatis, bounded on the north-east and south-west by rays from Proclus. The colour is peculiar; it has been described as brownish, greenish or yellowish, though to me these elusive tints are invisible. Barker considers that the hue is variable, but I regard this as unlikely. On the boundary of the Palus Somnii and the Mare Tranquillitatis are some low-walled craters, notably FRANZ and LYELL.

TARUNTIUS. An interesting crater, 38 miles in diameter, and with low narrow walls nowhere attaining more than 3,500 feet. There is a central mountain crowned by a pit, but the most notable feature is the presence of a complete inner ring on the floor, so that Taruntius is an excellent example of what Thornton has termed a 'concentric crater'. Well to the south-east lies SECCHI, an imperfect but quite conspicuous formation.

TRANQUILLITATIS, MARE. This is one of the major seas, and spreads from Section 1 into Section 4. It joins on to the Mare Serenitatis, Mare Vaporum, Mare Nectaris and Mare Fœcunditatis. The floor is decidedly lighter and patchier than that of the Mare Serenitatis, and its form is less perfect. Important craters on its floor include Cauchy (Section 1) and Maskelyne and Arago (Section 4).

UNDARUM, MARE. This is a lunabase area, but not a well-defined sea; it lies near the Mare Crisium, west of Firmicus and Apollonius. It is very dark near full moon, and can be found without difficulty.

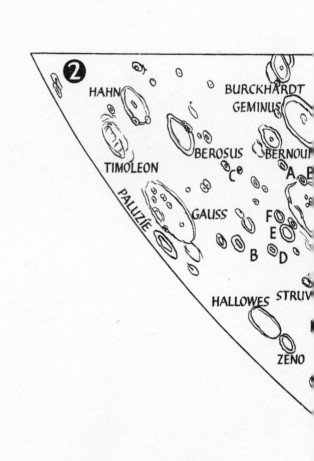

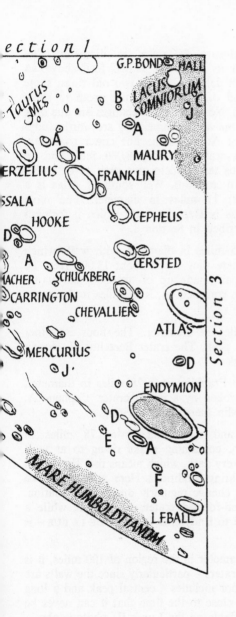

ATLAS. A magnificent enclosure 55 miles in diameter. The much-terraced walls rise to as much as 11,000 feet above an interior which contains much detail – one or two old rings, some delicate clefts, craterlets, and dark patches which seem to show changes during each lunation. No doubt these changes are due only to the altering illumination; but all the same, they are worth studying. Some way south-west of Atlas lies the fine crater FRANKLIN, 34 miles in diameter with walls reaching 8,000 feet, and in the Franklin area are various lesser enclosures such as CEPHEUS, ŒRSTED, CHEVALLIER and SHUCKBURGH. Well south of Atlas is a bright, deep crater, MAURY, 11 miles in diameter. The most important neighbour of Atlas is Hercules, with which it forms a noble pair; Hercules is described in Section 3.

BERNOUILLI. A fine crater 25 miles in diameter, with walls which are highest on the west, where they reach about 13,000 feet. To the west is another crater-pair made up of BEROSUS and HAHN. Berosus, the larger and more conspicuous, is 47 miles in diameter, with terraced walls.

BERZELIUS. A crater 24 miles in diameter. The floor is rather dark, and includes a central peak. The crater Berzelius H, closely west, also has a central peak.

CEPHEUS. The companion to Franklin; it is 28 miles in diameter, and its north-west wall is broken by a bright crater, Cepheus A. Between Cepheus and Franklin there is an old ring.

ENDYMION. An important and interesting crater 78 miles in diameter. Its walls are high, containing peaks rising to at least 15,000 feet, and the floor is very dark, which means that Endymion is easy to find under any lighting conditions. Here, as in Atlas, we have patches which seem to change regularly during the lunation. Close to Endymion is a well-formed crater, L. F. BALL, while a much larger enclosure, equal to Endymion in size – DE LA RUE – is shown in Section 3.

GAUSS. Since Gauss has a diameter in the region of 100 miles, it is one of the Moon's greatest craters – particularly since the walls are high and continuous. The floor includes a central peak and a long ridge. Unfortunately it is so close to the limb that it can never be properly studied. It is identifiable on the Lunik III photographs.

GEMINUS. The larger companion of Bernouilli. It is 55 miles in diameter, with broad, richly terraced walls attaining 16,000 feet in places. In the centre of the floor is a rounded hill with a pit on its summit. Nearby lies BURCKHARDT.

HUMBOLDTIANUM, MARE. A well-bordered sea, probably of the same sort as the Mare Crisium, but placed so near the limb that it is difficult to examine; the Lunik III photographs show it. The floor contains a number of craters and craterlets, most of which were discovered in the 1950s by K. W. Abineri.

MERCURIUS. A distinct crater 33 miles in diameter, with a low central peak. To the west lie HALLOWES. which is about the same size, and has been disturbed by a rather smaller crater. ZENO. Between Zeno and the limb is POLIT, a crater difficult to see from Earth, but identifiable in the Lunik III pictures.

MESSALA. An oblong enclosure nearly 80 miles in diameter, with walls which are broken and generally rather low. Near it is HOOKE, only 27 miles across, but deeper and more distinct. Between Messala and Zeno are SCHUMACHER, smooth-floored and 25 miles across, and STRUVE, a small ring with a central peak, easy to recognize because it lies upon a dark patch.

TAURUS MOUNTAINS. This upland area has been described in Section 1; it extends from the Berzelius area in the general direction of Rømer.

MARE SE

POSIDONIUS B
J
3 P
G
DANIELL

K

L A C U S
S O M N I O R U M

GROVE

O KELL
Ç Ç

B
MASON

PLANA
D
C
B

Lacus
Mortis

BÜRG

K° J

A
HERCULES

A

WILLIAMS

BAILY

F
° H
B
A

M A R E

F R I G O R I S

DE LA RUE

A
GÄRTNER

D
F

B

J

A
A

G
DEMOCRITUS
ARNOL

STRABO
THALES

G

ABINERI

T
N B

SCHWABE

A

CUSANUS

PETERMANN

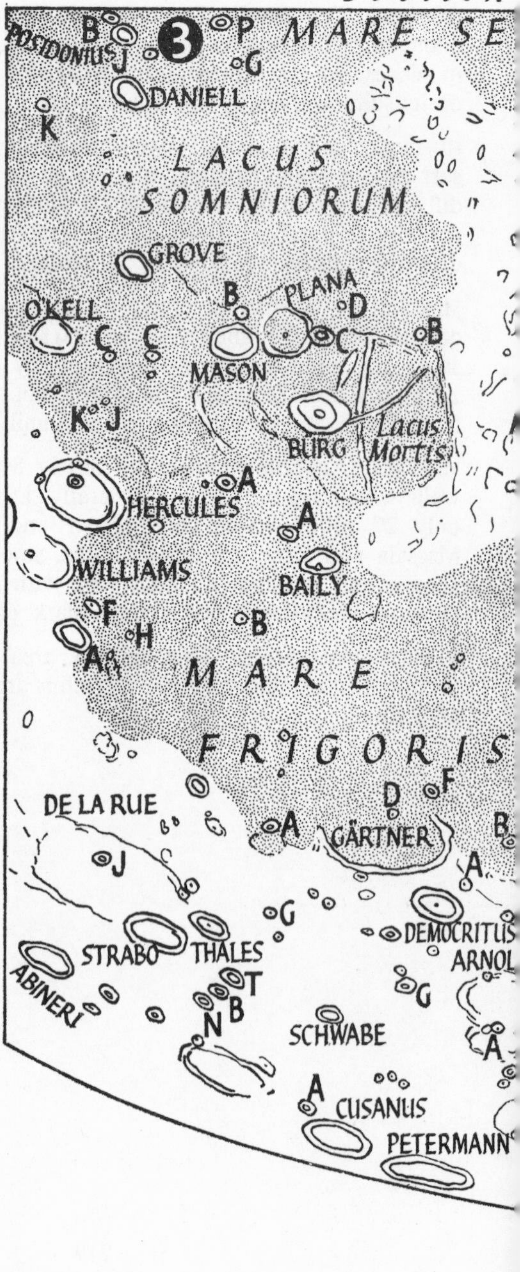

NITATIS   G   Caucasus Mts.   Palus ( )
Nebularum
THEÆTETUS
A   CALLIPUS   CASSINI
A B   Cape
F   Agassiz
ANDER   C   A L P S
D   E
LAMECH
EUDOXUS
D   TROUVELOT
EGEDE   Alpine Valley
E
ARISTOTELES   A   G
HELL
M A R E
R I G O R I S   PROTAGORAS
E   C   ARCHYTAS
SHEEPSHANKS
F   TIMÆUS
C.MAYER
KANE   B   W.C.
MOIGNO   BOND
NEISON
BARROW   A
TERS   B   GOLD-
E   B   METON   SCHMIDT
E   SCORESBY
LAUD   H   CHALLIS
D   EUCTEMON   GIOJA
NANSEN   MAIN

Section 6

ALPS. A bright mountain-range forming part of the rampart of the Mare Imbrium, from Plato toward Cassini. Part of it is shown here, and part in Section 6. The peaks are moderately high; MONT BLANC (Section 6), near the great Valley, rises to 11,800 feet. Note too the small but rather bright crater TROUVELOT, 6 miles in diameter, right in the uplands. The ALPINE VALLEY is 80 miles long, and has been described in the text; it is by far the finest formation of its type on the entire Moon.

ARCHYTAS. A bright crater 21 miles in diameter, on the north border of the Mare Frigoris. It has a triple-peaked central mountain, and walls which rise to 5,000 feet above the sunken interior. To the south-west lies a similar but rather smaller crater, PROTAGORAS.

ARISTOTELES. A great plain 60 miles across, with walls rising to 11,000 feet. The floor contains many low hills, and particularly notable are the rows of hillocks which seem to radiate outwards from the crater itself. Closely outside the west wall is a deep crater, MITCHELL. Aristoteles forms a notable pair with its slightly smaller neighbour Eudoxus, which lies to its south.

W. C. BOND. A vast enclosure almost 100 miles across, north of Archytas. It is clearly very old, and is in a dilapidated condition, so that it is easy to recognize only under low conditions of lighting. To the north is BARROW, 54 miles in diameter, and of the same general type. Many of the walled plains in this area have been badly ruined; Meton is another example.

BÜRG. A crater 28 miles in diameter, near the edge of the Lacus Mortis. The floor is concave, and the walls rise to 6,000 feet. Bürg is notable both because of its very large central mountain, which includes a summit crater, and because it stands on the western edge of a small dark plain which is riddled with clefts. Well to the north is the 12-mile crater BAILY.

CALIPPUS. A deformed crater 19 miles in diameter, at the northern end of the Caucasus Mountains which separate the Mare Serenitatis from the Palus Nebularum. Closely west of it is ALEXANDER, which is 65 miles in diameter, and which has a dark floor and very low, broken walls.

CASSINI. A peculiar object on the edge of the Palus Nebularum. It is 36 miles in diameter, with very irregular walls. On the floor is a deep, distinct crater A, in which lies a small 'basin' which has been nicknamed the Washbowl. The floor of Cassini also includes other details. The whole formation was strangely left out of the early maps, but there is not the slightest chance that is is of recent formation.

CAUCASUS MOUNTAINS. An important range, forming part of the border between the Mare Serenitatis and the Mare Imbrium (of which the Palus Nebularum is a part). Some of the peaks rise to 12,000 feet. The range extends from this Section into Section 4.

CHALLIS. Challis is 35 miles in diameter. It and its companion, MAIN, form a good example of overlapping craters; Main, 30 miles in diameter, is the intruding formation. The best 'pointer' in this area is the deep and distinct Scoresby. Challis and Main lie not far from the Moon's north pole, and are never well placed for observation.

DE LA RUE. A large enclosure not far from Endymion, and of about the same size. The walls are, however, very low and broken, and the formation is not distinct. Near by are two much more prominent craters; Thales, which is a ray-centre, and Strabo.

DEMOCRITUS. A very deep ring 23 miles in diameter; it is not regular in outline, and Wilkins described it as being 'shell-shaped'. It lies in the highlands north of the Mare Frigoris, close to the bay of Gärtner. There is a central mountain. To the east are two low-walled formations, KANE and MOIGNO. Moigno has a decidedly dark floor.

EGEDE. A peculiar object shaped rather like a diamond; its average diameter is 23 miles. The floor is dark, and the walls are very low. Egede lies roughly between Aristoteles and the Alpine Valley.

EUDOXUS. In many ways Eudoxus is similar to its companion Aristillus, but it is smaller (diameter 40 miles) and lacks the remarkable radiating rows of hillocks. The walls attain 11,000 feet. Close to Eudoxus is a strange, incomplete formation, LAMÈCH.

FRIGORIS, MARE. This is not one of the circular-type seas, and must be regarded as an 'overflow'. Its floor is comparatively light and patchy. Craters on it include Protagoras and Galle. The Mare separates the Alpine region from the highlands around the north pole.

GALLE. A small but distinct crater on the Mare Frigoris, north of Aristoteles.

GÄRTNER. A splendid example of a bay. It lies on the border of the Mare Frigoris, and the Mare-material has reduced its 'seaward' wall to such an extent that it is now barely traceable, though the 'landward' rampart is still quite high. Gärtner is 63 miles in diameter, and must once have been a grand formation. The floor contains a good deal of detail: I have discovered some clefts there, but these are too delicate to be seen except with large telescopes.

GIOJA. A 26-mile crater close to the north pole, and thus badly placed for observation. It abuts into a larger formation, SHACKLE-TON, while north-west again is a crater, PEARY, with a central peak.

GOLDSCHMIDT. An old ring, 68 miles in diameter, between Barrow and the very prominent Anaxagoras in the second quadrant (Section 6). Its walls are low and broken. Details may be seen on the floor.

HERCULES. The smaller companion of Atlas. Hercules is 45 miles across and with walls rising to 11,000 feet; these walls are richly terraced, and often appear very brilliant. The floor contains one prominent crater as well as a large amount of fine detail.

MASON. This crater is 15 miles in diameter; it forms a pair with Plana (24 miles) not far from Bürg. Both craters have low, broken walls. Plana has the darker floor. South-west of Mason, on the border of the Lacus Somniorum, is a more distinct and deeper crater, GROVE.

MORTIS, LACUS. A small and unremarkable dark plain near Bürg.

METON. Another of the large enclosures in the north polar region; it lies not far from the distinct Scoresby. Meton is over 100 miles long, but is really a compound formation, made up of several ringed plains which have run together. Between it and the limb, close to its wall, is a smaller but more perfect enclosure, EUCTEMON, and to the north-west is the broken crater BAILLAUD. Near the limb in this area are various other craters of some size, notably PETERMAN and CUSANUS.

NEBULARUM, PALUS. Part of the Mare Imbrium; the region of Aristillus and Autolycus (Section 6).

PLANA. The companion of Mason, and described with that crater.

SCORESBY. A very deep, distinct crater 36 miles in diameter, in the north polar highlands close to Challis. It has a twin-peaked central hill. Scoresby is usually easy to recognize, since it is much better-formed than any of its neighbours.

SOMNIORUM, LACUS. This is really a bay leading out of the Mare Serenitatis, but its floor is much lighter and patchier. On its southern border is the great enclosure Posidonius (Section 4), but the 18-mile DANIELL, the well-formed companion of Posidonius, is in this Section. Fine detail may be seen on the Lacus, and I have recorded a delicate cleft or two there.

STRABO. A 32-mile crater, close to De La Rue. The wall contains some high peaks, and the floor is smooth. Strabo is the centre of a very short and inconspicuous ray system, much less prominent than that of its neighbour Thales.

THALES. Thales, close to Strabo, is 24 miles across and a major ray-centre, so that it is very prominent near full moon. It is described in the text.

THEÆTETUS. A crater on the Palus Nebularum, near Cassini; it is 16 miles in diameter, and has been described in the text. Using the Meudon refractor in 1953 I discovered a low central mountain. It was near Theætetus that Charbonneaux recorded his 'cloud' in 1902, also with the Meudon refractor.

TIMÆUS. A bright crater, 21 miles in diameter, on the north border of the Mare Frigoris, not far from Archytas. The floor contains a double central hill. Timæus is the centre of a minor ray-system, and acts as a good guide to the large, broken enclosure of W. C. Bond.

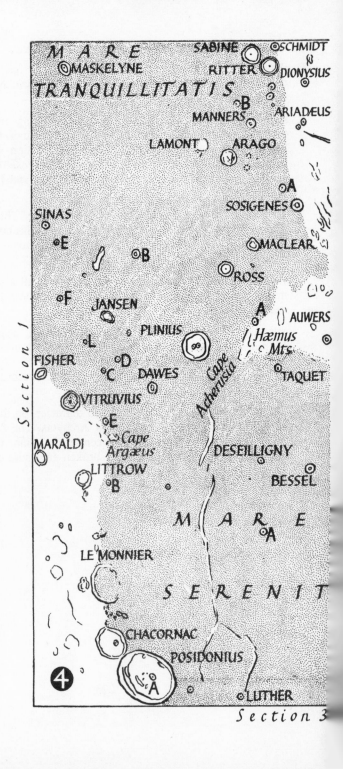

MARE

MASKELYNE

SABINE   SCHMIDT
RITTER   DIONYSIUS

TRANQUILLITATIS

B

MANNERS   ARIADÆUS

LAMONT   ARAGO

A

SOSIGENES

SINAS

E

MACLEAR

B

ROSS

F

A   AUWERS

JANSEN

PLINIUS   Hæmus
Mts

L

FISHER   D   Cape
C   DAWES   Acherusia   TAQUET

VITRUVIUS

E

MARALDI   Cape
Argæus   DESEILLIGNY

LITTROW

B   BESSEL

M   A   R   E
A

LE MONNIER

S   E   R   E   N   I   T

CHACORNAC

POSIDONIUS

④   A

LUTHER

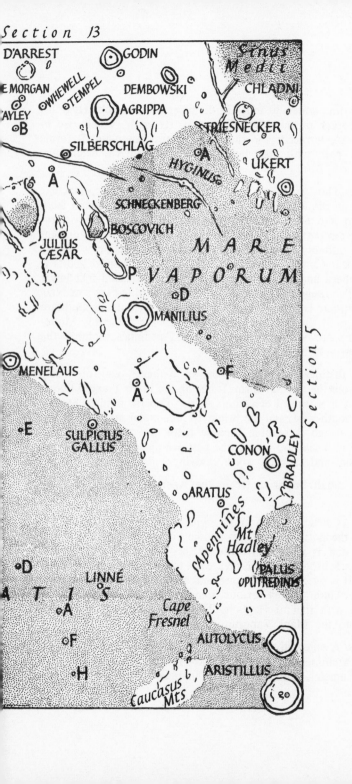

D'ARREST

GODIN

E MORGAN
WHEWELL
TEMPEL
DEMBOWSKI
AGRIPPA
AYLEY
B
SILBERSCHLAG

A

Sinus
Medii

CHLADNI

TRIESNECKER

HYGINUS
UKERT

A

SCHNECKENBERG

BOSCOVICH

JULIUS
CÆSAR

MARE

P VAPORUM

D

MANILIUS

F

MENELAUS

A

E
SULPICIUS
GALLUS

CONON

BRADLEY

ARATUS

Apennines

Mt
Hadley

PALUS
OPUTREDINIS

D

LINNÉ

ATIS

S

A

Cape
Fresnel

AUTOLYCUS

F

H

ARISTILLUS

Caucasus
Mts

AGRIPPA. A fine crater 30 miles in diameter not far from Hyginus, near the border of the Mare Vaporum. Its walls, which rise to 8,000 feet, are terraced; and there is a central mountain. It forms a notable pair with its slightly smaller southern neighbour, Godin.

APENNINES. The Apennines are certainly the most spectacular mountains on the Moon, though not the highest; they extend from this Section into Section 5, ending near Eratosthenes. They form part of the rampart of the Mare Imbrium, and make a magnificent sight when suitably lit. The loftiest peak in this Section is MOUNT BRADLEY, near Conon, which rises to 16,000 feet; MOUNT HADLEY, at the northern end of the range, is only one thousand feet lower than this. The range ends, to the north, at the jutting CAPE FRESNEL, after which there is a gap between the Mare Imbrium and the Mare Serenitatis until the border is resumed with the Caucasus Mountains. There are various craters in the Apennines, notably the 13-mile CONON, right in the uplands.

ARAGO. A distinct crater, 18 miles in diameter and obviously distorted from the circular form. It lies on the Mare Tranquillitatis; on the floor is a central elevation. A low, imperfect ring, LAMONT, lies to the south-west, and the bright 10-mile crater MANNERS to the south-east. Arago is notable because there are various domes to the east of it. These are among the best examples of domes on the whole Moon, and are well worth studying.

ARATUS. A small bright crater in the Apennines, south of Cape Fresnel.

ARIADÆUS. A bright 9-mile crater, with a smaller one in contact with it on the north-west. It lies on the border of the Mare Tranquillitatis, and is notable because of the great cleft nearby, discovered by Schröter in 1792 and easy to see with even a small telescope. It is over 150 miles long, and seems to be a genuine cleft, not a crater-chain. It has various branches, one of which connects the system with that of Hyginus. The main cleft runs across the uplands into the Mare Vaporum.

ARISTILLUS. A splendid crater on the Palus Nebularum, forming a trio with Archimedes (Section 5) and Autolycus. Aristillus is 35 miles in diameter, with walls rising in places to 11,000 feet. Its interior is of exceptional interest, and has been described in the text. Like Eratosthenes, the inner patches need close attention, since they show marked apparent variations each lunation. The floor includes a fine triple-peaked central mountain.

AUTOLYCUS. The southern companion of Aristillus. It is smaller (24 miles in diameter) but just as distinct, and the walls rise to 9,000 feet. Under high light Autolycus is seen to be the centre of an inconspicuous ray system, and under a low sun radiating ridges are seen extending from it.

BESSEL. The largest crater on the Mare Serenitatis. It is 12 miles in diameter, with walls rising to 3,600 feet above the depressed interior. With the Meudon refractor, I have been unable to see a central peak, though older observers believed in the existence of one. To the west lies a smaller crater, DESEILLIGNY.

BOSCOVICH. A low-walled formation on the border of the Mare Vaporum. It is about 27 miles across, but is irregular in form, and I believe it to be a compound structure. It is notable for the darkness of its floor, which makes it very easy to recognize; the same is true of its neighbour Julius Cæsar.

CAYLEY. One of the bright craters in the uplands between the Mare Vaporum and the Mare Tranquillitatis. It is 9 miles in diameter, and very distinct. The nearby TEMPEL and DE MORGAN are also bright, but only about 5 miles in diameter.

CHACORNAC. A pentagonal ring-plain about 30 miles in diameter, close to Posidonius on the edge of the Mare Serenitatis. There is considerable detail on the floor, including some clefts.

DAWES. A 14-mile crater between the Mare Serenitatis and the Mare Tranquillitatis; it is somewhat deformed. Two dusky bands run from the small central peak up the inner east wall. I first saw them in 1952 with my 12½-inch reflector, and they have been confirmed since.

DIONYSIUS. A brilliant crater, 12 miles in diameter, on the edge of the Mare Tranquillitatis not very far from Ariadæus. It stands on a light area, and is very conspicuous under high illumination. In 1950 F. H. Thornton found a dark band running up the inner north wall, and I have been able to confirm it.

GODIN. A crater 27 miles in diameter, slightly deformed, but with a central hill. It is the southern component of the Godin-

Agrippa pair. Between it and the Sabine-Ritter pair is a broken crater, D'ARREST.

HÆMUS MOUNTAINS. These mountains form part of the border of the Mare Serenitatis, and separate it from the Mare Vaporum. They are not lofty, but some of the peaks rise to about 8,000 feet. The glittering Menelaus lies in the range; so does the much smaller and less bright AUWERS.

HYGINUS. A crater-depression about 4 miles in diameter, notable because of its association with the famous crater-cleft. It has been fully described in the text. North of it lies the area of Hyginus N, and here too is an interesting spiral mountain, MOUNT SCHNECKEN-BERG, which requires a fairly high power to be well seen. Some branches of the Hyginus cleft-system join up with the system of Ariadæus.

JULIUS CÆSAR. An imperfect, very dark-floored enclosure between Mare Tranquillitatis and Mare Vaporum, not far from Boscovich. This is one of the darkest patches on the whole Moon, and is worth close attention.

LE MONNIER. A fine example of a bay; it lies on the border of the Mare Serenitatis, and is 34 miles in diameter. Of the seaward wall, only a few mounds now remain. The floor contains little detail, and must be one of the smoothest areas in this part of the Moon.

LINNÉ. This celebrated formation, on the Mare Serenitatis, has been fully described in the text.

LITTROW. A 22-mile crater between Le Monnier and Argæus, on the edge of the Mare Serenitatis. The walls are quite high, but broken in places.

MANILIUS. A splendid crater 25 miles in diameter, on the borders of the Mare Vaporum. Its walls are brilliant, so that it is very prominent near full moon. The walls are terraced, and there is considerable interior detail, including a central mountain.

MARALDI. This has been described with Rømer (Section 1).

MASKELYNE. A 19-mile crater on the Mare Tranquillitatis. The walls have inner terraces, and there is a low central peak. To the east is a conspicuous little crater, Maskelyne B.

MENELAUS. A brilliant crater in the Hæmus Mountains, striking under a high light even though it is only 20 miles in diameter. The walls rise to 8,000 feet above a floor which contains a peak not quite centrally placed.

PLINIUS. A superb crater 'standing sentinel' on the strait between the Mare Tranquillitatis and the Mare Serenitatis. It is 30 miles across, but appreciably distorted from the circular form. The central structure seems to be not a peak, but a twin crater. Plinius has high terraced walls, and is conspicuous under all conditions of illumination.

POSIDONIUS. A walled plain 62 miles in diameter, adjoining Chacornac and lying on the borders of the Mare Serenitatis and the Lacus Somniorum. The ramparts are rather low and narrow, and the floor is crowded with detail, including a nearly central craterlet, Posidonius A.

PUTREDINIS, PALUS. Part of the Mare Imbrium, in the Autolycus and Cape Fresnel area. It extends on to Section 5.

RITTER. This and its neighbour Sabine form a striking pair, not far from Ariadæus on the boundary of the Mare Tranquillitatis. Ritter is very slightly the larger, and is about 19 miles across. Nearby is a small but bright crater, SCHMIDT, and closely north of Ritter are two more bright craterlets, making up almost perfect twins of the sort so common on the Moon. Both Sabine and Ritter have central peaks.

ROSS. A crater with a central peak. It is 18 miles in diameter, and lies on the Mare Tranquillitatis. To the south-east lies MACLEAR, dark-floored and 11 miles across, east of which is a fine long cleft running to, and beyond, Sosigenes A.

SABINE. The companion of Ritter, and described with that crater.

SCHNECKENBERG, MOUNT. An extraordinary 'spiral mountain', described with Hyginus.

SERENITATIS, MARE. One of the most perfect of the circular seas. It covers an area of 125,000 square miles, slightly more than that of Great Britain. It is bordered, in part, by the Caucasus Mountains and by the Hæmus Mountains, ending at CAPE ACHERUSIA. The floor is relatively smooth, but contains some prominent ridges as well as Bessel, Deseilligny and – of course – Linné. Its floor is lighter than that of the Mare Imbrium, and in my view it is probably older.

SILBERSCHLAG. A small but bright crater, 8 miles in diameter, near Ariadæus. It is not unlike Cayley, though slightly smaller.

SOSIGENES. A 14-mile crater west of Julius Cæsar; it has a small central hill, and its walls are bright. To the south-west is Sosigenes A, which lies on the long cleft running from Maclear, and which is connected to Sosigenes itself by a ridge.

SULPICIUS GALLUS. An extremely bright crater, 8 miles in diameter and with walls which rise to about 8,000 feet. It lies just on the Mare Serenitatis, in the foothills of the Hæmus Mountains, In 1953 I found a small central peak, but this is a difficult object and needs a large telescope to be properly seen.

TAQUET. Another bright crater just on the Mare Serenitatis in the Hæmus region; it is about 6 miles across.

TRANQUILLITATIS, MARE. A major sea, extending on to Sections 1 and 13. It is less regular in outline than the Mare Serenitatis, and has a lighter, patchier floor which includes several notable craters as well as much fine detail.

TRIESNECKER. A crater in the Mare Vaporum-Sinus Medii area. It is 14 miles across, and is notable because of the very complex cleft-system to the west of it. The chief clefts are visible with a 3-inch refractor under suitable conditions, but the finer ones require large apertures.

UKERT. Another 14-mile crater, somewhat irregular in outline. Here too there are clefts, though the system is a minor one and does not rival that of Triesnecker, which lies not far off. Ukert itself has rather bright walls.

VAPORUM, MARE. One of the minor seas, but notable because of its darkness and because of the many interesting objects nearby – notably Boscovich, Manilius and the cleft-systems of Hyginus and Ariadæus. A small part of it extends on to Section 5.

VITRUVIUS. An interesting formation, just on the Mare Tranquillitatis near Mount Argæus. The walls are bright, but the floor is decidedly dark, containing a low central peak. Well to the south-east of it, right on the Mare, is JANSEN, which is 16 miles across and has very low walls, rising to only 300 feet above its darkish floor – which does not seem to be appreciably depressed below the level of the Mare. About the same distance south-east of Jansen is a well-marked small crater, SINAS. Closer to Vitruvius is the unremarkable crater FISHER.

232

SECOND (NORTH-EAST) QUADRANT

This is the 'sea' quadrant, and there is little true upland. Most of the area is covered by the two greatest maria on the Moon – the Mare Imbrium and the Oceanus Procellarum, together with various minor seas such as the Sinus Æstuum, the Sinus Roris and the lovely Bay of Rainbows, Sinus Iridum. Only along the limb do we find tremendous walled plains, of which Pythagoras and Xenophanes are good examples. On the Mare surface lie three of the most famous of all lunar craters, Copernicus, Archimedes and Aristarchus, while the dark-floored Plato is to be found on the border of the Mare Imbrium.

The southern part of the Apennine range lies in the quadrant, and there are also the less lofty Carpathian Mountains, near Copernicus, and the Jura Mountains, bordering Sinus Iridum. The Hercynian range, right on the limb, is probably higher, but its position makes it difficult to observe properly.

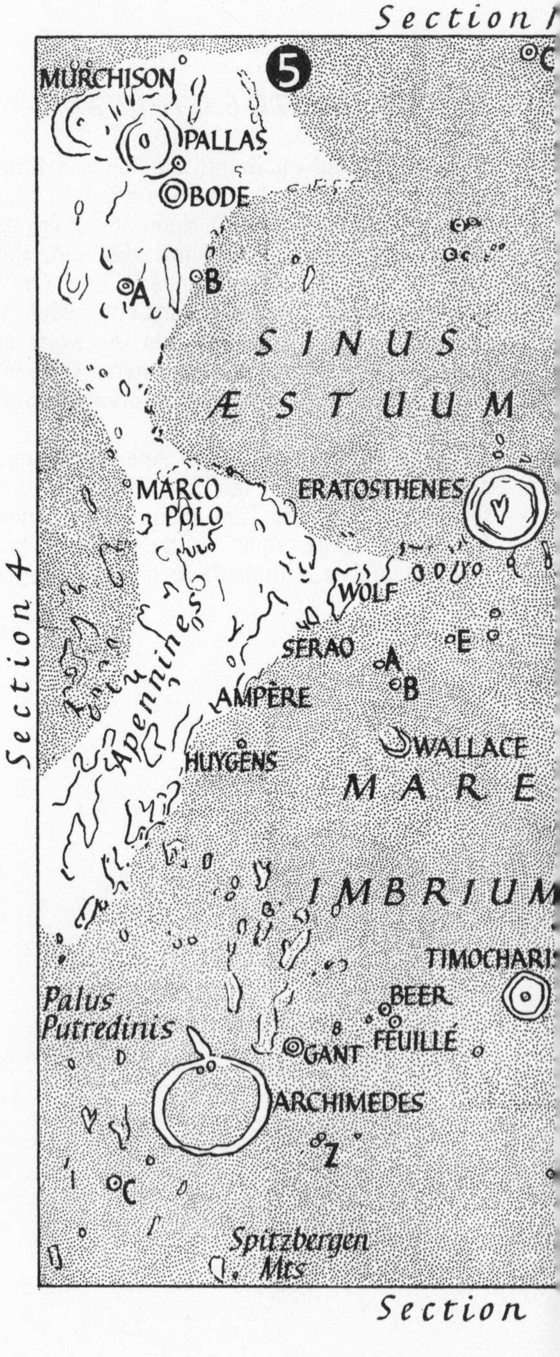

MURCHISON
PALLAS
BODE
A B

SINUS
ÆSTUUM

MARCO
POLO
ERATOSTHENES

WOLF
SERAO A E
AMPÈRE B
HUYGENS
WALLACE
MARE

Apennines

IMBRIUM

TIMOCHARIS
BEER
Palus
Putredinis
GANT FEUILLÉ
ARCHIMEDES
Z
C
Spitzbergen
Mts

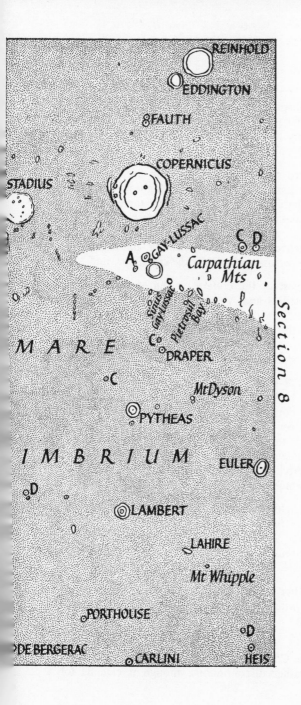

REINHOLD

EDDINGTON

FAUTH

COPERNICUS

STADIUS

GAY-LUSSAC

A

Carpathian Mts

C D

Sinus Gay-Lussac

Pietrosil Bay

C

DRAPER

C

MtDyson

PYTHEAS

M A R E

I M B R I U M

EULER

D

LAMBERT

LAHIRE

Mt Whipple

PORTHOUSE

D

DE BERGERAC

CARLINI

HEIS

Section 8

ÆSTUUM, SINUS. A conspicuous dark plain west of Copernicus, and and bordered by the southernmost extension of the Apennines. Eratosthenes lies at its boundary. The floor is relatively smooth, and there is not much detail on it.

APENNINES. This superb range stretches up from Section 4, ending at Eratosthenes. This part of it contains the highest peak, MOUNT HUYGENS, which probably reaches 18,500 feet; there is also the triangular mountain mass MOUNT WOLF, of at least 12,000 feet, as well as MOUNT AMPÈRE, around 11,000 feet. There are a few low-walled, rather distorted craters in the Apennine uplands, notably MARCO POLO, 12 miles across and with a darkish floor, and SERAO.

ARCHIMEDES. The largest of the craters on the Mare Imbrium; it forms a trio with Aristillus and Autolycus (Section 4). Archimedes is 50 miles in diameter, with walls around 4,300 feet above the slightly sunken floor; the rampart includes a few peaks reaching to at least 7,000 feet, but in general the wall has been much reduced. The floor is dark and smooth, with no vestige of a central mountain.

BEER. A crater about 8 miles in diameter, on the Mare Imbrium between Archimedes and Timocharis. It has an almost identical twin, Feuillé, closely north-east of it. Like Messier and Pickering, the relative sizes of Beer and Feuillé seem to vary; these apparent changes must be due only to optical effects, but they are worth studying, and any amateur with a modest telescope could do useful work here. Between Archimedes and the Beer-Feuillé pair is a deep small crater, GANT, which contains a central peak.

BODE. An 11-mile bright crater in the highlands separating the Sinus Medii from the Sinus Æstuum. Its walls reach 5,000 feet above the floor. Bode lies close to the semi-ruined crater-ring Pallas, and is conspicuous near full moon; it is the centre of a minor ray-system.

CARLINI. A small, rather bright crater on the Mare Imbrium. It is 5 miles in diameter, with a small central hill; its isolated position makes it conspicuous.

CARPATHIAN MOUNTAINS. A range forming part of the border of the Mare Imbrium, in the Copernicus area. It cannot compare with the Apennines, and is rather discontinuous, though it extends for a total of between 200 and 250 miles. Its highest peaks attain 7,000 feet, but most of the mountains are much lower than this. The eastern end of the range stretches into Section 8.

COPERNICUS. The 'Monarch of the Moon'. It has been described in the text, and no more need be said here except that it and its rays dominate this whole area of the lunar surface.

ERATOSTHENES. This also has been described in the text. It is 38 miles in diameter and extremely deep, with central elevations and a great amount of floor-detail. It lies at the southern end of the Apennine range. It is not a ray-centre.

EULER. A minor ray-centre on the Mare Imbrium, and therefore easy to find under high light. Euler is a well-marked crater 19 miles in diameter, with a central peak and walls which show some inner terracing.

FAUTH. A double craterlet south of Copernicus; its form makes it easy to identify. This whole area is dominated by ridges and crater-chains radiating from Copernicus.

GAY-LUSSAC. An irregular 15-mile crater in the Carpathian Mountains, north of Copernicus. Its floor contains some fine detail, including at least two delicate clefts. To the east, in the direction of Tobias Mayer, are two 'bays' in the Carpathian range which have been named SINUS GAY-LUSSAC and PIETROSUL BAY. Immediately south-west of Gay-Lussac itself is the smaller, deeper crater Gay-Lussac A.

HEIS. A small craterlet on the Mare Imbrium, between De L'Isle (Section 8) and Caroline Herschel (Section 7). It is very minor, but is easy to find because of its isolated position.

IMBRIUM, MARE. The greatest of all the circular-type seas. Most of it lies in this Section, but it also extends into Sections 6 and 8. It has been fully described in the text; we may repeat, however, that in area it is larger than Great Britain and France combined.

LA HIRE. A bright 5,000-foot mountain on the Mare Imbrium, north-east of Lambert. It has a summit craterlet.

LAMBERT. Lambert is only 18 miles across, and is not bright, but is nevertheless easy to find owing to its position on the Mare Imbrium. In place of a central mountain, it has a central crater – a type of feature not uncommon on the Moon; Plinius is another good example.

MURCHISON. The companion of Pallas, on the edge of the Sinus Medii. It has been badly distorted, and is clearly very old, so that its walls are now low and broken. It is about 35 miles in diameter.

PALLAS. Pallas, adjoining Murchison, is rather smaller (diameter 30 miles) but more complete, even though its walls have been broken by numerous passes. The central peak still exists. On the other side of Pallas is the smaller but much deeper crater-ring of Bode.

PUTREDINIS, PALUS. Part of the Mare Imbrium, to the west of Archimedes. There seems little real reason for it to have a separate name.

PYTHEAS. A very bright crater on the Mare Imbrium, with terraced walls and a central hill. It is a minor ray-centre, and is so conspicuous that it is surprising to find that its diameter is a mere 12 miles. Well to the south lies a much smaller crater, DRAPER, which has a still smaller craterlet, Draper C, close beside it. Rays from Copernicus cross this whole area.

REINHOLD. A 30-mile crater on the Oceanus Procellarum, southeast of Copernicus; its walls rise to 9,000 feet in places. Closely north-west of Reinhold is EDDINGTON, which has low walls and is about 15 miles across. Eddington has a relatively smooth, rather darkish floor.

STADIUS. The celebrated 'ghost', on the edge of the Sinus Æstuum, and forming a triangle with Copernicus and Eratosthenes. It has been fully described in the text.

TIMOCHARIS. An interesting crater on the Mare Imbrium, roughly east of Archimedes. It is 25 miles in diameter, with broad terraced walls reaching 7,000 feet. Like Lambert, it has a central crater. Timocharis is the centre of a rather faint ray-system, and is always easy to identify. D. P. Barcroft has reported obscurations inside it, and it should be carefully watched.

WALLACE. An incomplete crater between Archimedes and Eratosthenes. Either it has been ruined by the Mare-material, or else (as I believe) it was formed before the crust in that area had become solid enough to produce a really deep, well-formed crater. The ridges and clefts in the Wallace area are most interesting. With the Meudon refractor I have found a cleft inside Wallace itself, but large telescopes are needed to show it.

Section

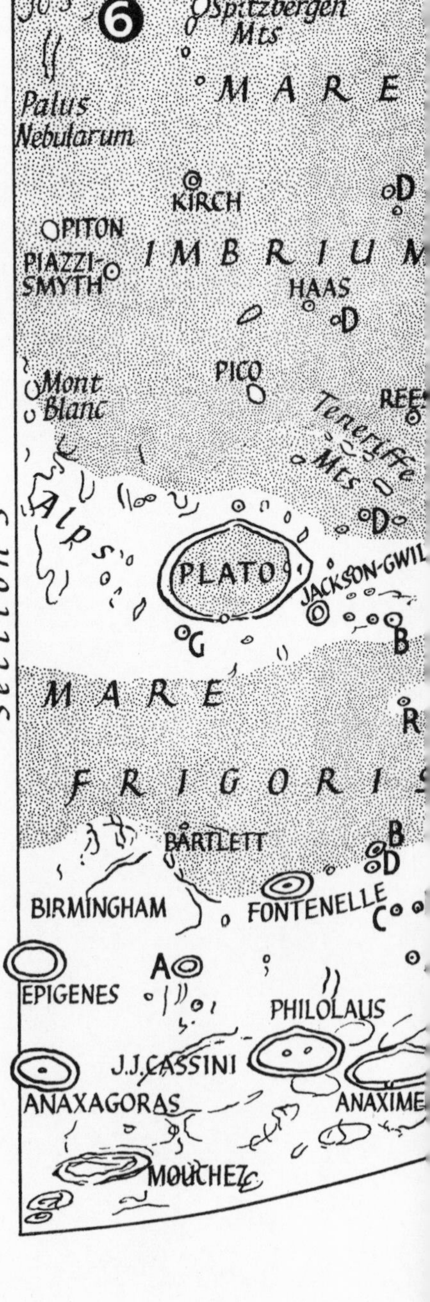

6
Spitzbergen Mts
MARE
Palus Nebularum
KIRCH
D
PITON
IMBRIUM
PIAZZI-SMYTH
HAAS
D
PICO
Mont Blanc
REE
Teneriffe Mts
Alps
D
PLATO
JACKSON-GWIL
G
B
MARE
R
FRIGORIS
BARTLETT
B
D
BIRMINGHAM
FONTENELLE
C
A
EPIGENES
PHILOLAUS
J.J.CASSINI
ANAXAGORAS
ANAXIME
MOUCHEZ

Section 3

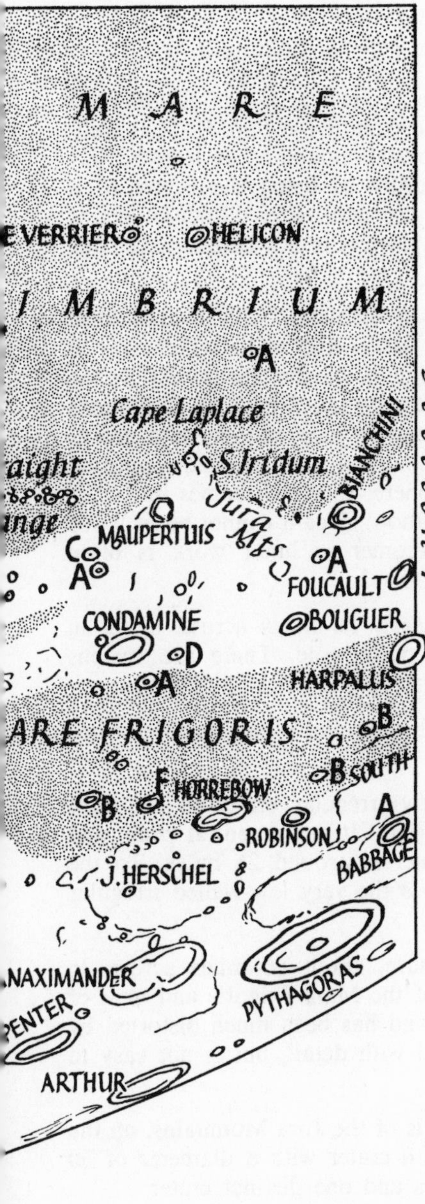

MARE

VERRIER⊙ ⊙HELICON

IMBRIUM

A

Cape Laplace

aight   S. Iridum   BIANCHINI

nge   Jura Mts

MAUPERTUIS   A

C   FOUCAULT
A

CONDAMINE   ⊙BOUGUER

D

A   HARPALLUS

MARE FRIGORIS   B

B SOUTH

B   F HORREBOW

ROBINSON   A

J. HERSCHEL   BABBAGE

NAXIMANDER   PYTHAGORAS

PENTER

ARTHUR

SECTION 6

ANAXAGORAS. A crater 32 miles in diameter, in the north polar highlands and closely east of Goldschmidt (Section 3). It is well-formed, with high walls and a central mountain. It is extremely bright, and is particularly noteworthy as being the centre of a major ray-system, so that it is easy to find under all conditions of illumination. It is a pity that Anaxagoras is not better placed for observation.

ANAXIMANDER. A crater 54 miles in diameter, with a good deal of floor-detail (though no central peak) and walls which rise in places to over 9,000 feet. Adjoining it, to the north-west, is the smaller but almost equally deep CARPENTER. The limb-formations in this area are of great interest, and include one splendid group, of which the chief craters are THORNTON and ARTHUR. Thornton actually lies on the averted hemisphere, so that it comes into view only under good conditions of libration; since it cannot be included on mean-libration maps, the newcomer to lunar work is often surprised to see it – as I originally was!

ANAXIMENES. A large enclosure nearly 50 miles across, again in the upland region bordering the north pole. There are various features on the floor. It adjoins the deeper crater Philolaus.

BARTLETT. 'Mädler's Square', near Fontenelle; it has been described in detail in the text.

BIANCHINI. A bright-walled, slightly irregular crater in the Jura Mountains bordering the Sinus Iridum. It has a central peak, and is usually easy to find. Its diameter is around 25 miles. To the west of it, also in the Jura range, is the very low-walled irregular enclosure MAUPERTUIS.

BIRMINGHAM. A very large enclosure, about 66 miles across, in the highlands immediately north of the Mare Frigoris and west of Fontenelle. It is clearly very old, and has been much distorted by later outbreaks. It is now crowded with detail, but is not easy to find under high illumination.

CONDAMINE. This lies in the foothills of the Jura Mountains, on the border of the Mare Frigoris. It is a crater with a diameter of 30 miles, with walls broken by passes and one distinct crater.

FONTENELLE. A bright formation with a central crater. It lies on the

242

northern edge of the Mare Frigoris, close to Bartlett, and is easy to find on account of its brilliance. North of it lies an ill-formed plain, J. J. CASSINI, bounded by irregular ridges.

FRIGORIS, MARE. The eastern part of the Mare Frigoris extends into this Section, from Section 3. The general aspect is the same as that of the western part, and the Mare is clearly an overflow rather than a genuine sea-formation in its own right.

HARPALUS. A conspicuous crater 22 miles across, near the borders of the Mare Frigoris and the Sinus Roris. It has a floor-hill some distance from its centre. This was the crater selected for the rocket landing-site in the famous film *Destination Moon* of the early 1950s, when space-travel was still regarded as something of a joke!

HELICON. This and Le Verrier form a conspicuous pair on the Mare Imbrium, near the Sinus Iridum. Helicon is 13 miles in diameter, Le Verrier 11; Helicon has a central craterlet, Le Verrier a central peak. Both have moderately high walls. Oddly enough Helicon is always easy to find, but Le Verrier often becomes so obscure near full moon that it is difficult to locate at all.

HERSCHEL, JOHN. A ridge-bordered enclosure on the edge of the uplands bordering the Mare Frigoris to the north. It is about 90 miles across. With the Meudon refractor I have recorded over fifty craterlets on its floor, together with peaks and ridges; any small telescope will show some of these, but the plain is so low-walled that it is not easy to identify except under low light. It is decidedly irregular in outline.

IMBRIUM, MARE. Part of the vast Mare Imbrium extends into this Section. The general aspect is the same as that of the area in Section 5.

IRIDUM, SINUS. The lovely 'Bay of Rainbows'; one of the most spectacular sights on the Moon near sunrise, when the floor is in shadow and the peaks of the Juras are illuminated. From the Mare, the level of the Bay gradually slopes down to the extent of 2,000 feet. The seaward wall has almost vanished; its site is marked now only by a few very low, irregular ridges and one or two small crater-lets. The Sinus Iridum has been fully described in the text.

KIRCH. A bright 7-mile crater on the Mare Imbrium, north of the Spitzbergen Mountains. Well to the north-east lies a somewhat smaller crater, HAAS, to the west of which is an isolated mountain arm.

LE VERRIER. This is the companion of Helicon, and has been described with it.

NEBULARUM, PALUS. Part of the Mare Imbrium. The region in this Section is of the same type as that in Section 3.

PHILOLAUS. A very deep, prominent crater 46 miles across, with walls rising a full 12,000 feet above a floor which contains a good deal of detail. Unusual shadow-colours have been reported here. Anaximenes adjoins Philolaus to the east; it is slightly larger than Philolaus, but not nearly so deep or conspicuous.

PICO. A bright mountain on the Mare Imbrium, south of Plato. It is triple-peaked; the highest attains 8,000 feet. The area between Pico and Plato is occupied by a very large ghost-ring; it was once known as Newton, but the name has now been transferred to a crater in the opposite part of the Moon, not far from the south pole, and the ghost has been relegated to anonymity. The bright TENERIFFE MOUNTAINS, some of which are almost as lofty as Pico, also lie near the boundary of the ghost, and may once have formed part of its wall, though more probably they are of considerably later date.

PITON. Another isolated mountain, 7,000 feet high and with a summit craterlet. It lies well to the south-west of Pico, and is always easy to find, because of its brightness. Between the two peaks, rather closer to Piton, is the bright 6-mile crater PIAZZI SMYTH.

PLATO. Hevelius' 'Greater Black Lake'; the 60-mile crater noted for the darkness of its floor, which some observers regard as variable in hue. It has been described in the text. Plato should be kept under constant watch, and amateur observers will be wise to study it on every possible occasion. To the north-east is the well-marked deep crater JACKSON-GWILT.

PYTHAGORAS. This too has been described in earlier pages. It is one of the noblest craters on the whole Moon, with its lofty, continuous walls and its central elevation, and it is a great pity that it lies too near the limb to be seen properly. Under favourable libration it can be a striking object.

SOUTH. This is a ridge-bounded enclosure about 60 miles across. It and its larger and even more ruined neighbour BABBAGE lie close to Pythagoras, and are full of detail, but their walls are so broken and discontinuous that they are often difficult to recognize. The nearby crater ROBINSON is only 17 miles in diameter, but is generally easier to find. Across the Mare Frigoris, in the Jura foot-hills, are some well-formed craters less than twenty miles across, of which the chief are BOUGUER and FOUCAULT.

SPITZBERGEN MOUNTAINS. A series of bright little hills north of Archimedes (Section 5). In 1948 I found that they lie on the western border of a very obscure ghost-ring which is now traceable only because of a slight difference in the hue of what must once have been its floor.

STRAIGHT RANGE. A remarkable line of peaks, rising to a maximum of 6,000 feet, on the Mare Imbrium between Plato on the one hand and CAPE LAPLACE, the jutting promontory of the Sinus Iridum, on the other. The peaks are less brilliant than Pico or Piton, but are still quite bright. The range is curiously regular, and there is nothing just like it anywhere else on the Moon.

TENERIFFE MOUNTAINS. These little peaks lie near Pico, on the border of the ghost-ring between Pico and Plato. They have been described with Pico.

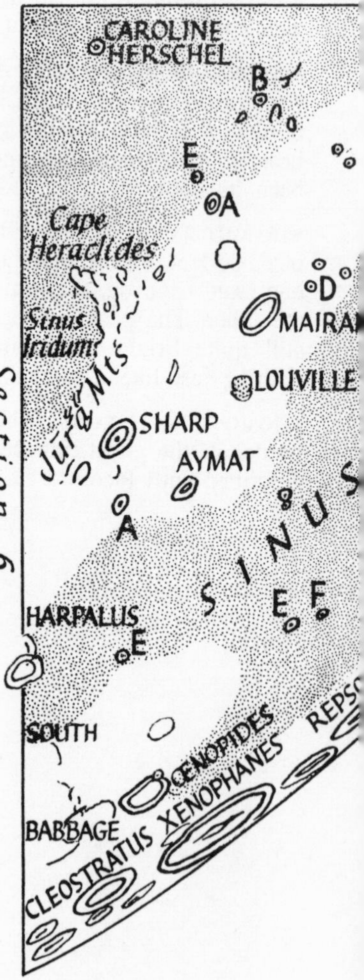
CAROLINE
HERSCHEL
B
E
A
Cape
Heraclides
D
MAIRA
Sinus
Iridum
LOUVILLE
Jura Mts
SHARP
AYMAT
A
SINUS
E
F
Section 6
HARPALUS
E
SOUTH
ŒNOPIDES
XENOPHANES
REPS
BABBAGE
CLEOSTRATUS

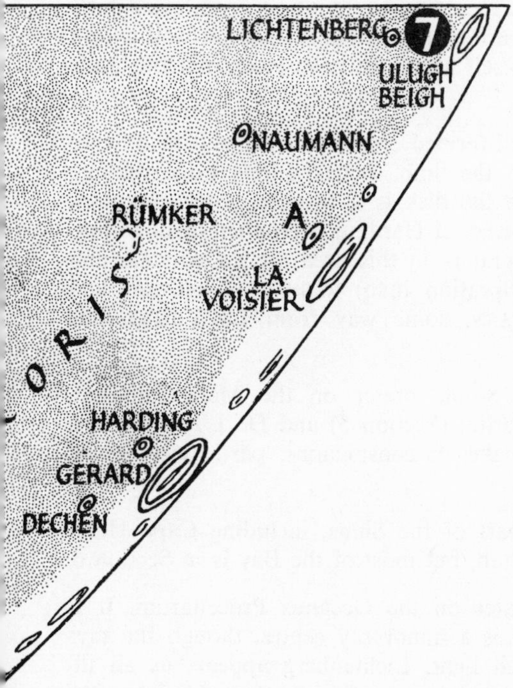

LICHTENBERG

7

ULUGH
BEIGH

NAUMANN

RÜMKER

A

LA
VOISIER

ORIS

HARDING

GERARD

DECHEN

SECTION 7

CLEOSTRATUS. A large and well-formed crater very close to the limb, not far from Xenophanes. On the libration zone, even more unfavourably placed, are various ringed plains, not yet well shown on any map. Cleostratus itself seems to have steep, narrow walls and a smooth floor.

GERARD. Another large, well-formed crater very difficult to observe because of its closeness to the limb. It has a long ridge running down its floor. Further on the disk is a 14-mile crater, HARDING, with low walls, and north-west of Harding is another small formation, DECHEN. Other limb-craters in this area are LA VOISIER, and (not shown on a mean libration map) RÉGNAULT, GALVANI and NAJERÁ. The crater NAUMANN, some way from La Voisier, has fairly bright walls.

HERSCHEL, CAROLINE. An 8-mile crater on the Mare Imbrium, forming a triangle with Carlini (Section 5) and De L'Isle (Section 8). Its isolated position makes it conspicuous, particularly as its walls are rather bright.

IRIDUM, SINUS. A small part of the Sinus, including Cape Heraclides, appears in this Section, but most of the Bay is in Section 6.

LICHTENBERG. A small crater on the Oceanus Procellarum. It is 12 miles in diameter, and is a minor ray centre, though the rays are very short. Under high light, Lichtenberg appears as an ill-defined whitish patch. As has been noted in the text, Mädler often recorded a reddish hue near the crater, recovered in modern times by Barcroft and Baum. Between Lichtenberg and the limb is a well-formed crater, ULUGH BEIGH, which is 30 miles across and has a central peak.

MAIRAN. A fine, well-formed crater in the Jura uplands. Its walls are very lofty, rising perhaps to as much as 15,000 feet in places, but there seems to be no central mountain. North of it, also in the Jura uplands, is the ill-defined depression LOUVILLE, which is not hard to identify because of its dusky floor.

ŒNOPIDES. A large crater near Cleostratus and Xenophanes. It is 42 miles in diameter, and has high walls, broken in the south-east by a considerable crater. There are some minor features on the floor, though Œnopides, like many of its large companions in this area, lacks a central peak. South-east of it, rather closer to the limb, is REPSOLD, which is almost 70 miles across, and would be an imposing object if better placed.

RORIS, SINUS. This Bay forms the 'outlet' of the Oceanus Procellarum into the Mare Frigoris. It is not particularly remarkable, and its surface has the same general aspect as that of the Oceanus Procellarum. On it are a few minor features, together with one peculiar formation, RÜMKER, which seems to be in the nature of a semi-ruined plateau thirty miles in diameter.

SHARP. A deep crater 22 miles in diameter, lying in the Jura Mountains and surrounded by high peaks. The floor includes a small central peak. North-east of it is AYMAT, 12 miles across, rather pear-shaped in outline and also with a minor central peak.

ULUGH BEIGH. This large crater lies near Lichtenberg, and has been described under that heading.

XENOPHANES. Xenophanes is one of the grandest craters in this part of the Moon. It is 67 miles in diameter, and has a massive, elongated central mountain crowned by a craterlet. The walls are lofty and terraced. Unfortunately it is very unfavourably placed, and is much too near the limb to be well seen even when libration is at its maximum.

Section 9

Section 5

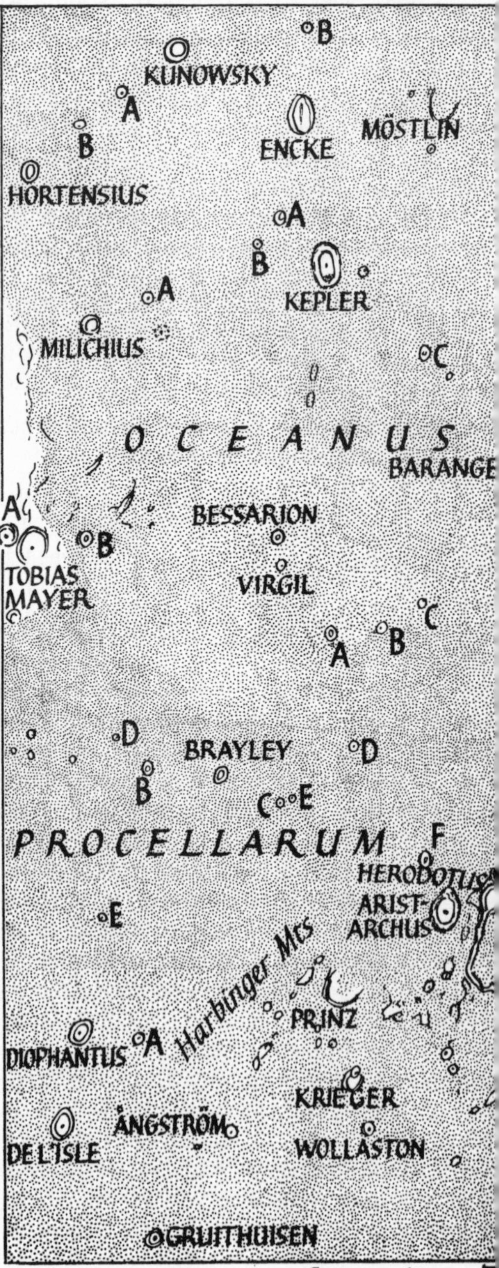

B
KUNOWSKY
A
B
ENCKE
MÖSTLIN
HORTENSIUS
A
B
KEPLER
A
MILICHIUS
C
OCEANUS
BARANGE
A
BESSARION
B
TOBIAS MAYER
VIRGIL
C
A
B
D
BRAYLEY
D
B
C
E
PROCELLARUM
F
HERODOTUS
ARISTARCHUS
E
Harbinger Mts
PRINZ
DIOPHANTUS
A
KRIEGER
ÅNGSTRÖM
DE L'ISLE
WOLLASTON
GRUITHUISEN

Section 7

SUESS

°C °G

°A

°B

REINER

HEVEL

INGALLS

SVEN HEDIN

CAVALERIUS

RALIN

°B

OLBERS

MARIUS

GALILEO

°A

OCEANUS B°

VASCO DA GAMA

CARDANUS

B

PROCELLARUM

KRAFFT

°A

SELEUCUS

°B

OTTO STRUVE

°A

SCHIAPARELLI

A

BRIGGS

B°

Hercynian Mts

8

ARISTARCHUS. This is one of the most interesting craters on the whole Moon, but it has been fully described in the text, and there is no need to say more here. Suffice to say that its extreme brilliance makes it conspicuous under any lighting conditions, and it is prominently visible when lit by nothing stronger than earthshine.

BESSARION. A bright 6-mile crater on the Oceanus Procellarum. It has a central hill, and a radial band runs across the floor up the south-east wall. North of Bessarion is a smaller but equally bright crater, VIRGIL.

BRAYLEY. Another crater on the Oceanus Procellarum, similar to Bessarion but rather larger (diameter 10 miles). It too has a low central hill and dusky radial bands in its interior. To the south-west is a small, bright craterlet, Brayley B.

BRIGGS. A 33-mile crater on the Oceanus Procellarum, not very far from Otto Struve. It is well-marked, and not hard to identify. Ridges connect it with Seleucus.

CARDANUS. This and KRAFFT form another notable pair in the limb-region at the very edge of the Oceanus Procellarum. Cardanus has a diameter of 32 miles and continuous walls attaining 4,000 feet. On the floor lie a central mountain and numerous crater-lets. To the south-west, between Cardanus and Reiner, lies the bright little crater GALILEO. Galileo is fairly bright, but a 9-mile formation is surely inadequate to honour the first man to turn a telescope toward the Moon!

CAVALERIUS. The northern member of the chain which includes Hevel as well as Lohrmann, Riccioli and Grimaldi (Section 9). Cavalerius is well-formed, with a diameter of 40 miles and a central ridge on its floor. The walls rise to 10,000 feet above the interior. It is a fine object when it lies on the terminator. Closely west of it is a superb example of a dome with a summit crater; I found it in 1954, but cannot understand why more attention has not been paid to it.

DE L'ISLE. De L'Isle is 16 miles in diameter, and forms a pair with the less regular 13-mile DIOPHANTUS, to the south. Both craters have central peaks. Various domes lie in the area, and are well worth studying.

ENCKE. A crater which may be regarded as the 'twin' of Kepler; but it is a dissimilar twin, since it is far less bright and is not a ray-centre. The diameter is 20 miles, and the walls are rather low. There is no central peak, but a ridge lies on the floor. To the east lies the inconspicuous and unremarkable formation MÖSTLIN.

GRUITHUISEN. A bright crater on the Oceanus Procellarum, 10 miles in diameter. The area between it and Aristarchus is of great interest. There are the small, bright craters ÅNGSTRÖM and WOLLAS-TON and the rather larger, less regular KRIEGER, together with clefts and domes. The incomplete ring PRINZ has domes on its floor, and others nearby. The HARBINGER MOUNTAINS do not form a proper range, but take the form of groups of hills, the highest of which rises to 8,000 feet; all the same, it is probable that the Harbingers once formed part of the border of the Mare Imbrium, perhaps connecting the modern Carpathians with the Jura Mountains.

HERCYNIAN MOUNTAINS. A limb-range near Otto Struve. It is difficult to observe well, but its peaks probably exceed 7,000 feet in height.

HERODOTUS. The companion crater to Aristarchus. It is 23 miles across, and has a darkish floor, in striking contrast to the brilliance of its neighbour. Its walls rise to about 4,000 feet, but the shape of the crater is not quite regular. Associated with Herodotus is the great Valley, sometimes known as Schröter's Valley. There has been a controversy as to whether the Valley starts inside Herodotus or not; my own work with the Meudon 33-inch refractor indicates that it does, but I may be wrong. The Valley has been described in the text.

HEVEL. A grand 70-mile crater in the Grimaldi chain. Its walls are almost linear in places, but rise to 6,000 feet above a decidedly convex floor which contains a central mountain. Hevel is noted for the system of clefts inside it, and there are also domes nearby.

HORTENSIUS. A deep 10-mile crater in the Oceanus Procellarum. It is well-formed, and has rather bright walls. It is interesting because of the group of domes which lies to the north of it. Studies by P. J. Cattermole and myself show that several of these domes have summit pits.

KEPLER. In diameter (22 miles) and form Kepler is very like Encke, but it is far brighter, and is the centre of a major ray-system. There is a central mountain, and the walls are so heavily

253

terraced that they seem to be double in places. To the south-west is a small, deep craterlet, Kepler A. It is also worth noting that Kepler, like the even more brilliant Aristarchus, includes some radial bands, though they are nothing like so conspicuous as those of Aristarchus.

KUNOWSKY. A small crater 12 miles across, south-west of Encke. Its floor contains a rather low central ridge.

MARIUS. A well-marked crater 22 miles in diameter, on the Oceanus Procellarum. It has a very low central hill, as well as bright streaks on its floor. Well to the south-east is its 'twin', REINER, slightly smaller (diameter 20 miles) with brightish walls but a dark floor.

MAYER, TOBIAS. A crater in the Carpathian Mountains, 22 miles across, and with a central hill; adjoining it to the west is Tobias Mayer A, which is smaller but which also has a central hill. There are clefts and domes in this region which are worthy of close attention.

MILICHIUS. A small bright crater 8 miles in diameter, on the Oceanus Procellarum east of Copernicus. East of it lies a magnificent dome with a summit pit, and there are various other domes not far off.

OLBERS. A 40-mile crater close to the limb, not far from Cavalerius. It is a pity that it is so badly placed, since it is a major ray-centre. Like all ray-craters, it is very bright. Other formations even closer to the limb come into view under favourable conditions of libration.

PRINZ. An incomplete ring in the Harbinger Mountains, described with Gruithuisen.

PROCELLARUM, OCEANUS. The vast 'Ocean of Storms' has an area of two million square miles, much larger than our Mediterranean, but it is not one of the well-formed circular seas, and may be an overflow from the Mare Imbrium into the depression left by an older formation produced in the very early days of the Moon's history – though this is speculation, and may be quite wrong. At any event, the surface is much lighter and patchier than that of the Mare Imbrium. It extends on to Sections 5 and 9, and joins the Mare Nubium, Mare Humorum, Mare Imbrium and the Sinus Roris. Of the numerous craters on its floor, by far the most imposing is

Copernicus. With unfavourable libration the Oceanus spreads almost to the limb of the Moon, though none of it lies on the reverse hemisphere.

REINER. Reiner is not unlike Marius, and has been described with it.

SELEUCUS. This may be regarded as the twin of Briggs, to which it is connected by ridges. It is 32 miles in diameter, with terraced walls rising to 10,000 feet above an interior which contains a central peak. North-west of Seleucus is the distinct 18-mile crater SCHIAPARELLI; a light streak runs south-eastwards from it, so that Schiaparelli is easy to find under high light.

STRUVE, OTTO. A vast enclosure made up of two old rings, each about 100 miles across, which now make up one formation, while the east wall is really a ridge parallel to the Hercynian Mountains. In 1952 I discovered a vast crater, containing a central crater, beyond Otto Struve toward the limb, only visible under extreme libration; it has since been fully confirmed, and named CARAMUEL. It is a superb object, but is of course extremely difficult to see. I have also charted other large craters in the area, but better maps are needed.

SVEN HEDIN. A large 60-mile formation, irregular in shape and with broken walls, between Hevel and Cavalerius on one side and the limb on the other. It is difficult to study even under the best possible libration, but is very complex, and deserves attention. In the north its wall is broken by a distinct crater, BAUM.

VASCO DA GAMA. Though 50 miles in diameter, and with a central ridge rising to a peak in its mid-point, Vasco da Gama is difficult to examine on account of its unfavourable position very close to the limb. It lies north of Olbers and east of Cardanus and Krafft. It is one of a group of major ringed plains which are not yet properly charted.

THIRD (SOUTH-EAST) QUADRANT

The Moon's third quadrant includes most of the tremendous Mare Nubium as well as the Mare Humorum and a small part of the Oceanus Procellarum, but much of the quadrant is composed of rugged uplands. There are mountain ranges along the limb, of which the Dörfels are the highest, but few true ranges along the Mare coasts, apart from the Percy Mountains on the border of the Mare Humorum. There are many huge craters, notably Bailly, Schickard, Grimaldi, Riccioli, and the Walter and Ptolemæus chains, as well as the superb enclosure Clavius. Cleft-systems include those of Hippalus, Hesiodus and Sirsalis, and here too we have the celebrated lunar plateau Wargentin, as well as the remarkable fault known as the Straight Wall.

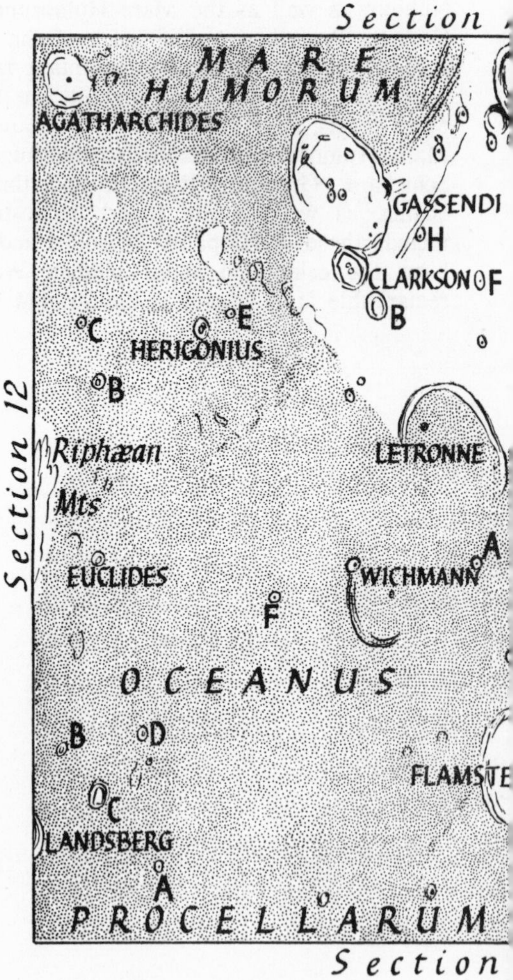
Section
MARE
HUMORUM
AGATHARCHIDES
GASSENDI
H
CLARKSON
F
B
E
C
HERIGONIUS
B
Section 12
Riphæan
Mts
LETRONNE
A
EUCLIDES
WICHMANN
F
OCEANUS
B
D
C
LANDSBERG
A
FLAMSTE
PROCELLARUM
Section

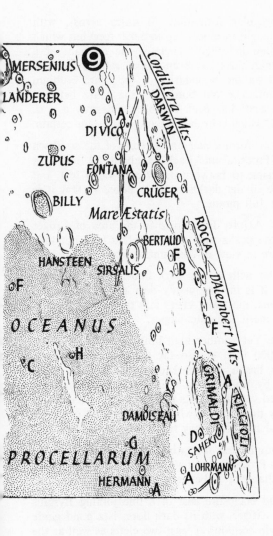

AGATHARCHIDES. An irregular formation 30 miles across, with walls which are of fair height in places (up to 5,000 feet) but which have been almost levelled in others. There is the remnant of a central mountain. Agatharchides has been considerably ruined by Mare-material, and lies on the boundaries of the Mare Nubium and the Mare Humorum. The old border of the Mare between Agatharchides and Gassendi has been completely destroyed – if, of course, it ever existed, which is probable but by no means certain.

BILLY. This and HANSTEEN form a pair on the edge of the southern part of the Oceanus Procellarum. Each is about 32 miles in diameter, with walls rising to between 3,000 and 4,000 feet, but Billy is notable because of the darkness of its floor, so that it is readily identifiable near full moon.

CORDILLERA MOUNTAINS. A lofty limb-range in the area of Crüger and Darwin. Some of the peaks may exceed 18,000 feet, but they are very hard to measure in view of their unfavourable position.

CRÜGER. A 30-mile crater with a very dark floor, resembling that of Billy. Unfortunately it is inconveniently near the limb. Near it are two small dark plains, the MARE VERIS and the MARE ÆSTATIS, which hardly seem to merit separate names.

D'ALEMBERT MOUNTAINS. Yet another high limb-range; some of its peaks may exceed 20,000 feet, but so far there are no reliable measures. In this area lies a well-marked little 'sea', the MARE ORIENTALIS, discovered by Wilkins and visible only under extreme libration. I have recorded various details in it, including what seems to be a cleft, but I very much doubt whether the present charts of it are at all reliable, and my 'cleft' may turn out to be a ridge.

DAMOISEAU. A very complicated formation west of Grimaldi, on the edge of the Oceanus Procellarum, made up of several old craters and ridges. The total diameter is between 20 and 30 miles.

DARWIN. A large, ruined enclosure east of a line joining Byrgius (Section 10) to Crüger; Crüger, with its dark floor, is a good guide to it. The floor of Darwin contains at least two clefts as well as the important and exceptional dome which has been described in the text. To the north-west of Darwin is the deep 15-mile crater DE VICO; the nearby crater De Vico A lies at the southern end of the great Sirsalis Cleft.

EUCLIDES. A remarkable little crater close to the Riphæn Mountains (Section 12). It is only 7 miles in diameter and 2,000 feet deep, but it is surrounded by an extensive bright nimbus which makes it very prominent. There are several smaller bright craters nearby.

FLAMSTEED. A bright 9-mile crater on the Oceanus Procellarum. It lies on the south rim of a large ghost-ring 60 miles across, which has incomplete and very low walls, but which is quite distinct under high light.

FONTANA. A 30-mile crater west of Crüger, with low but bright walls and a central hill. There are various clefts nearby, probably forming part of the extensive Sirsalis system.

GASSENDI. This is one of the most superb formations on the Moon. It it 55 miles in diameter, and lies on the north border of the Mare Humorum. The wall is quite high on the west, but on the south the Mare-material has largely destroyed it, and there are numerous gaps and passes. There is a central mountain, and the floor includes an extremely intricate cleft system – one of the finest known, and worth close study. In the north, the already battered wall has been further distorted by a prominent, well-formed crater, CLARKSON.

GRIMALDI. The famous walled plain near the east limb. It is 120 miles in diameter, so that it is one of the largest craters on the Moon, and its floor is definitely the darkest patch on the entire surface, so that Grimaldi is always unmistakable. The walls are discontinuous, but include some peaks which exceed 8,000 feet. The ramparts are extremely complex, and include hills, ridges, and clefts near their foot. The chief feature on the floor is the well-marked crater SAHEKI, but there is a mass of detail too complex for ready description. It has been suspected that the hue is variable, though I personally regard this as being due to nothing more significant than changes in illumination. Between Grimaldi and the limb at extreme libration are various other considerable craters, notably BUSS, LOWE and GREEN, while I have also found a 40-mile crater with a central hill, now named BOLTON. More accurate maps are needed.

HANSTEEN. This is the companion-crater to Billy, and has been described with it. Unlike Billy, it has a fairly bright floor.

HUMORUM, MARE. A small part of this interesting Mare is shown in the present Section, but most of it lies in Section 10.

LETRONNE. A good example of a bay. It has a diameter of 70 miles, and borders the Oceanus Procellarum, north-east of Gassendi. Its north wall has been destroyed, and the floor is fairly smooth, though it contains the wreck of a central peak. Letronne must once have been a noble formation, possibly the 'twin' of Gassendi.

LOHRMANN. A 28-mile crater lying between Hevel (Section 8) and Grimaldi, so that it is a member of the celebrated chain. It has a darkish floor, on which is a central hill, and there are many clefts nearby. West of it, on the Oceanus, is the bright 10-mile crater HERMANN.

MERSENIUS. An important and interesting crater, 45 miles across, near the border of the Mare Humorum. Its walls are terraced, rising to something like 8,000 feet in places, and the floor is markedly convex; Hevel is another large formation with this peculiarity. Mersenius is associated with an extensive cleft-system; some of the clefts lie on the Mare Humorum, others to the south of Mersenius (Section 10) in the direction of Liebig and De Gasparis. Closely outside the east wall of Mersenius is a distinct ten-mile crater, LANDERER.

PROCELLARUM, OCEANUS. A small part of the Oceanus extends into this Section, and includes the craters Wichmann, Flamsteed and Hermann as well as the great bay Letronne.

RICCIOLI. The smaller companion of Grimaldi. It is 100 miles in diameter, and has one patch on its floor which is almost as dark as any area in Grimaldi. The interior contains much detail, including hills, ridges and clefts. If Grimaldi and Riccioli lay nearer the centre of the disk, they might quite well have been classed as minor Maria.

ROCCA. A large crater, 60 miles in diameter, with a central ridge. It lies near the limb in the D'Alembert Mountains region, and is not easy to study.

SIRSALIS. A 20-mile crater which overlaps its slightly larger neighbour BERTAUD, so that the two form a striking pair rather similar to Steinheil and Watt in the fourth quadrant (Section 14). Sirsalis, the intruding formation, is also much deeper than Bertaud. Nearby is the famous cleft, visible with any small telescope when well placed, which forms part of a very complex cleft-system, and which extends from the border of the Oceanus Procellarum southward as far as Byrgius (Section 10).

WICHMANN. A bright 8-mile crater on the Oceanus Procellarum. north-west of Letronne. Like Flamsteed it lies on the rim of a large ghost crater, but the Wichmann ghost is even more ruined than that of Flamsteed.

ZUPUS. A very low-walled formation only about 12 miles across, north of Billy. It is, however, easy to find, because its floor, like those of Billy and Crüger. is extremely dark.

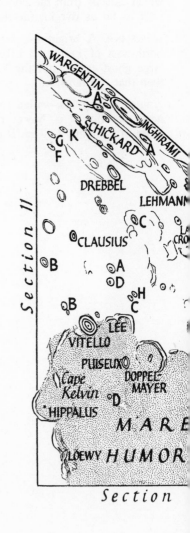

BOUVARD

Rook Mountains

AZZI

D

LA GRANGE
FOURIER

A

MIERI

VIETA

DE GASPARIS

8

BYRGIUS

A

LIEBIG   CAVENDISH

LA PAZ

PAUL
HENRY

JIYAH

PROSPER HENRY

EICHSTADT

BYRGIUS. A low-walled and rather obscure enclosure about 40 miles in diameter, not far from the limb. It is easy to find because the small crater on its western crest, LA PAZ, is a ray-centre, and so is prominent under high light. Well to the north-east of Byrgius. much closer to the limb, is the regular low-walled EICHSTÄDT. 32 miles across, but very badly placed for observation.

CAVENDISH. A formation with a diameter of 32 miles. Its walls are of fair height, attaining 7,000 feet in places, but are disturbed by smaller craters. It lies south-east of Mersenius (Section 9) and east of the Mare Humorum. Between it and the Mare border are the smaller LIEBIG, DE GASPARIS and JIYAH.

DOPPELMAYER. Another splendid lunar bay, this time on the coast of the Mare Humorum. The 'landward' wall is quite high, and there is a central mountain, but the 'seaward' wall has been so ruined that it is now very low and discontinuous, with wide gaps. Adjoining it is LEE, another incomplete formation which has been ruined by Mare material, but which is much less impressive than Doppelmayer. PALMIERI, roughly between Doppelmayer and Vieta. is a curious enclosure whose floor is crossed by at least two clefts.

FOURIER. A 36-mile crater close to Vieta. Its walls are terraced. and the floor contains a central crater in lieu of a central peak.

HUMORUM, MARE. A superb example of a minor circular sea; its area, amounting to 50,000 square miles, is about the same as that of England. It provides probably the best example of faulting on the Moon, and there are also many clefts and bays in and near it. The floor is fairly smooth, and the only formation on it given a separate name is the very low-walled ghost PUISEUX. Partly in this Section. and best described with it. is another great bay, HIPPALUS, which is 38 miles in diameter and has a central peak, though the seaward wall is now barely traceable. Hippalus is associated with a fine system of parallel clefts. A much less prominent bay, LOEWY. lies near it, rather to the north-east.

INGHIRAMI. A beautiful walled plain 60 miles in diameter, between Schickard and the limb. It has high terraced walls, with peaks rising to 10,000 feet, and a central mountain. Unfortunately it is too near the limb to be well seen. From it a ridge runs toward the even larger BOUVARD, 80 miles across, and which has a central ridge rising to a peak at its mid-point.

PERCY MOUNTAINS. A mountain arm running south-east from Gassendi (Section 9) and so forming part of the border of the Mare Humorum.

ROOK MOUNTAINS. A lofty mountain range on the limb. Some of the peaks may exceed 20,000 feet, but the measures are not reliable. Nearby are the large but badly-placed formations LAGRANGE and PIAZZI.

SCHICKARD. This is one of the Moon's great walled plains, and has been referred to frequently in the text. Its diameter is 134 miles, and its walls are rather low, averaging less than 5,000 feet and with its highest peaks rising to about 8,200 feet. The floor contains some interesting dark patches as well as various craterlets and hills. Adjoining it on the north-east is the 28-mile LEHMANN, whose floor is connected by passes to that of Schickard. Not far off is the 18-mile, well-formed crater DREBBEL, as well as the small but quite prominent CLAUSIUS and the ill-defined, rather dark-floored formation LACROIX. The most interesting of Schickard's neighbours is, of course, Wargentin, described separately, while Phocylides and Nasmyth (Section 11) are also members of the Schickard group.

VIETA. A large crater 50 miles in diameter. Its walls are uneven in height, but in places rise to 15,000 feet; there is a minor central peak.

VITELLO. This is particularly interesting as being a splendid example of what Thornton terms a concentric crater – even though the complete inner ring is not quite concentric with the main wall. Vitello is 30 miles across, and has a central peak crowned by a craterlet. It lies on the border of the Mare Humorum, west of Doppelmayer and Lee, and its seaward wall has clearly been reduced by the Mare material, though elsewhere the rampart rises to over 4,000 feet above the interior.

WARGENTIN. This is one of the most remarkable formations on the whole Moon, and represents the only example of a really large, well-preserved lunar plateau. It is 55 miles in diameter, so that in size it is the equal of Copernicus, and it is a great pity that it lies so near the limb. In small telescopes its floor appears smooth apart from a couple of ridges, but with the Meudon refractor I have been able to chart about sixty features, mainly ridges and hills. There is a 'wall' in places, but the whole floor is considerably raised – by about 1,400 feet – so that it is unique among major formations. It has been described in the text. Wargentin is a member of the group which includes Schickard, Nasmyth and Phocylides.

11 NEWTON
GRUEMBERGER
CYSATUS
CASATUS LEGENTIL WILSON
KLAPROTH
BLANCANUS
RUTHERFURD
CLAVIUS
SCHEINER
KIRCHER
B
PORTER
DELUC
C
C H
H E B D A
MAGINUS
LONGO-
MONTANUS
D K G
M
STREET D
PROCTOR D
SAUSSURE A
PICTET
BROWN
HUGGINS
ORONTIUS BARKER
TYCHO
D C
B
A
SASSERIDES A
A
HEINS
A C
B
BALL
C
A
WALTER
LEXELL
A
DESLANDRES A
GAURICUS
HELL
WURZEL-
BAUER
HÖRBIGER
B
PITATUS
REGIO-
MONTANUS
M A R E
N U B I U M
PURBACH
Stags Horn
Mts
LIPPERSHEY
G

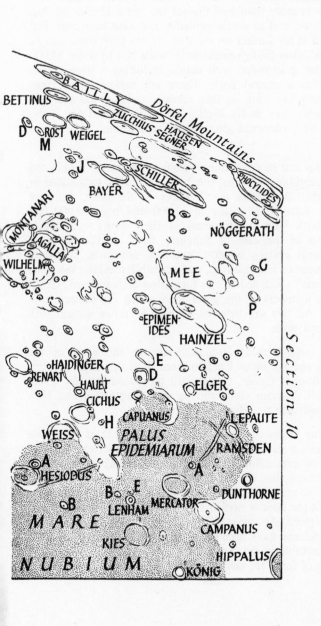

BETTINUS

BATLY

Dörfel Mountains

D ROST WEIGEL
M

ZUCCHIUS HAUSEN
SEGNER

J

SCHILLER

PHOCYLIDES

BAYER

B

NÖGGERATH

MONTANARI
AGALLA
WILHELM
I.

MEE

G

P

EPIMEN-
IDES

HAINZEL

HAIDINGER
RENART
HAUET
CICHUS

E

D

ELGER

H

CAPUANUS

L'EPAUTE

WEISS

PALUS
EPIDEMIARUM

RAMSDEN

A
HESIODUS

A

B

B E
LENHAM MERCATOR

DUNTHORNE

MARE

KIES

CAMPANUS

NUBIUM

HIPPALUS

KÖNIG

BAILLY. The largest formation on the Moon officially classed as a crater. Its area is more than half that of the Mare Humorum, but it has a light floor, and so would probably not have been reckoned as a sea even if it lay further on the disk. It has been described as 'a field of ruins', even though peaks in its walls rise to about 14,000 feet; the interior is crowded with detail, including a deep crater, HARE, which has a central peak. There are various other large formations along the limb in this section, notably HAUSEN and LEGENTIL, which – like Bailly itself – are badly placed for study, and can be well observed only under conditions of extreme libration.

BLANCANUS. This and its companion SCHEINER are rather dominated by their vast neighbour Clavius, but both are major formations in their own right. Blancanus is 57 miles in diameter, Scheiner 70; both have lofty walls, rising to 12,000 and over 15,000 feet respectively; both have much detail in their floors – a nearly central craterlet in the case of Scheiner. Close to the limb are several prominent craters, WILSON, KIRCHER, BETTINUS, ZUCCHIUS and SEGNER, more or less lined up, and probably marking the same 'line of weakness' which led to the formation of Schickard, Grimaldi and other members of the great chain along the eastern limb of the Moon. All five are between 40 and 50 miles across, with lofty, continuous walls.

CAMPANUS. A well-formed, 30-mile crater at the edge of the Mare Nubium and the Palus Epidemiarum. It is the 'twin' of Mercator, but its floor is lighter, though still on the dusky side. There is a central hill. Various clefts run between Campanus and Hippalus, associated with the Hippalus system.

CAPUANUS. This is an extraordinary formation. It is 35 miles across, and lies on the coast of the Palus Epidemiarum; its floor has been to some extent flooded with lunabase, and appears darkish. Wilkins considered that the interior was elevated above the surrounding area, so making Capuanus a plateau, but my own observations show that the floor is neither raised nor depressed with regard to the outer regions. At any rate, the walls have been disturbed on the seaward side, and have been badly ruined in places. What makes Capuanus so notable is the fact that at least eight domes exist on its floor; some of them are visible with very small telescopes. There

272

is no other known case of a large crater so rich in domes. Closely outside Capuanus is an imperfect formation, ELGER.

CASATUS. This and KLAPROTH form another example of overlapping craters – this time on a grand scale, since Casatus is 65 miles in diameter, with extremely high walls which, according to some measures, exceed 20,000 feet. Klaproth is shallower, with a much smoother floor. Not far from Klaproth is GRUEMBERGER, which belongs to the Moretus group (Section 14), while between Casatus and the limb at extreme libration is a large, interesting and decidedly broken formation, DRYGALSKI. This whole area is shown very poorly on most maps, since it is so crowded, and so badly placed, that it is extremely difficult to study properly.

CICHUS. A prominent 20-mile crater west of Capuanus, just beyond the border of the Mare Nubium. On its eastern crest is a well-formed crater, Cichus G, about 5 miles in diameter. Nearby is the crater HAUET, and to the north of Cichus is WEISS, which is really an enclosure bordered by irregular ridges rather than a true crater. There are various clefts in this area, probably associated with the Hesiodus system.

CLAVIUS. Apart from Bailly, Clavius is the largest of the so-called craters, since it is 145 miles in diameter, and with mighty walls rising to at least 12,000 feet. Every lunar observer knows it well. The north-west wall is broken by a large crater, PORTER, and there is a chain of craters across the floor, of which RUTHERFURD is the largest. When on the terminator, Clavius is distinctly visible with the naked eye, and it is easy to find telescopically under any conditions of lighting.

DÖRFEL MOUNTAINS. A very high limb-range, extending roughly from Bailly as far as Inghirami (Section 10). Owing to the great foreshortening, the altitudes are difficult to measure, but some peaks may exceed 20,000 feet, so that of all the lunar mountains only the Leibnitz are higher.

EPIDEMIARUM, PALUS. A conspicuous little dark plain extending out of the Mare Nubium. Mercator and Capuanus lie on its borders. It is notable chiefly because there are many clefts in and near it, known as the Ramsden system, though the crater of RAMSDEN itself is only 15 miles in diameter and is entirely unremarkable. In complexity, the Ramsden system rivals that of Triesnecker, and is well worth close attention.

GAURICUS. An irregular enclosure with a diameter of about 40 miles and walls which are uneven in height. It lies close to the Pitatus group, and may be regarded as a member of it.

HAINZEL. A curious formation which seems to be made up of two almost equal rings which have coalesced. The north-south diameter is 60 miles. Under oblique lighting it is conspicuous, but is hard to find near full moon. West of it is the small crater EPIMENIDES. and to the south is a large, decidedly ruined enclosure. MEE, with low walls.

HEINSIUS. A very peculiar structure between Tycho and Capuanus, rather closer to Tycho. The north wall is quite high, but to the south the rampart has been broken by three considerable craters. one of which really lies on Heinsius' floor. The diameter is about 45 miles.

HELL. A 20-mile crater with a low central hill. lying near the edge of the vast enclosure Hörbiger.

HESIODUS. This is the companion of Pitatus, to which it is connected by passes in their common wall. It is 28 miles across, and its walls have been somewhat reduced by the Mare material: the floor contains an almost central crater. From Hesiodus a famous cleft runs across to the mountain arm north of Cichus; it is easy to see with a small telescope when well placed. Other, less prominent clefts are associated with it.

HÖRBIGER. One of the largest enclosures of the crater type; it seems to have been named after the originator of various peculiar astronomical theories, including the ice hypothesis of the lunar surface, but other maps term it 'Hellplain'. Hell lies inside it; on the border are BALL, which is 25 miles across and has high terraced walls, and the 39-mile LEXELL, whose north wall has been reduced to such an extent that it resembles a bay opening out of Hörbiger. even though it retains the wreck of a central peak. The only other prominent crater in Hörbiger is DESLANDRES. The formation is easy to locate. since it adjoins the Walter chain to the east.

KIES. This cannot be termed a ghost-ring, but it lies on the Mare Nubium, and its walls are now very low, nowhere exceeding 2,500 feet; the floor is dark, and evidently covered with lunabase. East of it lies a superb example of a dome with a summit pit. and there are other domes in the area. Other. smaller craters in the area include LENHAM, KÖNIG, and the formation marked as MOORE (Section 12) in some maps – because I once discovered a radial band inside it, though many people will prefer to retain its title of Agatharchides A! Lenham, too, contains a radial band. The Hippalus cleft-system lies closely east of this area, and Moore actually lies on a cleft.

KLAPROTH. This large crater has been described with its companion, Casatus.

LONGOMONTANUS. A very large enclosure, 90 miles in diameter, with complex walls and considerable detail on its floor. It is easy to find, though it is not nearly so prominent as Clavius. North of it is the small but well-formed crated MONTANARI.

MAGINUS. With a diameter of 110 miles, Maginus is one of the greatest craters on the Moon, and would be even more striking were it not close to the even more majestic Clavius. Maginus has walls of uneven height, and a rather rough floor; to the south-east the ramparts are broken by a 30-mile crater, Maginus C, while another crater of about this size, PROCTOR, lies between Maginus and Saussure. Oddly enough Maginus is difficult to identify near full moon – even if it does not vanish entirely, as some books maintain.

MERCATOR. The 'twin' of Campanus, on the edge of the Palus Epidemiarum. It has a dark floor, with walls rising in places to 5,000 feet; there is only a trace of a central peak, but detail lies on its floor, including a delicate cleft.

NEWTON. This is generally regarded as the deepest of the lunar craters. Some estimates make the wall 30,000 feet above the floor at its highest point; this may well be an over-estimate, but Newton is certainly very deep indeed. Evidently it is a compound formation, made up of the fusion of two or more rings, but it is so near the limb, and so appallingly badly placed for observation, that maps of it are by no means reliable. It lies on the borders of this Section and Section 14, not far from Gruemberger.

NUBIUM, MARE. Part of the Mare Nubium is shown here, but most of it lies in Section 12.

ORONTIUS. An irregular formation about 52 miles in diameter, north-west of Tycho. It is one of a group which includes Miller and Nasireddin in Section 14, and Huggins and Saussure in this

Section. Orontius has been disturbed by HUGGINS, and must therefore be older. The whole area is crowded with detail, but includes no particularly notable features.

PHOCYLIDES. A most interesting formation, 60 miles in diameter. It is a member of the Schickard group (Section 10), also including NASMYTH (between Phocylides and Wargentin), and Wargentin itself, as well as Phocylides C, which merits a separate name. Considerable detail is visible on the floor, and some years ago W. Cameron Walker reported the existence of an unusual 'step-fault', though my own observations indicate that no such fault exists. Between Phocylides and Mee lies the unremarkable NÖGGERATH.

PITATUS. A grand formation 50 miles across. It lies on the border of the Mare Nubium, and gives the impression of a large lagoon; its walls have been badly damaged, especially on the seaward side, and are almost non-existent in places. Passes connect the floor with that of Hesiodus. Pitatus has no true central peak, but there is a hill not quite centrally placed. Other members of the Pitatus group are Gauricus and Wurzelbauer.

PURBACH. This great ring-plain, 75 miles in diameter and with walls rising 8,000 feet in places, is a member of the chain which includes Regiomontanus and WALTER. The floor contains considerable detail. The outline of Purbach is not entirely regular, and the northern part of the rampart has been badly disturbed by later outbreaks. The circular LACAILLE lies north-west.

REGIOMONTANUS. This is a distorted formation between Purbach and Walter. Its east-west diameter is 80 miles, but the distance from north to south is only 65 miles; one has the impression that the whole crater has been 'squashed' between Purbach and Walter. There is abundant floor-detail, including some considerable mountains not quite in the centre. The walls are of irregular height, but there are peaks reaching 7,000 feet. In places the rampart is common with that of Purbach and Hörbiger.

SASSERIDES. An irregular enclosure north of Tycho, with a diameter of about 60 miles. Its north wall has been largely destroyed by four smaller craters, and the floor includes numerous pits and hills. To the south-east is Sasserides A, which has a central peak; and between Sasserides and Orontius lies the unremarkable formation BARKER.

SCHEINER. This great plain may be regarded as the twin of Blancanus, though it is the larger and deeper of the two. It is described with Blancanus.

SCHILLER. A compound formation in the area between Schickard and Clavius. It is 112 miles long, but only 60 wide at its broadest point, and is clearly the result of the fusion of at least two old rings; I have seen vague traces of the old border between them. The floor contains some ridges and pits. The region bounded by Schiller, Phocylides and Segner is fairly smooth, and I suspect that it is an old crater whose walls have now been destroyed. Closely outside Schiller is the well-formed BAYER, 32 miles across, and with high terraced walls attaining 8,000 feet in places.

TYCHO. This crater, 54 miles in diameter, is in a class by itself, as it is the centre of by far the greatest ray-system on the Moon; under high light it dominates the entire lunar scene. It has been fully described in the text. Its neighbours include PICTET, STREET and BROWN, as well as Sasserides and the Orontius group; had Tycho been formed by a meteorite late in lunar history, it is hard to see how any of these formations could have survived in recognizable shape.

WALTER. A majestic, complex walled plain, 90 miles in diameter.

WILHELM I. A 60-mile enclosure with walls which are uneven in height, but which contain a few peaks reaching 11,000 feet above the floor. Outside it, to the south-east, lies the irregular and pear-shaped formation LAGALLA. Wilhelm I is easy enough to find, as it lies not far from Tycho, but becomes very obscure under high illumination.

WURZELBAUER. Wurzelbauer is one of the Pitatus group, and is about 50 miles in diameter, but its walls are irregular and even discontinuous in places. The floor contains a mass of complex detail.

ZUCCHIUS. This is one of a chain which includes Segner, Bettinus, Wilson and Kircher. It has been described with Blancanus. Between Zucchius and Longomontanus lie two unremarkable but quite distinct craters, WEIGEL and ROST. I have found a feature inside Zucchius itself which appears to be a dome of considerable size.

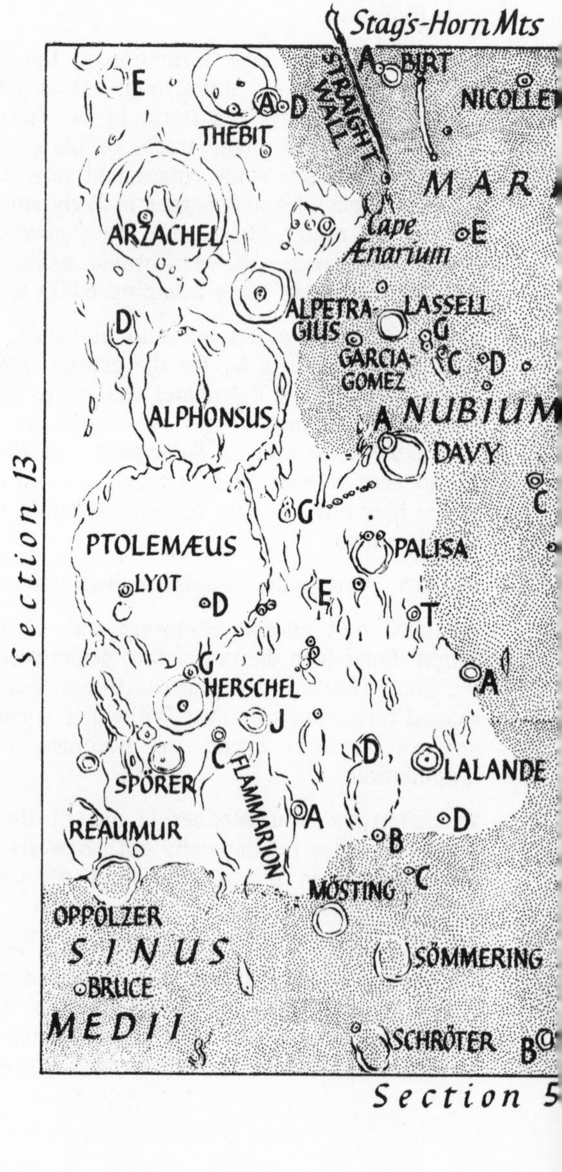
Stag's-Horn Mts
STRAIGHT WALL
A
BIRT
NICOLLET
E
A
D
THEBIT
MARE
ARZACHEL
Cape Ænarium
E
ALPETRAGIUS
LASSELL
D
G
GARCIA-GOMEZ
C
D
NUBIUM
A
ALPHONSUS
DAVY
C
G
Section 13
PTOLEMÆUS
PALISA
LYOT
D
E
T
G
HERSCHEL
A
J
D
C
LALANDE
SPÖRER
FLAMMARION
A
D
RÉAUMUR
B
C
MÖSTING
OPPÖLZER
SINUS
SÖMMERING
BRUCE
MEDII
SCHRÖTER
B
Section 5

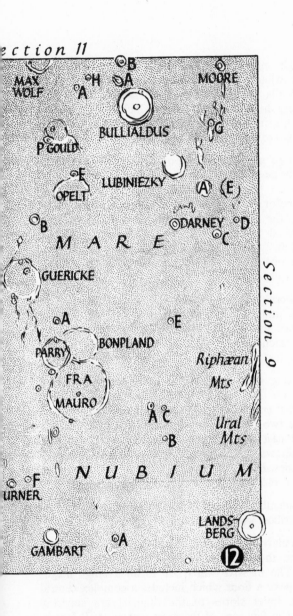

MAX
WOLF

B

H

A

A

MOORE

BULLIALDUS

G

P GOULD

E

LUBINIEZKY

A

E

OPELT

B

DARNEY

D

C

M A R E

GUERICKE

A

E

PARRY

BONPLAND

Riphæan
Mts

FRA

MAURO

A C

B

Ural
Mts

N U B I U M

F

URNER

LANDS-
BERG

GAMBART

A

⑫

ALPETRAGIUS. Though only 27 miles in diameter, Alpetragius is a splendid sight when seen under good conditions. It lies closely outside the walls of Alphonsus and Arzachel, and is distinguished for its very high terraced walls, which exceed 12,000 feet in places, and for its enormous central mountain, which is rounded and which is crowned by two summit pits.

ALPHONSUS. Little more need be said about this great formation, since it has been fully described in the text; it achieved particular notoriety in 1958 when Kozirev reported an outbreak inside it, but for many years before it had been regarded as a possible site of mild activity. It is the middle member of the Ptolemæus chain, and is slightly distorted in form. The floor contains a mass of detail, including a cleft system. It is hardly necessary to add that Alphonsus should be observed on every possible occasion, in case any further outbreaks occur inside it.

ARZACHEL. The southern member of the Ptolemæus chain. It is 60 miles in diameter, and has high walls, reaching 13,500 feet in places; the floor detail includes a central mountain and a deep, prominent crater, Arzachel A. Wilkins gives the height of the central peak as 4,900 feet.

BIRT. A very interesting little crater 11 miles in diameter, close to the Straight Wall, on the Mare Nubium. Its south-west wall is disturbed by a smaller crater, and on the common rampart is a minute pit. There are two radial bands inside Birt, running to the north-west and south-east wall. Closely outside, to the east, is a famous cleft, which shows crater-like enlargements at its northern and southern extremities. Birt is quite deep, and may be found even under high light, when the Straight Wall is completely invisible.

BONPLAND. This is a member of the Fra Mauro group on the Mare Imbrium, and is described with Fra Mauro.

BULLIALDUS. A particularly fine crater; it has been described as a miniature Copernicus, though it is a full 39 miles across and is not a ray-centre. The massive walls rise to an average height of about 8,000 feet above a floor which includes a complex central mountain group; the inner slopes of the rampart are superbly terraced. Bullialdus is, in fact, one of the most perfect of all formations of its type.

DAVY. A 20-mile crater near the edge of the Mare Nubium, between Alphonsus and the Fra Mauro group. The wall is quite high in places, but there is a gap in the north, while in the southwest the rampart is broken by a small, deep crater, Davy A. To the south is the low-walled 14-mile crater LASSELL, and between Lassell and Alpetragius there is a very symmetrical bright crater, GARCIA-GOMEZ, 6 miles in diameter. Some way north of Davy is a low-walled ring, PALISA. The area between Palisa and Davy seems to represent the ruins of a very old crater.

FLAMMARION. An irregular enclosure north-east of Ptolemæus and Herschel, with a maximum diameter of 45 miles. Its walls are incomplete, particularly in the north, where they have presumably been damaged by material from the adjacent Mare.

FRA MAURO. This is the largest member of a group of craters in the Mare Nubium; the others are Bonpland, Parry and Guericke. Fra Mauro itself, with a diameter of 50 miles, is the largest and presumably the oldest; its walls have been much reduced, and it almost, though not quite, comes into the category of a ghost. Bonpland (36 miles across) is in a slightly better state of preservation, and PARRY (26 miles) has still higher walls. These three formations have common boundaries, and are crossed by various clefts. Further south is GUERICKE (often, though wrongly, spelled Gueriké), with incomplete walls, very broken in the north and indeed almost levelled in places. The interior contains considerable detail, including a crater-chain, pits and ridges, several delicate clefts, and a considerable crater, Guericke A.

HERSCHEL. A fine crater 28 miles across, with terraced walls and a large central peak. It lies closely north of Ptolemæus, and is very distinct. Adjoining it to the north is SPÖRER, much less complete, and with indications of having been partly filled with lava. Closely west of Herschel is a prominent valley, beyond which is a low-walled depression.

LALANDE. A well-formed crater 15 miles in diameter, with a low central hill. A very old ring lies between it and Flammarion.

LANDSBERG. The more correct spelling is 'Lansberg', but the alternative form has been in use for many years, and it would be pedantic to alter it now. It lies on the Mare Nubium, north of the Riphæan Mountains, and is a fine example of a ringed plain, 28 miles in diameter, with massive walls pitted on the south by crater-like depressions. Well to the west lies the shallower and less regular GAMBART; between Gambart and Landsberg is a distinct little crater. Gambart A; and between Gambart and Lalande lie two craterlets, TURNER and Gambart F.

LUBINIEZKY. A ruined crater on the Mare Nubium, north-east of Bullialdus; its walls are everywhere low, and in places discontinuous, while the floor is as dark as the surrounding Mare. To the north lies the well-formed little crater DARNEY. There are numerous ghost rings in this area (GOULD and OPELT are others) and the whole region is worthy of close attention.

MEDII, SINUS. The Central Bay. Part of it lies in this Section; Mösting, Sömmering and Schröter lie near its boundary.

MÖSTING. A well-formed crater 16 miles across, with a low central hill. To the south-south-west is Mösting A, actually on the borders of Flammarion. which is very bright. and is a minor ray-centre.

MOORE. A small crater lying between Hippalus (Section 10) and Bullialdus. It has been described with Kies.

NICOLLET. A distinct 10-mile crater on the Mare Nubium, roughly east of Birt. Some distance away is MAX WOLF. low-walled and irregular in outline.

NUBIUM, MARE. One of the largest of the lunar seas; much of it lies in this Section, though parts extend into Sections 9 and 11. It is lighter and patchier than the Mare Imbrium, though less so than the Oceanus Procellarum, and I believe that it is made up of an overflow into an already existing, very ancient formation. There are no really high ranges of mountains to mark its border. Craters on it include Bullialdus and the interesting Fra Mauro group.

PARRY. This is in the Fra Mauro group, and has been described with it.

PTOLEMÆUS. Ptolemæus is one of the most famous craters on the Moon. It is over 90 miles across, and lies fairly near the middle of the disk, so that it is excellently placed for observation. Its floor is darkish in hue, but contains a great many objects as well as the well-marked craterlet LYOT; by visual observation and with the help of photographs. Wilkins and I have constructed a chart showing well over 100 separate features on the interior. The walls are generally broken. but contain some high peaks, one of which seems to reach 9,000 feet or so. Ptolemæus is a member of a great chain of walled formations, including Alphonsus and Arzachel.

RIPHÆAN MOUNTAINS. A low mountain range in the Mare Nubium, probably marking part of the wall of an old ghost crater. Its highest peaks rise to no more than 3,000 feet. The URAL MOUNTAINS, to the north, are really part of the Riphæans. The best means of identification is provided by Euclides (Section 9), whose bright nimbus makes it easy to find under any conditions of illumination.

SCHRÖTER. A semi-ruined, 20-mile crater between the Mare Nubium and the Sinus Medii. It has clearly been badly reduced by the Mare material, and its walls are incomplete in the south. It is worth noting that it is nowhere near Schröter's Valley; the Valley lies in the second quadrant, near Aristarchus, and to avoid confusion I personally prefer the alternative name for it of the Herodotus Valley.

SÖMMERING. Another ruined ring, 17 miles across, close to Schröter and Mösting. Its walls are low everywhere, with a gap in the south.

STRAIGHT WALL. As has been pointed out in the text, this formation is not straight, and it is not a wall. It is, nevertheless, a particularly interesting object, and has been described earlier. It lies between Thebit and Birt, and ends to the south in the group of hills termed the STAG'S-HORN MOUNTAINS – which, according to my observations, are really part of the border of an ancient crater lying to the east.

THEBIT. This also has been described in the text. It may be a true member of the Walter chain, and is always identifiable, even near full moon. It lies on the edge of the Mare Nubium, and some way north-east lies the cape known as PROMONTORIUM ÆNARIUM – a misspelling of the proper name of Tænarium, but which has become generally accepted.

TURNER. This small crater has been described with Landsberg and Gambart.

FOURTH (SOUTH-WEST) QUADRANT

This quadrant contains few seas; the Mare areas are in fact limited to part of the Mare Fœcunditatis, all of the Mare Nectaris, and a very small portion of the Sinus Medii, apart from the lunabase area known as the Mare Australe on the south-west limb. Most of the quadrant is occupied by rugged uplands, and there are craters of all sorts, ranging from the huge, ruined Janssen down to superb formations such as Theophilus, smaller rings, and hundreds upon hundreds of craterlets. The Leibnitz Mountains, on the limb, are extremely high, but otherwise there is only the feature once known as the Altai Mountain range but now, following Spurr, as the Altai Scarp. Various features near the limb are also shown on the Lunik III photographs.

⓭

FERMAT

ROMAÑA

POLYBIUS

FRACAS-
TORILIS

Altai Scarp

A

C F

A

C

D

F
G

A

P

CATHARINA

BEAUMONT

A

M A R E

C

TACITUS

B

NECTARIS

CYRILLUS

A

D

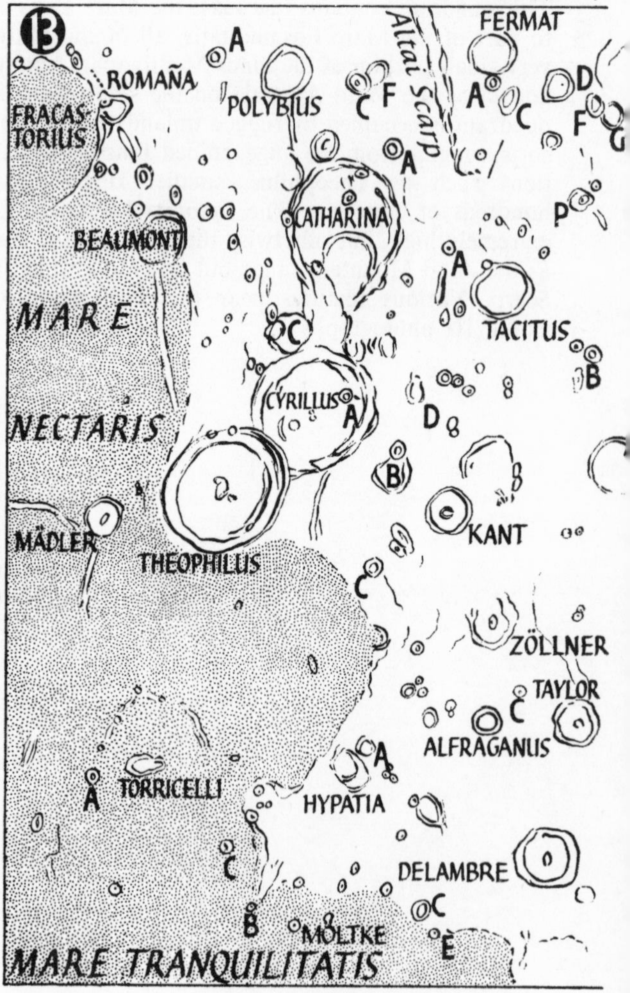

B

MÄDLER

THEOPHILUS

KANT

C

ZÖLLNER

TAYLOR

C

ALFRAGANUS

A
TORRICELLI

A
HYPATIA

DELAMBRE

C

C

C

E

B
MOLTKE

MARE TRANQUILITATIS

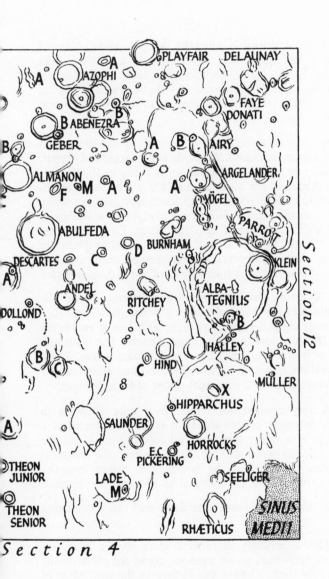

PLAYFAIR DELAUNAY

A

AZOPHI

A

FAYE
DONATI

B

B ABENEZRA

GEBER

A B AIRY

B

ALMANON

ARGELANDER

F M A

A

VÖGEL

ABULFEDA

PARROT

D BURNHAM

DESCARTES

C

KLEIN

ANDEL

ALBA-
TEGNIUS

RITCHEY

A

B

DOLLOND

HALLEY

B

C

C HIND

MÜLLER

A

X

HIPPARCHUS

SAUNDER

HORROCKS

E.C.
PICKERING

THEON
JUNIOR

LADE
M

SEELIGER

THEON
SENIOR

SINUS
MEDII

RHÆTICUS

ABENEZRA. This forms a notable pair with Azophi. The two are of about the same size (27 miles in diameter), and have high walls, exceeding 10,000 feet. The ramparts have inner terraces, particularly in the case of Abenezra. To the south-east, just on Section 14, is another unremarkable ring, PLAYFAIR, equal in size to Abenezra and Azophi.

ABULFEDA. Another interesting pair is formed by Abulfeda and Almanon, not far from Abenezra. Abulfeda is the larger and deeper, since it is 40 miles in diameter and has walls rising to 10,000 feet; the figures for Almanon are 30 miles and 6,000 feet. An interesting crater-valley runs from north-east to south-west between them, and is continued in the general direction of Polybius; undoubtedly it is associated with the system of the Altai Scarp. To the north are the low-walled rings of DESCARTES and ÅNDĚL, as well as the bright 6-mile DOLLOND. Dollond borders a large, ruined enclosure, and some maps give the name to the ruin instead of to the deep craterlet.

ALBATEGNIUS. A great crater 80 miles in diameter, near the Ptolemæus chain (Section 12) and forming a companion to Hipparchus. The walls are generally quite high, with one or two peaks reaching to 14,000 feet, and there are large terraces. The walls are, however, broken in the south-east by a large crater, KLEIN. There is a central mountain, as well as various craterlets and other features on the floor. Albategnius is a fine sight under oblique lighting.

ALFRAGANUS. A very conspicuous crater. It is only 12 miles in diameter, but is intensely bright, and as it is also the centre of a minor ray-system it is easily found at full moon. Near it are the triangular, 30-mile HYPATIA, on the Mare-border; the elliptical TAYLOR, 25 miles across; and the low-walled, rather irregular ZÖLLNER, none of which can be regarded as of particular interest.

ALMANON. This crater has been described with its companion Abulfeda.

ALTAI SCARP. This is certainly more of a scarp than a mountain range. It rises to 6,000 feet, on an average, above the plain on the west, but only very slightly above the surface to the east. Most of it lies in Section 14, but it extends past Fermat as far as Tacitus.

ARGELANDER. A 20-mile crater south-west of Albategnius, with terraced walls and a central peak. Its 'twin' is the nearby AIRY, rather similar to it, and also with a central peak.

AZOPHI. This adjoins Abenezra, and has been described with it.

BEAUMONT. An excellent example of a bay. It lies on the coast of the Mare Nectaris, between Fracastorius and Cyrillus, and is 30 miles in diameter; it retains its landward wall, but the rampart toward the Mare has been largely destroyed. Small craterlets exist on the floor, but are hardly likely to be seen with small telescopes.

CATHARINA. The southernmost member of the Theophilus chain. It is about 55 miles in diameter, with rugged walls; the floor contains a large, low-walled, ruined ring. There is no central peak. The area between Catharina and Cyrillus is high, and is a splendid sight under oblique illumination.

CYRILLUS. Cyrillus lies between Catharina, from which it is separated by an upland area, and Theophilus, which overlaps it – showing that Theophilus is younger than Cyrillus. As usual, the walls of the broken formation remain intact up to the point of the junction, so that Theophilus can hardly have been formed by any violently explosive process. The floor of Cyrillus contains a reduced central hill, as well as a considerable crater, Cyrillus A, and much fine detail. The diameter is about 60 miles, but this is only an average, as the formation is by no means perfectly circular even allowing for the intrusion of Theophilus. Closely west is Cyrillus C, recently re-named PAVLOV.

DELAMBRE. A well-formed crater 32 miles in diameter, east of the Mare Nectaris. It has high walls, with some peaks reaching 15,000 feet. Close beside it lie the two bright craters known as the Theons. Delambre has a central peak with a summit pit.

DELAUNAY. A most peculiar formation lying well to the south of Albategnius. It seems to consist of two distinct craters separated by a high ridge, but its details are very complex, and I can understand why F. H. Thornton once referred to it as 'Puzzle Corner'.

FAYE. This and DONATI are two irregular, imperfect formations close to Delaunay. Each is about 22 miles in mean diameter.

GEBER. A very regular 25-mile crater between Almanon and Abenezra. Its walls are high and terraced, but slightly disturbed to the east by a much smaller crater, Geber A.

HALLEY. This and HIND are two well-formed, terraced craters close to Hipparchus and Albategnius. Halley is 22 miles in diameter, Hind 16. Halley has been referred to in the text in connection with the Rutherfurd photograph, but any change there is highly unlikely. A broad valley runs from Halley into Hipparchus in one direction, and to the western glacis of Albategnius in the other. East of Halley is the low-walled, rather irregular MÜLLER, and some way south of Hind is another very irregular and deformed object, RITCHEY.

HIND. This crater has been described with its larger companion, Halley.

HIPPARCHUS. This tremendous enclosure, almost equal to Ptolemæus in size, has been considerably ruined, but even so it is striking when seen under low illumination. A grid system is very evident in this area, and Hipparchus contains a great amount of fine detail as well as the prominent 18-mile crater HORROCKS. Outside Hipparchus, to the north-west, are the ruined formations SAUNDER and LADE and the more regular but smaller crater E. C. PICKERING. Hipparchus itself is, of course, much less imposing than Ptolemæus (Section 12).

KANT. A very deep crater, 20 miles in diameter, east of Theophilus. It is distinguished by its huge, rounded central mountain, which contains a summit pit. Kant is one of the craters whose floor has been suspected to be subject to obscuration – as was, for instance, reported by the French astronomer Trouvelot on 4th January 1873, when he stated that the crater was 'filled with mist'.

MÄDLER. An irregular but prominent crater 20 miles across. It lies on the Mare Nectaris, west of Theophilus. Its floor is crossed by a ridge, which joins the central mountain mass. Mädler lies near the eastern border of a ghost ring which extends in the direction of Isidorus (Section 16).

MEDII, SINUS. A small part of the Sinus appears in this Section, in the area of Rhæticus.

NECTARIS, MARE. Part of the Mare Nectaris appears here; the rest is on Section 16. It is basically circular, but has been considerably distorted, with a good deal of faulting. Mädler lies near its junction with the Mare Tranquillitatis; note also the great bays of Beaumont and FRACASTORIUS. Fracastorius is 60 miles across, and its sea-ward wall has been almost completely levelled. It joins this Section with Section 16. Abutting on it is the irregular, somewhat triangular walled depression ROMAÑA.

PARROT. A complex irregular formation, around 40 miles across, south of Albategnius. It presents no features of particular interest.

POLYBIUS. A fairly regular 20-mile crater south-west of Catharina.

RHÆTICUS. This and RÉAUMUR (Section 12), each 28 miles in diameter, lie on the border of the Sinus Medii. Both are somewhat ruined, with low walls. There are various clefts and valleys in this region.

TACITUS. A somewhat polygonal formation, 25 miles in diameter, between Catharina and Abulfeda. The walls are terraced, and rise in places to 11,000 feet, while the floor contains a central craterpit.

THEON JUNIOR and THEON SENIOR. Two prominent craterlets, respectively 10 and 11 miles in diameter, closely east of Delambre. Both are bright – my observations indicate that Theon Junior is slightly the more brilliant of the two – and in many ways they resemble Alfraganus.

THEOPHILUS. There can be little doubt that Theophilus is, with the possible exception of Copernicus, the grandest crater on the whole Moon. It is extremely deep, with walls rising to 18,000 feet; there is a splendid, many-peaked central mountain mass, and the inner ramparts are terraced. It is always a magnificent sight, and may be recognized under any conditions of illumination. It is the northern member of a chain of three great walled plains, and actually intrudes into its neighbour Cyrillus.

TORRICELLI. A curious compound formation on the Mare, north of Theophilus. It is made up of two rings, the larger one, to the west, having a diameter of 12 miles; it gives the general impression of a pear-shaped enclosure, and there are interesting features inside it, including some clefts.

TRANQUILLITATIS, MARE. A small part of this large Mare appears in this Section, but most of it lies in Section 4. Near the border of the Mare is a distinct small crater, MOLTKE, which is quite conspicuous.

VOGEL. A most peculiar formation near Albategnius. It consists of at least three craters which have fused together, and it may indeed be regarded as a short crater-chain. There are also various clefts in the neighbourhood.

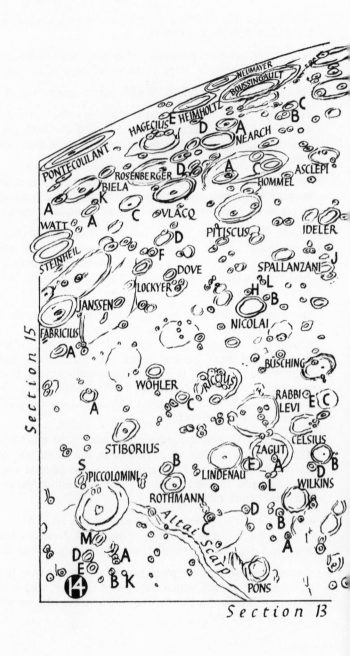

NEUMAYER
BOUSSINGAULT
HELMHOLTZ
HAGECIUS E
D A
NEARCH
PONTECOULANT
ROSENBERGER D
BIELA
K
A A
WATT
C
VLACQ
A
STEINHEIL
D
F
DOVE
LOCKYER
JANSSEN
FABRICIUS
A
ASCLEPI
HOMMEL
PITISCUS
IDELER
J
SPALLANZANI
L
H
B
NICOLAI
BÜSCHING
WÖHLER
RICCIUS
RABBI E C
LEVI
A
C
CELSIUS
STIBORIUS
ZAGUT
B
E A
LINDENAU
D B
S
L
WILKINS
PICCOLOMINI
ROTHMANN
D
C
B
M
A
D
A
E
14
B K
Altai Scarp
PONS

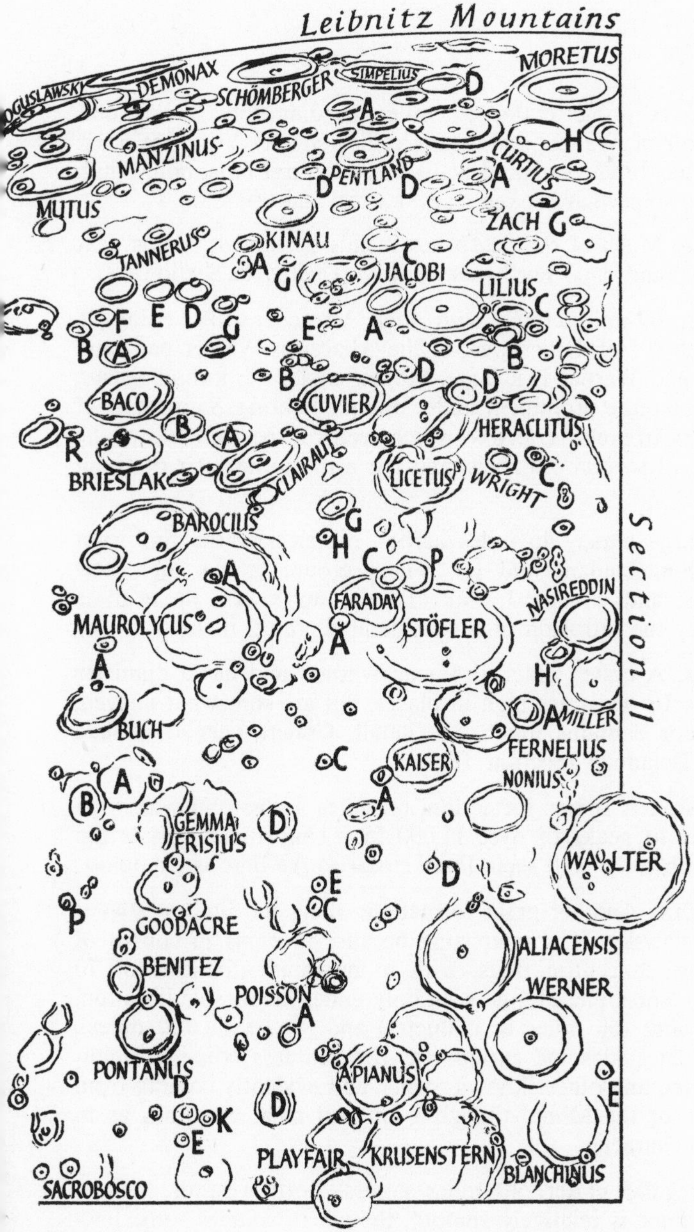

MORETUS

H

DEMONAX
SCHÖMBERGER SIMPELIUS D
BOGUSLAWSKI
A
CURTIUS
MANZINUS D PENTLAND D A
ZACH G
MUTUS
TANNERUS KINAU
A JACOBI LILIUS
F E D G G E A C
B A B B
BACO CUVIER D D HERACLITUS
R B A D C
BRIESLAK CLAIRAUT LICETUS WRIGHT C
BAROCIUS G
H C P NASIREDDIN
A FARADAY STÖFLER
MAUROLYCUS A
A H
BUCH A MILLER
FERNELIUS
B A C KAISER NONIUS
GEMMA A
FRISIUS D WALTER
P E
C
GOODACRE
BENITEZ ALIACENSIS
POISSON WERNER
A
PONTANUS D APIANUS E
D K D
E
SACROBOSCO PLAYFAIR KRUSENSTERN BLANCHINUS

ALIACENSIS. A noble crater 52 miles in diameter. It lies outside the wall of Walter, and has a rather smaller 'twin', Werner.
Aliacensis has broad, terraced walls and a central mountain. South
of it lie two somewhat broken rings, KAISER and NONIUS.

ALTAI SCARP. Much of the Scarp lies in this Section; it begins near
Piccolomini, and runs north-eastward to Tacitus in Section 13.

APIANUS. A 39-mile crater with high terraced walls rising in
places to 9,000 feet. It lies west of the Aliacensis-Werner pair, and
between it and Werner is a large, broken enclosure, KRUSENSTERN,
which can be quite prominent under oblique lighting. South-west of
it is the very irregular POISSON, which seems to be made up of the
coalescence of several old rings, and has a mean diameter of about
45 miles.

BIELA. A large crater, 46 miles across, rather near the limb, not
far from Pontécoulant and the Vlacq group. It has high, terraced walls, and a central peak. To the north-west the wall is
disturbed by the intrusion of a considerable crater, Biela A.

BLANCHINUS. A crater which lies near Werner, and has a diameter
of 33 miles. Its walls are high in places, but are somewhat uneven,
and the floor contains much fine detail. Craters near it include
Faye and Delaunay (Section 13).

BOGUSLAWSKY. A major formation, 60 miles across and with high
walls, rising to peaks of over 11,000 feet. Unfortunately it is too
near the limb to be well seen. Even closer to the limb is Demonax.

BOUSSINGAULT. Another great formation, along the limb westward
from Boguslawsky. It is interesting because it seems to consist of
three almost concentric rings, with a maximum diameter of 70
miles. Even worse placed, and seen only under favourable libration,
are HELMHOLTZ (60 miles in diameter) and NEUMAYER (50 miles).
In 1954 I detected some curious ray-like features crossing Helmholtz, not like any others known to me, and evidently coming from
the far side of the Moon, though I am still most uncertain as to
their exact character.

BUCH. A regular crater, 30 miles across, north-west of Maurolycus. The floor is relatively smooth, though it includes some low-
rimmed pits. Adjoining it to the north-west is –

BÜSCHING, slightly larger (diameter 36 miles) but less regular, and with a much rougher floor. The surrounding regions of Buch and Büsching are thickly crowded with craters and craterlets.

CURTIUS. An exceptionally deep crater, 50 miles across, in the south polar region, not far from Moretus. Its walls are massive and terraced, and the floor contains considerable detail. It is a great pity that Curtius is not better placed; if it were, it would be a most imposing object.

CUVIER. A moderately regular, 50-mile crater, with high terraced walls and a minor central hill. It lies in the uplands, west of the Licetus-Heraclitus group. Close by are CLAIRAUT, which has been deformed by the intrusion of two considerable craterlets, and BACO, 40 miles across, which has lofty walls and a low central peak. North of Baco lies BREISLAK, which is slightly smaller, while between Breislak and Baco may be seen a small, rather deep craterlet.

DEMONAX. This great enclosure, with a diameter of 75 miles, lies between Boguslawsky and the limb, but may be seen only under favourable libration. This is a pity, since it is majestic and complex. Even worse placed is its smaller companion CORTÉS, which actually lies on the far hemisphere; and I have found a similar crater about 1½ diameters west along the limb from Cortés. which is excessively difficult to examine.

FABRICIUS. A walled plain 55 miles in diameter, breaking into the vast ruin Janssen. There is a central mountain on the generally rough floor, while the walls attain 9,500 feet in places. A long cleft runs north from outside the east wall.

FARADAY. A very irregular formation, around 40 miles in diameter, which has broken into Stöfler. There are two deep craters which break into the walls of Faraday itself, and the whole terrain is very complex. The floor is much rougher than that of Stöfler.

GEMMA FRISIUS. A large, irregular enclosure, much broken by smaller craters, and with a decidedly rough floor which contains a nearly central hill. In the north it has been disturbed by the 30-mile GOODACRE, which also has broken walls and a low central peak.

HAGECIUS. A most peculiar formation; it is included in the Vlacq group, and is not very far from the limb. Its diameter is about 50 miles, but its west wall has been ruined by the intrusion of no less than five craters. The floor is relatively smooth, but includes several craterlets. one of which is of fair size.

HERACLITUS. A strange, irregular enclosure, with a central ridge. It is one of a group of three formations, the others being Cuvier and Licetus. LICETUS is 46 miles across, with uneven walls and a low central hill; the rampart has been broken on the south, so that its interior connects with that of Heraclitus. The whole group can be very prominent when well placed, and is not difficult to find, since it lies not far south of the dark-floored and always prominent Stöfler.

HOMMEL. A huge crater, 75 miles in diameter, sufficiently far from the limb to be quite well seen under good conditions of libration. It has walls of fair height, and is notable because the floor has been broken by two large craters, one of which has a central hill. Outside Hommel, to the east, are the twenty-mile craters ASCLEPI and TANNERUS, while Pitiscus adjoins Hommel to the north.

JACOBI. A 41-mile crater, with walls rising in places to almost 10,000 feet. It lies south-west of the Heraclitus group. Its neighbours are KINAU (26 miles across) and LILIUS (32 miles), both of which have high walls and central peaks, but present no features of particular note. A considerable crater lies between Lilius and Jacobi.

JANSSEN. This great ruin has a diameter of over 100 miles (Goodacre's figure is 121 miles, but may be an over-estimate). It is thus one of the Moon's major formations, but it is in a sad state, and is prominent only when on the terminator. Its walls are broken in the north by Fabricius and in the south by the bright-walled, 30-mile crater LOCKYER; the floor is light, and is crowded with detail, including a conspicuous valley-cleft from which extend several branches.

KINAU. This well-marked crater has been described with Jacobi.

LEIBNITZ MOUNTAINS. These peaks, right on the Moon's southern limb, are said to be the highest on the whole Moon, but they are so badly placed for observation that I personally doubt whether any measures of their altitudes are accurate.

LICETUS. One of the Heraclitus group, and described with Heraclitus.

LILIUS. This has already been described with Jacobi.

MANZINUS. A large crater, 55 miles across, and with high terraced walls reaching 14,000 feet here and there. It is placed rather inconveniently close to the limb, in the Boguslawsky area.

296

MAUROLYCUS. A crater with an average diameter of 68 miles, lying west of the darker-floored Stöfler. Its walls are of some altitude, but are broken in several places by craterlets and landslips. There is a central mountain group, and the floor in general is rough, containing some ruined rings. Immediately outside Maurolycus, to the south-west is BAROCIUS, 50 miles across, whose high walls are broken in the north-west by two considerable craters. One of the interesting things about the Maurolycus-Barocius group is that Maurolycus itself has encroached upon an old formation to the south; the broken formation – which also touches Barocius – is not equal in size to Maurolycus, and this may be one of the excessively rare cases in which a large formation has broken into a smaller one. I am not convinced about it, however, as the whole region is extremely complex, and the 'broken' ring may simply have been badly distorted by crustal forces.

MILLER. This and NASIREDDIN are two 30-mile craters east of Stöfler. They really make up part of the group which includes Orontius and Huggins, and which has been described in Section 11.

MORETUS. Moretus is one of the most well-formed craters on the Moon, and if it were better placed it would probably outrank even Copernicus and Theophilus. It is larger, with a diameter of 75 miles, and has a high, broad and terraced wall. The floor is somewhat dark, and there is a magnificent central mountain, which may well be the 'highest on the Moon; it is thought to attain 9,000 feet, and is crowned by a small pit. Unfortunately Moretus is very near the limb, in the south polar zone, and moreover lies in a crowded area. Nearby is a 29-mile, high-walled crater, CYSATUS (Section 11).

MUTUS. A 50-mile crater near Manzinus. Its walls are high, rising to peaks of 14,000 feet. Mutus has two large craters on its floor, so that the arrangement resembles that of the decidedly larger Hommel, and makes the formation easy to recognize. The area between Mutus and Tannerus is crowded with small craters.

NASIREDDIN. This has been described with its companion Miller.

NEARCH. This 38-mile formation lies near Hommel and Hagecius, and may be regarded as a member of the Vlacq group. The floor contains half a dozen craterlets of some size, and in the south the rampart is broken by the intrusion of a deep crater, Nearch A. which has a central peak.

NICOLAI. A regular crater 27 miles in diameter, roughly between Janssen and Maurolycus. The walls rise to 6,000 feet. Nicolai lies right in the upland area, but there are no large craters close to it, and this is one of the 'smoother' parts of the area, even though it is still very rough judged by general lunar standards.

PENTLAND. A 45-mile crater near Curtius, with terraced walls and a double-peaked central mountain. A considerable crater, Pentland A, abuts on it to the south. Nearby lies ZACH, which is of about the same size, and is rather similar in aspect, though it has a nearly central craterlet instead of a central mountain.

PICCOLOMINI. A splendid crater at the end of the Altai Scarp. It is 56 miles across, with high, terraced walls with peaks attaining 15,000 feet; the southern wall has unusual structure. To the northeast, on the western side of the Scarp, I have found a good example of a lunar dome. Between Piccolomini and the Zagut group lies the well-formed crater ROTHMANN, which has a peak slightly displaced from the centre of the floor.

PITISCUS. A crater 50 miles in diameter, adjoining Hommel to the north. Its walls have peaks rising to 10,000 feet, but are narrow in places; the floor contains several craters, one of which is of considerable size. To the east, in the general direction of the Maurolycus group, lie several craters, notably IDELER and SPALLANZANI.

PONS. A 20-mile crater close to the Altai Scarp, north-east from Piccolomini. Its walls are abnormally thick. Nearby lies the irregular, 52-mile SACROBOSCO.

PONTANUS. A well-formed 28-mile crater, with broad walls which are disturbed in places. There is no central peak, but a crater lies very near the middle of the floor. Adjoining Pontanus to the south is a smaller formation, BENITEZ.

PONTÉCOULANT. This lies on the borders of the present Section and Section 15, and is too near the limb to be well seen; but it has a diameter of 60 miles, while the darkish floor includes a nearly central crater, some hills, and at least one cleft.

RABBI LEVI. This is one of a group lying some way south-east of Piccolomini; the other members are RICCIUS, LINDENAU, ZAGUT, CELSIUS and WILKINS. Rabbi Levi is 50 miles across, but is irregular in shape, with rather low walls, while the rough floor includes numerous craterlets and pits. Celsius, separated from Rabbi Levi by a broad valley, is smaller, and has a deep craterlet some way from the centre of its floor. Riccius (50 miles in diameter) also has broken walls and a rough, pitted floor; Lindenau is 35 miles across, with high terraced walls and a group of low mounds near its centre; Wilkins is an irregular enclosure with a mean diameter of 40 miles; and Zagut is of the same type, though larger (50 miles in diameter). The whole group is complex, but in no way remarkable.

RICCIUS. This has been described with Rabbi Levi.

ROSENBERGER. This is included in the Vlacq group. It is 50 miles in diameter, with a darkish floor and a low central peak; in the south its walls have been broken by a smaller crater.

SCHÖMBERGER. A large crater, over 40 miles in diameter, near the limb in the general region of Boguslawsky. Still closer to the limb are SCOTT and AMUNDSEN, each 66 miles across according to measures by D. W. G. Arthur; Amundsen, the shallower, seems to have been damaged by Scott's wall. Both contain much detail, and are interesting objects, but they are not easy to study, and Amundsen cannot be seen at all under conditions of mean libration. Better placed, and again not far from Schömberger, is the rather distorted but quite prominent SIMPELIUS.

STEINHEIL. This and WATT form a splendid example of a pair of overlapping craters, and have been described in the text. They lie outside the south-west wall of Janssen. Steinheil is 45 miles across, while the walls rise to 11,000 feet in the east; Watt has some ridges and craterlets on its floor. The pair is similar to that of Sirsalis-Bertaud, but is considerably larger.

STIBORIUS. A well-marked 23-mile crater south of Piccolomini; its walls are terraced, broken by a crater in the north, while the floor includes a peak slightly displaced from the centre. Further south lies a much smaller, rather elliptical crater, WÖHLER, which has no special points of interest.

STÖFLER. A grand enclosure, 90 miles across, with a dark floor which makes it identifiable under any conditions of lighting. Part of the rampart has been destroyed by the intrusion of Faraday. The interior contains much fine detail, as well as darker patches which appear to vary according to the state of the lunation, so that Stöfler merits close attention. To the north is the 40-mile, rather irregular FERNELIUS.

VLACQ. A deep, well-formed crater 56 miles in diameter, with a central hill and walls that rise to 10,000 feet in places. It is a member of a group which includes Hommel, Nearch, Rosenberger, Pitiscus and Hagecius.

WERNER. The 'twin' of Aliacensis. It is smaller than Aliacensis, and has a diameter of 45 miles, but is extremely regular, with high terraced walls probably attaining peaks of 15,000 feet. There is also a splendid central peak. Werner has been mentioned in the text in connection with a bright spot at the foot of the north-east wall, which has been held (probably quite wrongly) to have faded since Mädler's time.

WRIGHT. A well-formed, 18-mile crater some way east of Licetus.

WILKINS. One of the Rabbi Levi group, and described with it.

ZAGUT. This also has been described with Rabbi Levi.

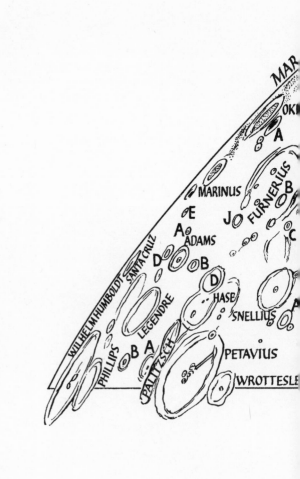

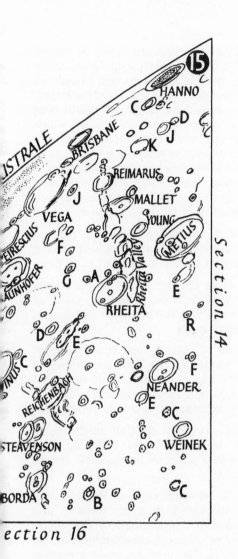

HANNO

C

BRISBANE

D

K J

REIMARUS

USTRALE

MALLET

J

YOUNG

VEGA

METIUS

PEIRESCIUS

F

E

AUNHOFER

G A

RHEITA

Rheita Valley

E

R

D

E

F

INUS C

NEANDER

REICHENBACH

E

C

STEAVENSON

WEINEK

BORDA

B

C

AUSTRALE, MARE. The so-called Southern Sea can hardly be classed as a true Mare, as it consists of disconnected patches of lunabase rather than a true sheet; but it covers a large area, and extends on to the reverse hemisphere, as is shown by the Lunik III photographs. I have seen several old rings on its floor. Right on the limb at extreme libration are the craters of PRATDESABÁ and IBAÑÉZ, which would be imposing if better placed, while further on the disc are some large, rather low-walled rings such as PEIRESCIUS and VEGA. In places the walls of Vega rise to some height, while the floor is smooth; the diameter is 50 miles. This whole area needs more attention than it has received up to now. Naturally, it is best seen very shortly after full moon, when it is on the terminator.

BORDA. A low-walled, 26-mile crater between Santbech (Section 16) and Steavenson, the companion of Reichenbach. It has a central hill, as well as a low ring on the south-west part of its floor.

FRAUNHOFER. A crater 30 miles in diameter, west of the Rheita Valley. It has walls rising to 5,000 feet, but broken in places by smaller craters. On the floor are several craterlets, one of which is nearly central, as well as some low ridges.

FURNERIUS. A great walled plain 80 miles across. It is a member of the great 'Western Chain' which includes Petavius, Endymion and probably the Mare Crisium. The terraced walls are somewhat broken, while the floor contains details such as craterlets, hills and delicate clefts, as well as one prominent bright crater, Furnerius B.

HANNO. A dark-floored, 40-mile crater near the limb in the region of Pontécoulant (Section 14). In the limb-area extending from Hanno to the Mare Australe there are various considerable craters, such as BRISBANE and REIMARUS.

HASE. An enclosure 48 miles in diameter, close to Petavius. The walls are broken and the shape rather irregular, while I have found that the floor is covered with vast numbers of tiny crater-pits, together with one prominent crater of considerable size. To the outer north-east of Hase, F. H. Thornton has noted a peculiar arrangement of ridges which show up at sunset as an illuminated cross, but I have yet to see this appearance, though I have often looked for it.

HUMBOLDT, WILHELM. This formation, on the limb and close to the border of Sections 15 and 16, is one of the grandest craters on the Moon, and it is a great pity that it is so badly placed. The diameter is 120 miles, and the majestic walls rise to 16,000 feet; the floor contains a chain of hills rising in the centre to a lofty mass, as well as some craterlets and at least two clefts. Abutting on the southwest wall is another great crater, WHITAKER, 70 miles across, while southward along the limb is the 50-mile SANTACRUZ. The eastward companion of Wilhelm Humboldt is PHILLIPS. 75 miles in diameter, with a long central ridge and some low rings on the northern part of its floor. Between Phillips and the west wall of Petavius is a deep craterlet of some size.

LEGENDRE. A low-walled crater 46 miles in diameter, between Hase and Wilhelm Humboldt. The floor contains a discontinuous central ridge. Close to Legendre is ADAMS, which has a central crater, while closely outside it is Adams A, which is of considerable depth and has brilliant walls.

MARINUS. A 30-mile crater in the Mare Australe area. It has moderate walls, and a central hill.

METIUS. This large formation really belongs to the Janssen group (Section 14). It is 50 miles in diameter, with terraced walls containing one peak of 13,000 feet. The floor contains a central mountain with a summit pit. Metius may be regarded as the 'twin' of its neighbour Fabricius.

NEANDER. A well-formed crater 30 miles across, between Reichenbach and Piccolomini. The inner slopes of the wall contain two prominent craterlets. Some distance north-eastward is the smaller but quite conspicuous crater WEINEK.

OKEN. A 50-mile crater in the Mare Australe area, easy to find because of its dark floor. The walls tend to be linear in places, but rise here and there to 6,000 feet; to the east is Oken A, which also has a darkish floor upon which stands a low central hill.

PALITZSCH. This extraordinary formation lies closely outside the western wall of Petavius. Many authorities describe it as an irregular, gorge-like structure, 60 miles long by 20 wide, possibly formed by a meteor ploughing through the lunar surface layers. In 1952, however, I examined it with the 25-inch Newall refractor at the Cambridge Observatory, and found that it is nothing more nor less than a vast crater-chain made up of several major rings which have coalesced. Outside, to the west, is Palitzch A, which has continuous walls and three hills on its floor. There is nothing else quite like Palitzsch on the whole Moon, and it deserves careful study.

PETAVIUS. A magnificent crater, certainly one of the finest on the Moon. It is over 100 miles in diameter, and has walls which reach a maximum of 11,000 feet; the ramparts are very complex, and in places double. The floor is somewhat convex, and contains a grand central mountain group; the main peak exceeds 5,500 feet. A particularly conspicuous cleft runs from the central area to the south-east wall. Under low and moderate illumination Petavius dominates the whole area, but it becomes strangely obscure under high light, and is difficult to find at full moon. It is, of course, a member of the Western Chain. Palitzsch lies closely west, and abutting on Petavius to the east is the well-marked, 34-mile crater WROTTESLEY, which has a twin-peaked central mountain and walls rising to 8,000 feet in places.

PHILLIPS. This has been described together with its larger companion, Wilhelm Humboldt.

REICHENBACH. In itself Reichenbach is not remarkable; it is 30 miles in diameter, with lofty walls. North of it is STEAVENSON, 22 miles across and with a central peak, which has broken into a somewhat larger ring-plain to the east of it. The chief interest in this area is the splendid REICHENBACH VALLEY, south-west of Reichenbach, and narrowing steadily as it passes southward. It is really a crater-chain, and is thus similar in character to the Rheita Valley, though it is neither so conspicuous nor so well-formed.

RHEITA. A crater 42 miles across, with walls rising to 14,000 feet; the crests are unusually sharp. Associated with it is the imposing RHEITA VALLEY, which has been fully described in the text, and is easily seen with a small telescope when suitably lit. It is 115 miles long, and the breadth across the widest part is about 15 miles. In the Valley area are various unremarkable rings, such as MALLET and YOUNG.

SNELLIUS. This and STEVINUS form a good example of twin formations. Each is high-walled, and about 50 miles in diameter; each has a central mountain. Snellius has rather the lighter floor. Both are easy to find except under very high light.

STEVINUS. This is described with Snellius.

306

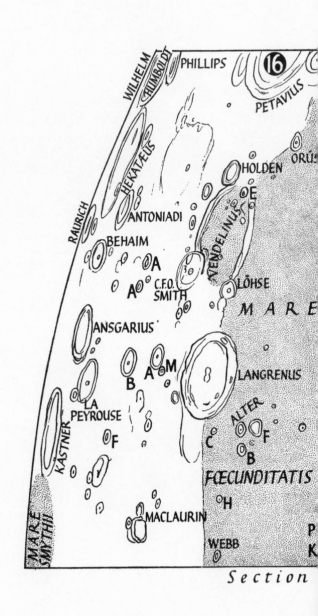

PHILLIPS

WILHELM
HUMBOLDT

PETAVIUS

16

HOLDEN

ORÚ

HEKATEUS

RAURICH

ANTONIADI

E

BEHAIM

VENDELINUS

A

LÔHSE

A

C.F.O.
SMITH

MARE

ANSGARIUS

A M

B

LANGRENUS

LA
PEYROUSE

ALTER

F

F

KÁSTNER

C

B

FŒCUNDITATIS

H

MARE
SMYTHII

MACLAURIN

WEBB

P
K

Section

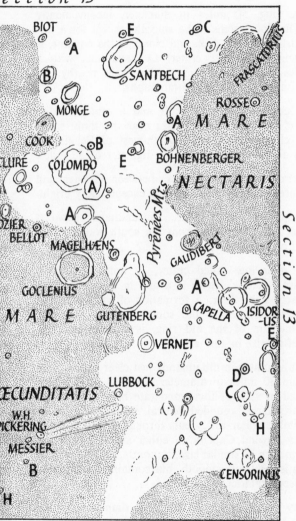

BIOT

A

E

C

B

SANTBECH

FRASCATORIUS

MONGE

ROSSE

COOK

B

A MARE

:LURE

COLOMBO

E

BOHNENBERGER

A

NECTARIS

)ZIER

A

Pyrenees Mts.

BELLOT

MAGELHÆNS

GAUDIBERT

GOCLENIUS

A

MARE

GUTENBERG

CAPELLA

ISIDOR
-US

VERNET

E

LUBBOCK

D

C

H

:ECUNDITATIS

W.H.
PICKERING

MESSIER

B

CENSORINUS

'H

ANSGARIUS. A large ring, 50 miles in diameter, inconveniently close to the limb. The floor seems to be smooth, except for a few low hills. Slightly further on the disk, and closer to the equator, is a similar though slightly smaller crater, LA PEYROUSE, with a diameter of 45 miles. There are various other rings nearby. La Peyrouse is shown on the Lunik III photographs.

BEHAIM. A 35-mile crater, with high walls and a central crater. The floor also includes a cleft. Behaim lies near the limb, south of Ansgarius; even closer to the limb, south-west of Behaim, is RAURICH, which has continuous walls and a diameter of 30 miles.

BELLOT. A small crater 12 miles across, between Crozier and Magelhæns. It is interesting because its floor is exceptionally bright.

BIOT. A 10-mile crater near the Mare Fœcunditatis, between Petavius and Santbech. A cleft runs from the south wall of Biot toward the east wall of Petavius.

BOHNENBERGER. A rather low-walled crater, 22 miles across, on the edge of the Mare Nectaris. There is a gap in the north wall, while a ridge runs across the floor. A formation of equal size, but with even lower ramparts, lies to the south; between this and Bohnenberger, on the rim of the old ring, is a deep craterlet. Various delicate clefts exist in this area.

CAPELLA. An interesting crater in the uplands just clear of the Mare Nectaris. It is around 30 miles in diameter, and has walls which are remarkably broad in view of their moderate height. The floor contains a particularly large, rounded central mountain, crowned by a craterlet. A notable crater-valley cuts through it, and is traceable for a long way beyond Capella to either side. Capella has intruded on to a formation of similar size, ISIDORUS, lying east of it; the floor of Isidorus is relatively smooth, but contains one prominent and decidedly deep craterlet.

CENSORINUS. A very small crater, 3 miles in diameter, in the uplands between the Mare Fœcunditatis and the southern extension of the Mare Tranquillitatis. It is one of the brightest points on the whole Moon, and is always conspicuous, particularly under high illumination. It lies, moreover, on a bright patch. A moderately large but very low-walled depression lies to the west.

COLOMBO. A large enclosure, 50 miles across, disturbed in the north-east by Colombo A, about half the size and with a central hill. Well to the south-west lies COOK, which is 26 miles in diameter and whose walls are low, but which is easy to recognize because of its dark floor; while south-east of Cook is a somewhat deformed crater of similar size, MONGE.

CROZIER. A 15-mile crater near the Colombo group. It has a central hill.

FŒCUNDITATIS, MARE. Most of the Mare Fœcunditatis lies in this Section, though some of it extends on to Section 1. It is one of the less regular of the great seas, and there are not many large craters on it; the most interesting object is probably the Messier pair. The Mare has no high mountain borders, and is connected with the Mare Tranquillitatis.

FRACASTORIUS. The great bay on the coast of the Mare Nectaris. It lies partly in Section 13, and has been described there.

GOCLENIUS. The companion of Gutenberg. It is 32 miles in diameter, with walls rising to 5,000 feet; as it lies on the edge of the Mare Fœcunditatis, it has been damaged by the Mare material. It has a low central hill, and the floor is cut through by a cleft which extends beyond the crater. There are various other clefts in the region.

GUTENBERG. Gutenberg is larger than Goclenius, since its diameter is 45 miles, but it has been distorted, and its wall is broken in the north-west by a 14-mile crater. There is a partly ruined central peak. To the north-east lies VERNET, which has incomplete walls, but is quite conspicuous; the central mountain is rather rounded. Clefts abound in the whole area, and are worth close attention.

HEKATÆUS. A vast, somewhat pear-shaped crater close to the limb. Observations by K. W. Abineri and myself indicate that it may be made up of two formations which have coalesced, but its position makes it very difficult to examine properly. To the north-east is the broken ring ANTONIADI, while Abineri has recorded three narrow valleys connecting the floor of Hekatæus with that of Wilhelm Humboldt.

WILHELM HUMBOLDT. This magnificent crater lies mainly in Section 15, and has already been described.

ISIDORUS. The companion of Capella, and described with it.

KÄSTNER. Yet another large crater too close to the limb to be well seen. It has a diameter of eighty miles, and it has high walls; the floor is relatively smooth apart from a ridge running from the north wall to the centre Between Kästner and the limb, and so very hard to study, is a smaller but still considerable crater, WATTS.

LANGRENUS. A tremendous walled plain, 85 miles across. It is one of the Western Chain, and is comparable with Petavius. The walls are high and massive, rising to 9,000 feet, and the floor contains a bright, twin-peaked central mountain. Langrenus is imposing under low light, and appears as a bright patch near full moon. To the north-east are three craters forming a triangle; one is the 17-mile ALLER, the others Langrenus B and Langrenus F.

LA PEYROUSE. This crater has already been described, with Ansgarius.

MAGELHÆNS. A 25-mile crater near Goclenius. It has a rather dark floor, and is joined to the south-west by a smaller crater with a central hill, so that Magelhæns gives the impression of being a double formation.

MESSIER. This and its companion W. H. PICKERING have already been dealt with in the text. The curious double 'comet' ray spreads across the Mare in the general direction of LUBBOCK, a bright 8-mile craterlet lying on the north border of a larger and much less perfect ring. Goodacre recorded several ruined rings along the comet-ray, but I have never been able to find them, though I have looked for them on hundreds of occasions.

MONGE. An unremarkable crater near Cook. It has been described with Colombo.

NECTARIS, MARE. Part of the Mare lies here, and part in Section 13. Note the bright, deep craterlet ROSSE, 10 miles in diameter, connected by ridges to Fracastorius.

PYRÉNÉES MOUNTAINS. A small range of mountains, lying roughly between Gutenberg and Bohnenberger.

ROSSE. A bright craterlet in the Mare Nectaris, and described with it.

SANTBECH. A large walled plain, 44 miles in diameter, with walls which rise to a maximum of 15,000 feet, though the average height is much less than this. Santbech lies in the uplands between

312

the southernmost parts of the Mare Nectaris and the Mare Fœcund-itatis. The floor is rough, and includes considerable detail, including an ancient ring and a hill silghtly displaced from the centre of the crater.

VENDELINUS. A majestic irregular formation, over 100 miles from north to south. It has been considerably ruined, and therefore seems to be older than Langrenus or Petavius, which are of much the same size. The floor contains craterlets, hills and some clefts. To the north-west the rampart is broken by the intrusion of a large crater, C. F. O. SMITH, 45 miles across; the rather smaller LOHSE abuts on the north-east; and to the south of Vendelinus lies HOLDEN, 25 miles in diameter, with a crater and a ridge on its floor. East of Holden is ORÚS, which is 19 miles across and has a central hill. Vendelinus and its companions make a grand picture under oblique illumination.

WEBB. A bright 14-mile crater, with a darkish floor and a central hill. I have found it to be the centre of a short, inconspicuous system of rays. Webb lies near the border of the Mare Fœcund-itatis, not far from the lunar equator, and in the uplands to the west is MACLAURIN, which has a diameter of 30 miles, uneven walls, and a somewhat concave floor. On the limb in this region is the MARE SMYTHII, but most of it lies in Section 1, and has been described there.

Index to Formations Described in the Map

Tralles, 1
Tranquillitatis, Mare, 1-4-13
Triesnecker, 4
Turner, 12
Tycho, 11
Ukert, 4
Ulugh Beigh, 7
Undarum, Mare, 1
Vaporum, Mare, 4
Vasco da Gama, 8
Vendelinus, 16
Vieta, 10
Vitello, 10
Vitruvius, 4
Vlacq, 14

Vogel, 13
Wallace, 5
Walter, 11-14
Wargentin, 10
Webb, 16
Werner, 14
Wichmann, 9
Wilhelm I., 11
Wilkins, 14
Wright, 14
Wurzelbauer, 11
Xenophanes, 7
Zagut, 14
Zucchius, 11
Zupus, 9

The Reverse Side of the Moon

So far, our knowledge of the other side of the Moon depends entirely upon the photographs taken from Lunik III in 1959. A chart has been drawn up by Y. N. Lipski and his colleagues in Russia, and shows a great many formations, though the details and natures of some of them are naturally uncertain. To correlate the photographs with features already known, the Soviet scientists used the lunar map compiled by H. P. Wilkins, and they have also followed Wilkins' nomenclature.

The photographs showed some already-known features, notably the Mare Crisium, and the limb-seas Mare Australe, Mare Humboldtianum, Mare Marginis and Mare Smythii are identifiable. Craters identified with fair certainty are Alhazen, Behaim, Gauss, Hahn, Hallowes,* Hanno, Hekatæus, Kästner, La Peyrouse, Legendre, Liddiard, Lower, Maclaurin, Marinus, Neper, Oken, Phillips, Polit, Plutarch, Raurich, Schubert, Seneca, Timoleon and Wilhelm Humboldt. On the other hand there is still a region which remains unphotographed, and so even our preliminary knowledge of the far side of the Moon is extremely incomplete.

It may be worth while to give a brief description of the named features on the hitherto unseen regions. These have, of course, been drawn from the official Russian accounts.

ASTRONAUTARUM, SINUS. A concavity in the outline of the Mare Moscoviæ.

CLERK MAXWELL. This shows up as a grey spot, and is probably a crater on a light background, with a wide wall narrowing in the south. The floor is brightest in the east.

DESIDERII, MARE. A dark segment near the edge of the photographed area. It is probably not a continuous Mare, but made up of a number of smaller formations which cannot be separately distinguished. It may spread on to the unexplored region.

EDISON. This shows as a dark spot, and is probably a crater. A light area adjoins it to the north and north-east.

GIORDANO BRUNO. Since this object appears as a bright spot, it is

* There are three mis-spellings in the English translation of the Russian atlas – 'Lover', 'Halloways' and 'Lyddiard' for Lower, Hallowes and Liddiard.

322

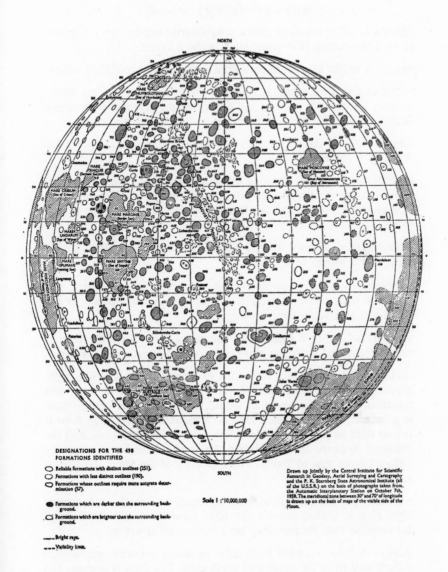

NORTH

MARE HUMBOLDTIANUM
(Sea of Humboldt)

Giordano Bruno

MARE MOSCOVAE
(Sea of Moscow)

Karpinskiy

Cleomedes

MARE PANGUAE
(German Sea)
Joliot-
Curie

Sinus Astronauticum
(Bay of Astronauts)

MARE CASLIM
(Sea of Crises)

Popov
Hertz

MARE MARGINIS
(Border Sea)

Mendeleev

MARE UNDARUM
(Sea of Waves)

MARE SMYTHII
(Sea of Smyth)

MARE SPUMANS
(Foaming Sea)

Langemak

Pasteur

MARE FOECUNDITATIS

Vandelinus

Pavlov

Sklodowska-Curie

Tsiolkovskiy

MARE AUSTRALE
(Southern Sea)

Jules Verne

Lomonosov

SOUTH

Drawn up jointly by the Central Institute for Scientific
Research in Geodesy, Aerial Surveying and Cartography
and the P. K. Sternberg State Astronomical Institute (all
of the U.S.S.R.) on the basis of photographs taken from
the Automatic Interplanetary Station on October 7th,
1959. The meridional zone between 30° and 70° of longitude
is drawn up on the basis of maps of the visible side of the
Moon.

**DESIGNATIONS FOR THE 498
FORMATIONS IDENTIFIED**

⬭ Reliable formations with distinct outlines (251).

⬭ Formations with less distinct outlines (190).

⬭ Formations whose outlines require more accurate determination (57).

⬤ Formations which are darker than the surrounding background.

⬭ Formations which are brighter than the surrounding background.

▬▬ Bright rays.

▬ ▬ Visibility limit.

Scale 1 : 10,000,000

either a brilliant crater or else a mountainous region. Since it seems to be a ray-centre, it is more likely to be a crater.

HERTZ. A bright formation on a grey background, probably a crater.

JOLIOT-CURIE. Dark spot; it seems to be a crater on a grey background. The floor is uneven, and darkest in the east and west, where dark spots can be seen. Probably it has a central mountain.

JULES VERNE. A dark spot with a well-defined outline. It is almost certainly a crater.

KURCHATOV. A crater, showing up as a bright spot. The wall is best defined from the north-west side, becoming less distinct from the side of the Mare Moscoviæ. Kurchatov seems to be elongated in form.

LOBACHEVSKY. A dark spot, probably a crater, and edged to the west with a bright background.

LOMONOSOV. A dark, prominent spot, almost certainly a crater, and probably with a central mountain. The wall is less distinct in the south-east and south-west.

MENDELEIEV. A dark spot in the equatorial zone. Since the floor is even in tone and there are signs of a wall, it is certainly a crater.

MOSCOVIÆ, MARE. A dark formation of Mare type on a bright background, with a sinuous outline. The floor is uneven in tone, and therefore probably uneven in height, while near the centre there is a bright formation which may be a mountain mass. The floor is not so dark as that of the Mare Smythii or Mare Marginis, and the diameter appears to be between 180 and 190 miles – not very different from that of Bailly. The concavity of the Sinus Astronautarum lies in the south.

PASTEUR. A light spot. It consists of rounded formations; a narrow light ring is visible around the light formation, with dark strips between, so that Pasteur may be a compound structure.

POPOV. A light, rounded formation, probably a crater, edged with a dark wall from the north and south sides. The floor is uneven, and darker in the south, so that Popov may be made up of two separate formations which cannot be distinguished on the photographs.

SKLODOWSKA-CURIE. An extremely bright formation on a grey background, with poorly-defined outlines; it may consist of a number of separate craters, but its exact nature is very difficult to determine.

SOVIET RANGE. A bright formation on a grey background, composed of a great number of separate details. It may well be a mountain range.

TSIOLKOVSKII. A dark formation of crater type on a grey background, with a well-defined, wide wall which is brightest on the west. There is also a bright area in the north-east part of the wall. The floor is dark and uneven, with a central mountain, while in the south-west part of the wall there is a dark formation with a light spot.

TSU-CHUN-CHJI. A bright spot, probably a crater, on a grey background. The floor and walls are almost equal in brilliancy, and are considerably lighter than the surrounding surface.

Latin and English Names of the Lunar Seas

Sinus Astronautarum	The Bay of the Astronauts
Mare Australe	The Southern Sea
Mare Autumni	The Autumn Sea
Mare Crisium	The Sea of Crises
Mare Desiderii	The Dream Sea
Palus Epidemiarum	The Marsh of Epidemics
Mare Fœcunditatis	The Sea of Fertility
Mare Frigoris	The Sea of Cold
Mare Hiemis	The Winter Sea
Mare Humboldtianum	Humboldt's Sea
Mare Humorum	The Sea of Humours
Mare Imbrium	The Sea of Showers
Sinus Iridum	The Bay of Rainbows
Mare Marginis	The Marginal Sea
Sinus Medii	The Central Bay
Lacus Mortis	The Lake of Death
Mare Moscoviæ	The Sea of Moscow
Palus Nebularum	The Marsh of Mists
Mare Nectaris	The Sea of Nectar
Mare Nubium	The Sea of Clouds
Mare Orientalis	The Eastern Sea
Oceanus Procellarum	The Ocean of Storms
Palus Putredinis	The Marsh of Decay
Sinus Roris	The Bay of Dews
Mare Serenitatis	The Sea of Serenity
Sinus Æstuum	The Bay of Heats
Mare Smythii	Smyth's Sea
Palus Somnii	The Marsh of Sleep
Lacus Somniorum	The Lake of the Dreamers
Mare Spumans	The Foaming Sea
Mare Tranquillitatis	The Sea of Tranquillity
Mare Undarum	The Sea of Waves

Index